# BASIC RADIATION BIOLOGY

# BASIC RADIATION BIOLOGY

**DONALD J. PIZZARELLO, Ph.D.**

Associate Professor of Radiology (Radiation Biology)

*and*

**RICHARD L. WITCOFSKI, Ph.D.**

Assistant Professor of Radiology (Medical Physics)

*The Bowman Gray School of Medicine*
*Wake Forest University*
*Winston-Salem, North Carolina*

LEA & FEBIGER • PHILADELPHIA • 1967

Copyright © 1967 by Lea & Febiger

All Rights Reserved

Library of Congress Catalog Card Number 67-19140

Printed in the United States of America

To our friend, Dr. Meschan

# Preface

This text is intended as a teaching tool for an *introductory* course in radiation biology. It is written for individuals who have a limited background in radiation physics and modern biology. Among those who should find it useful are college undergraduates, beginning graduate students, medical students, residents in radiology, radiologists, and radiation physicists with interests in radiation biology.

A narrative style has been used throughout and simple illustrations have been employed. The experiments cited have been selected as examples of general principles and important techniques. While complete coverage has been our aim, treatment of any one subject or of all of them is not *exhaustive*.

The book is divided into two parts. Part I deals with radiation physics that forms the physical foundation of radiation biology. Only those points most pertinent to radiation biology are presented; detailed and complex calculations have been avoided. When possible, words have been used in place of mathematics. We realize that much of this material is available elsewhere, but for those students already familiar with the subject, this presentation will serve as a useful review.

In Part II the core of radiation biology is portrayed. Included in it are two chapters which present a capsule review of cytogenetics for those who may not have a working knowledge of this subject.

In accordance with the over-all concept of a general introductory text, general studies have been listed as references wherever possible. These will provide the reader with a more exhaustive treatment of any phase that interests him as well as with a detailed bibliography.

We wish to express our appreciation to Mr. F. C. Watts for critically reading the manuscript, to Mr. Leonard Miller who prepared the illustrations, and to Mrs. Nancy Deitrick, Mrs. Edna Snow, and Mrs. Ernestine Godfrey, who typed the manuscript.

DONALD J. PIZZARELLO
RICHARD L. WITCOFSKI

# Contents

## PART I: Review of Pertinent Physics

## PART II: Interactions of Radiations with Living Systems

# PART I

## Review of Pertinent Physics

# 1

## Introduction: Review of
## Pertinent Atomic Physics

**1.1  Introduction.** The *biologic* effects of ionizing radiation represent the efforts of living things to deal with energy left in them after an interaction of one of their atoms with an ionizing ray or particle. For any living system, this energy will be in excess of the system's requirements for normal function; it will be a deviation from the proper energy relationships within that system. Radiation biology, then, is the study of the sequence of events within organisms which follows the absorption of energy from ionizing radiation. It is the study of the efforts of organisms to restore proper energy relationships within themselves, and of the damage to the organisms which may be produced by this excess of energy.

**1.2  The Atom.** Since all matter (whether living or not) is made up of atoms, and since radiation interactions with matter occur at the atomic level, the understanding of atomic structure itself is fundamental to the understanding of radiation interactions in general and, in particular, for the understanding of the development of radiation damage in living things. An atom (any atom) may be compared to the solar system; there is a central, massive portion (the nucleus) and a number of small bodies (orbital electrons) which rotate about it in discrete orbits. The distances between the sun and the planets and between the planets themselves are very great, so that most of the solar system is empty space. The atom also is mainly empty space. If an atom could be increased to the size of an ordinary room, the nucleus would occupy a space in the center of the room about the size of the period at the end of this sentence (and the nucleus would be much larger than *all* its orbital electrons combined). Because of the "emptiness" of matter, ionizing radiations may pass through the space of many atoms before they chance to interact with a portion – nuclei or electrons – of any one of them.

**1.3   The Atomic Nucleus.**   This, the massive central portion of the atom, consists of two major components — *positively charged* protons and *uncharged* neutrons (Table 1.1). The mass of the protons and that of the neutrons is nearly the same. The *number of protons* in any atom determines and is designated by the *atomic number* (Z); the *atomic mass* (A) is the number of protons and neutrons in the nucleus.

Both neutrons and protons in the nucleus are in constant motion. The protons repel each other (they are positively charged and like charges repel), exerting a force against each other which would tend to make them fly apart. But the repulsive force between protons is held in check by an opposite, cohesive force, one that binds the mutually repellent protons together. The energy required to do this is known as the *binding energy* of the nucleus.

**1.4   Isotopes.**   Elements exist in which member atoms have the *same* number of protons in their nuclei but *different* numbers of neutrons (same *atomic number* but a different *atomic mass*). These various members of that element or atomic species are called *isotopes*. In some isotopic forms of elements the *binding energy* of the nucleus is enough to hold the nucleus together; these elements are stable. But in other isotopic forms the binding energy is *not* enough to hold nuclear particles together. Parts of the nucleus are lost. This process, the process of nuclear disintegration, is called *radioactive decay*. Isotopic forms of elements, those which are unstable and undergo this process, are called *radioisotopes*. The term *isotope*, then, implies that more than one form of the *same* element exists. Another widely used term, *nuclide*, is used in reference to an atomic form with a *specific* atomic number *and* atomic mass; it does not designate whether or not there is any other elemental form.

**Table 1.1.**   The Elementary Particles

| Particle | Symbol | Charge | Mass° | Where It Is Located in the Atom |
|----------|--------|--------|-------|---------------------------------|
| Proton   | p      | +1     | 1.00759 | Nucleus       |
| Neutron  | n      | 0      | 1.00899 | Nucleus       |
| Electron | e      | −1     | 0.00055 | Extra-nuclear |

°Atomic masses are based upon oxygen which is arbitrarily assigned the value 16.0000. Since oxygen has 8 protons and 8 neutrons, each must have a mass very near to one (2).

**1.5   The Orbital Electrons.**   In atoms there is, practically speaking, a segregation of mass and charge; most of the mass and *all* of the *positive* charge reside in the nucleus. All the *negative* charge is in *extra-nuclear*, orbital electrons (Table 1.1). Furthermore, the charges are balanced. In the atom the number of protons in the nucleus and the number of electrons in the orbits are equal. The *number* of positive and negative charges then are equal, and atoms, as a whole, are electrically neutral.

The cloud of moving orbital electrons is found at a relatively great distance from the nucleus. Each electron rotates about the nucleus and is held at a particular distance from the nucleus (within orbits or shells) by the *attraction* of the positive protons *in* the nucleus. That attractive force, that force which binds electrons in their shells (does not permit them to drift away from the nucleus) is called the *binding energy* of the *orbit*.

The orbit *closest* to the nucleus is designated the *K* shell; shells at progressively greater distances are called L, M, N, and so on down the alphabet. According to the laws of electricity the *attractive* force of the nucleus upon the electrons (the binding energy of the orbits) *increases* as the *distance* between them (between nucleus and electron orbit) becomes smaller (Figure 1.1).

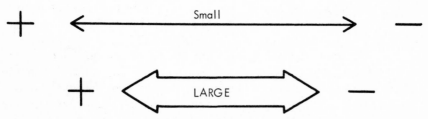

**Figure 1.1** The change in intensity of electrical attraction as it is related to distance is depicted. The force binding an electron in the K shell of an atom is greater than that binding an electron in the L shell. Electrons at progressively greater distance from the nucleus (K, L, M, N), therefore, are subject to a progressively weakening attractive force (smaller binding energy).

The elements with high atomic numbers (large numbers of protons) have a large central positive charge – larger than elements having low atomic numbers. They will attract the electrons in any given orbit more strongly than the electrons in the same orbit of an element with a low atomic number. For instance, the binding energies of electrons of the K shells of aluminum (13 protons), copper (29 protons), and lead (82 protons) differ greatly because of the different number of protons. The K shell binding energy of copper is almost six times that of aluminum, while the K shell binding energy of lead is almost sixty times that of aluminum.

Electrons in the *outermost* electron shell are called "valence electrons" (they are responsible for *chemical* combinations and interactions with other atoms). Since they are at the greatest distance from the nucleus, they are relatively loosely bound. If a small amount of energy is given them, they will be able to overcome the energy that binds them in their orbit and move out, even further away from the nucleus, to orbits beyond the valence shell. Those orbits are called "optical orbits," and the electrons occupying them are said to be *excited*. But electrons cannot be excited for long periods of time. Eventually they fall back, closer to the nucleus, into their regular orbit. The *excitation energy*, the energy that caused them to move in the first place, is not lost. It will be *radiated* from the atom.

A general rule is: when *any* electron moves from *any* outer to *any* inner shell, the energy *difference* in the binding energies of the two shells will be radiated from the atom. If this transition involves the outer optical shells, *optical* (ultraviolet) radiation is produced. If, however, *inner* shells are involved, more energy is involved, and more energetic radiation, ionizing radiation (x rays), is given off (Section 2.3).

**1.6   Ionization.**   The principal means by which *ionizing* radiations dissipate their energy in matter is by the *ejection* of orbital electrons from atoms. The removal of one or more of these orbital electrons is called *ionization*. Because each electron is held within its orbit by a specific binding energy, *work* must be done (energy given to the atom) when any orbital electron is removed. That energy must be equal to or greater than the binding energy of the electron shell. If it were not, the nucleus would continue to attract its electron, and it could not have been removed from its orbit. In order for an ionizing ray to produce an ionization, it must possess a *threshold* or minimum energy which it supplies to the atom. To remove a *K* electron from an atom, the radiation must have energy at least equal to or *greater* than the binding energy of the *K* shell of *that* atom. Since the binding energy of the K shell will vary from atom to atom (those with many protons bind it more tightly than those with fewer protons), this threshold energy will, of course, be different for different atoms.

Atoms are electrically neutral, but when they are ionized the loss of an orbital electron leaves them positively charged. The *ionized atom* and the dislodged electron constitute an *ion pair*.

In addition to the charge that the atom acquires, the atom will also be in an unstable energy state. It will possess an excess of energy *equal* to the binding energy of the electron shell that was occupied by the dislodged electron. The fault or empty place in the orbit must be filled. If an inner orbital electron were the one ejected, an electron from an orbit further from the nucleus would move in to fill the orbital "hole." This will follow the general rule governing the movement of electrons; the difference in energies will be radiated by the atom (Section 1.5).

The energy required to produce an ion pair will, of course, vary. It will be dependent upon the electron shell involved and the atomic number (the number of protons or the attractive force of the nucleus). The *average* energy required to form an ion pair (it is represented by the symbol, W) in various gases, however, has been determined. In *air*, 33.7 electron volts (eV) are required to form one ion pair—or W= 33.7 eV (an electron volt is a unit of energy and is that amount of energy acquired by an electron falling through a potential difference of one volt).[1] The amount of energy is only slightly different for other gases. W is meaningful, then, for gases in which electrons can be collected and their number determined, but it is at best approximate for condensed systems (such as tissue) in which it has not yet been determined experimentally.

**1.7 Excitation.** Not every interaction between ionizing radiation and matter need result in ionization. *Excitation*, a less drastic process than ionization, may also occur. In it an electron in an atom is raised to a higher energy state, moved to a more distant orbit, but not ejected. Excitation is the most important mode of energy dissipation by ultraviolet light, and probably forms a significant percentage of the energy dissipated by ionizing radiations in tissue. Johns[2] has estimated from the data of Lea and Fano that approximately 20 per cent of the energy released in tissue equivalent material by a fast electron (1 Mev) is through the mechanism of excitation.

## SUMMARY

1. The atom consists of a massive central portion, the nucleus, which contains the positive protons and the uncharged neutrons.
2. The nucleus is surrounded by negatively charged electrons which are found in discrete orbits at relatively great distances from the nucleus.
3. In the normal atom the number of protons is equal to the number of electrons—the atom is electrically neutral.
4. Radiations may have sufficient energy to remove an electron completely from an atom and produce an electrical charge (ionization) or perhaps only to move an electron to an orbit further from the nucleus (excitation).
5. These processes, particularly ionization, are responsible for the biologic damage produced by ionizing radiations.

## Text References

1. International Commission on Radiological Units and Measurements (National Bureau of Standards Handbook 85).
2. Johns, H. E.: *The Physics of Radiology*. Charles C Thomas, Springfield, Ill., 1961.

# 2

## The Origins and Types of Ionizing

## Radiations

**2.1 Introduction.** Ionizing radiations may be classified according to their origin (they are the products of radioactive decay, x-ray machines, particle bombardment, or nuclear reactors) or, more commonly, according to their physical properties. They fall into two general categories: those which have mass (corpuscular or particulate) and those which are energy only (non-particulate or electromagnetic). Those with mass may be charged or uncharged, but non-particulate radiations are never charged. The characteristics and origins of the ionizing radiations are summarized in Table 2.1.

**2.2 Radioactive Decay.** Atoms are not stationary; they are in *constant* motion. The electrons move continuously about the nucleus, and the protons and neutrons within the nucleus are also in continuous motion. The result of motion within the nucleus is collision between the particles and the rapid transfer of energy back and forth among them. Associated with all nuclei are forces of attraction between individual nuclear particles which tend to hold the nucleus together and to prevent the escape of component particles. The major difference between a stable and a radioactive nucleus is that the forces of attraction in a stable nucleus are such that no individual particle ever acquires enough energy to escape; in the radioactive nucleus it is possible on a *random* basis for an individual particle to acquire enough energy to escape from the nucleus.

The decay of radioactive atoms is described as a *disintegration* process. The term is misleading, however, because the atom does not truly disintegrate; instead a small portion of the nucleus is ejected.

Radioactive atoms are found throughout the periodic table of elements. The majority of the naturally occurring ones are found among the heavier elements (those which contain large numbers of the protons and neutrons), but radioactive forms are spread throughout the entire spectrum, examples being: tritium ($^3$H), carbon-14, potassium-40.

**Table 2.1.** Types of Ionizing Radiation

| Type | Mass | Charge | Description | Produced by |
|------|------|--------|-------------|-------------|
| Alpha | 4 | +2 | Doubly ionized helium atom | Radioactive decay primarily of heavy atoms |
| Beta (negatron) | 1/1837 | −1 | Negative electron | Radioactive decay and betatrons |
| Beta (positron) | 1/1837 | +1 | Positive electron | Radioactive decay and pair production |
| Protons | 1 | +1 | Hydrogen nuclei | Van de Graaff generators and cyclotrons |
| Heavy nuclei | Have a range of masses | Have a range of charges | Any atom stripped of one or more electrons and accelerated will be an ionizing particle. Deuterons and carbon atoms are examples | Accelerators |
| Neutrons | 1 | 0 | Neutron | Atomic reactor, cyclotrons |
| Gamma rays | 0 | 0 | Electromagnetic radiation | Radioactive decay |
| X rays | 0 | 0 | Electromagnetic radiation | X-ray machine and from the rearrangement of orbital electrons |

With the development of high energy machines, such as the cyclotron and other types of accelerators, and nuclear reactors it has been possible to make radioactive forms of commonly occurring stable elements (those that do not occur in nature in a radioactive form). In these cases, the new radioactive isotopes (or more properly, radionuclides) are formed by bombarding stable atoms with particles such as high energy protons, alpha particles, or, more commonly, neutrons. When these particles strike the nuclei of the stable atoms, they are absorbed. The addition of their mass and their energy is sufficient to change the stable configuration to an unstable one.

The ejection of a nuclear particle occurs by chance; there is no way to determine when or if a particular radioactive atom will undergo decay. Yet, if there are a great many unstable nuclei, a certain percentage of these may be expected to undergo decay in any given period of time. The *sudden disintegration* of these individual nuclei brings about, over a period ot time, a *gradual decrease* in their number. The total number of radioactive atoms decreases gradually (at very constant rate), but the gradual decrease is a result of the very sudden decay of individual radioactive atoms. The rate of decrease in the numbers of radioactive atoms per unit time will be a fixed percentage of those present; the change in the number ($\Delta N$) in any short period of time ($\Delta t$) will be be directly related to the total number (N) of atoms present. This may be expressed as the proportionality:

$$\Delta N \propto N\Delta t \qquad (2\text{-}1)$$

The symbol $\Delta$ simply is used to signify a *small* change. The proportionality may be made an equality by the addition of a constant of proportionality.

$$\Delta N = -\lambda N\Delta t \qquad (2\text{-}2)$$

The constant of proportionality ($\lambda$) is the *decay* or *transformation constant* and is a measure of the fraction of the radioactive atoms transformed per unit time (a measure of the rate of disintegration). The number of radioactive atoms is decreasing, so that there is a negative sign. This equation holds only for short periods of time (the time period in which N is essentially unchanged). An expression may be written which takes into consideration the constantly changing number of atoms so that the number present at any time (Nt), as related to the initial number (No), can be expressed as

$$N_t = N_o e^{-\lambda t} \qquad (2\text{-}3)$$

Instead of utilizing the decay constant to express the rate of decay, a more widely used term is *half-life*. The half-life is defined as the time period required for one half of the radioactive atoms present to undergo radioactive decay. By substituting in equation 2-3, $N_t = 1/2$ $N_o$ (the amount remaining after one-half life), one arrives at the relationship between half-life and the decay constant. This relationship is as follows:

$$\lambda = \frac{0.693}{T_{1/2}} \qquad (2\text{-}4)$$

Thus, with knowledge of the half-life one can compute the decay constant and vice versa. Another useful quantity, particularly in the calculation of radiation dosage, is the concept of *average life*. The average life is a measure of the average life expectancy of *all* of the radioactive atoms in a certain sample. The *assumption* is made that the radioactive decay rate remains constant for a specific period of time and then drops abruptly to zero. (Obviously this does not really occur, but this mathematical concept serves a very useful purpose.) Mathematically, it can be shown that the average life (Ta) is equal to $1/\lambda$. Since $\lambda = \dfrac{0.693}{T_{1/2}}$ a direct substitution for $\lambda$ yields a relationship between the half-life and the average life.

$$Ta = \frac{1}{\lambda} = \frac{T_{1/2}}{0.693} = 1.44\ T_{1/2} \qquad (2\text{-}5)$$

The unit which expresses the *quantity* of radioactivity is the *curie* (Ci). This is defined as a decay rate of $3.7 \times 10^{10}$ disintegrations per second. Thus, that amount of any radionuclide which is disintegrating at that rate (independent of the types of radiations it ejects) is defined as one curie. Other useful terms which are fractions of the curie are the millicurie ($1\ mCi = 3.7 \times 10^7$ d/sec) and the microcurie ($1\ \mu Ci = 3.7 \times 10^4$ d/sec).

**2.3  Alpha Disintegration.**  The alpha particle (it is the nucleus of the helium atom) consists of two protons and two neutrons. It is a large and highly charged particle. When a disintegrating nucleus emits an alpha particle, there will be a sizeable reduction in atomic number and atomic mass. The loss of these nuclear particles will lead to a more stable nuclear configuration. An example of alpha decay would be the disintegration of the familiar element, radium.

$$\underset{\text{(Radium)}}{^{226}_{88}Ra} \xrightarrow{\ T_{1/2}\ =\ 1622\ yrs\ } \underset{\text{(Radon)}}{^{222}_{86}Rn} + \underset{\text{(alpha particle)}}{^{4}_{2}He} \qquad (2\text{-}6)$$

Radium decays to radon by the emission of 2 different alpha particles. Most of the alpha particles will have an energy of 4.79 Mev (in 98.8 per cent of the disintegrations it is one of these which is emitted), while the others have an energy of 4.61 Mev. When one of the latter alpha particles is emitted, radiation of the excess energy (0.18 Mev) will be in the form of a gamma ray. Although some alpha emitters give off one alpha particle, others may eject two or more. Irrespective of the number, each one will have its own specific energy. Although alpha particles have energies which are normally quite high (up to several Mev), ionization is intense along their paths, and their energy is lost quite rapidly. Thus they travel only a short distance in tissue (microns).

**2.4  Beta Disintegration.**  Beta particle (electron) emission during radioactive disintegration is of two kinds: emission of the positive beta particle (positron) and the negatively charged beta particle (negatron). The nucleus of the atom contains only positively charged protons and uncharged neutrons; the orbits contain the negative electrons. Since the radioactive disintegration process involves the emission of particles (or energy) from the *nucleus,* some explanation is necessary to understand how electrons of either charge can originate there.

Negatron emission may be considered the result of conversion of a neutron within the nucleus to a proton and a negative electron:

$$\begin{array}{ccc} {}_{0}^{1}\text{n} & \longrightarrow & {}_{+1}^{1}\text{p} & + & {}_{-1}^{0}\text{e} & \qquad (2\text{-}7) \\ \text{(neutron)} & & \text{(proton)} & & \text{(negatron)} \end{array}$$

There will be no change in the atomic mass but the atomic *number* (Z) will increase by one since there is one more proton and one less neutron than was there before. On the other hand, positron decay may be considered the result of the conversion of a proton to a neutron and a positron.

$$\begin{array}{ccc} {}_{+1}^{1}\text{p} & \longrightarrow & {}_{0}^{1}\text{n} & + & {}_{+1}^{0}\text{e} & \qquad (2\text{-}8) \\ \text{(proton)} & & \text{(neutron)} & & \text{(positron)} \end{array}$$

In this case, the atomic number will decrease by one (there is one less proton), but, again, there will be no change in the atomic mass.

There is associated with beta decay, as in alpha decay, a specific energy difference between the initial and final product. However, the beta particle which is ejected from the nucleus of the radioactive atom may have any energy ranging from zero up to the characteristic maximum energy of the transition, the total energy difference between the initial and the final product (Figure 2.1).

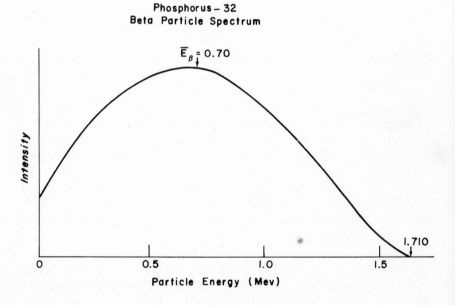

**Figure 2.1.** Beta energy distribution spectrum for phosphorus-32.

The distribution varies from zero energy to the maximum energy; the most probable energy (the average energy $\bar{E}_\beta$) is somewhat less than the maximal (E max). A useful approximation is that the average energy is about one third of the maximum energy. When a beta particle with an energy less than the maximum transition energy is emitted, the difference between it and the maximum energy will be irradiated as a neutrino, a neutral particle with a mass much less than that of the electron. Thus, the spectrum of energies related to beta decay is due to a sharing of the disintegration energy between the emitted beta particle and the neutrino. Because the neutrino has a mass which is small compared to that of the electron and no charge, it is of no known radiobiologic importance. A typical example of beta decay is the decay of radioactive phosphorus-32 (Figure 2.2).

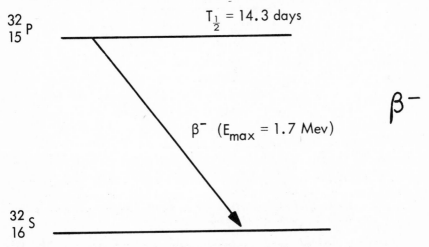

$$^{32}_{15}P \qquad\qquad T_{\frac{1}{2}} = 14.3 \text{ days}$$

$$\beta^- \; (E_{max} = 1.7 \text{ Mev}) \qquad\qquad \beta^-$$

$$^{32}_{16}S$$

**Figure 2.2** illustrates the decay of $^{32}$P to stable $^{32}$S. The beta particle is shown by a slanting arrow directed to the right. The emission of the beta particle results in an increase of one in atomic number and a product atom $^{32}$S with the same atomic weight.

The electron, because of its charge and small size, follows a tortuous path through matter giving up its energy through ionization. The ionizations, each representing a loss of energy, occur much further apart than those of the alpha particle, so that beta particles travel further. A 1 Mev beta particle has a range of about 1 cm in tissue, while an alpha particle of the same energy will have a range of 10 microns.

**2.5  Gamma Decay and Isomeric Transitions.** Atoms may also be unstable and therefore radioactive because they possess an excess of energy. The stable state of a nuclide is the "ground state"; an energy state higher than that will be called an *excited* or *isomeric state*. It is not uncommon in some types of beta decay for the nucleus, after the ejection of a beta particle, to be left in an excited or isomeric state. Such an instance is followed quite rapidly by the emission of a gamma ray from the excited nucleus. The decay of radioactive cobalt-60 is an example of such a decay scheme.

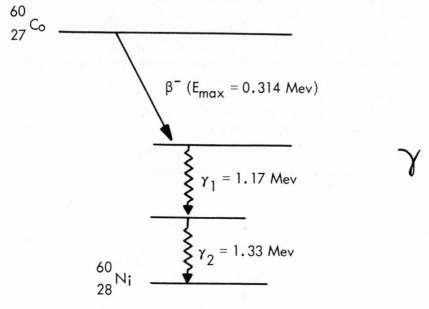

**Figure 2.3**  The decay scheme of cobalt-60. The beta particle is followed by the emission of two gamma rays. Cobalt-60 decays by beta emission to an excited state of $^{60}$Ni. This transition is instantaneously followed by the emission of two gamma rays, one after the other (cascade), to the stable form of the isotope.

Gamma rays belong to the electromagnetic spectrum (Table 2.1). Although they have a characteristic wavelike nature, their interactions are more easily understood if the radiations are considered as behaving as if they were small bundles of energy traveling at the speed of light. This bundle of energy is called a *quantum* or a *photon*. The amount of energy which is carried by the individual photon is related directly (is proportional) to the frequency of the wave form. It is not uncommon in some types of beta decay for the nucleus, after the ejection of a beta particle, to be left in an excited or isomeric state. Such an instance is followed quite rapidly by the emission of a gamma ray from the excited nucleus. The decay of radioactive cobalt-60 is an example of such a decay scheme.

**2.6  Other Forms of Radioactive Decay.**  Although alpha, beta and gamma emission constitute the majority of the decay processes, this should not imply that these are the only ones. Included among the less common ones are electron capture and internal conversion. In the former, one of the orbital electrons is "captured" by the nucleus (usually a K electron since these are closest to the nucleus) and a nuclear proton is converted to a neutron. The process normally leaves the nucleus in an excited energy state. The excess energy is subsequently released as a gamma ray. Very weak x ray is also produced because the outer orbital electrons will rearrange themselves to fill the vacancy in the K orbit. This results in the production of characteristic x rays (characteristic x rays will be discussed in Section 2.8). Thus, as a result of electron capture, gamma rays as well as characteristic x rays are produced.

In some of the heavier atoms there is a finite probability that orbital electrons (K electrons) may actually pass through the nucleus itself. If such a nucleus happens to be in an excited energy state, it is possible for electrons passing through it to acquire the excess energy and be ejected in what appears to be beta emission. These electrons, however, are called *conversion electrons*. A major difference between this type of beta emission and beta decay is that the electrons which are emitted during internal conversion have specific energies related to the specific excited state, whereas electrons produced by beta decay are emitted in a continuous spectrum of energies.

**2.7 The X-Ray Machine.** Whenever any substance is bombarded by high-speed electrons, x rays are produced. The production of x rays may be compared to what occurs when a rock is thrown against a wall. The rock (an object with mass) is thrown and given velocity (kinetic energy). When the rock strikes the wall, its energy is given up to the wall. The energy is then emitted from the wall as sound waves (another form of energy). The high-speed electrons are analogous to the rock and the x rays are analogous to the sound waves. The *x-ray* tube produces the electrons and accelerates them so that they may be used to bombard a target. It is the target in the tube which produces the x rays.

The conventional x-ray tube (Figure 2.4) consists of an evacuated glass envelope, a filament, a target, and a window through which the x rays pass. The purpose of the filament is to produce a cloud of negative electrons. This is accomplished by heating a filament of tungsten wire (by a filament heater circuit) to white heat so that electrons are literally "boiled off." If high voltage is applied across the tube between the filament and the target (the filament is made very negative and the target very positive), the electrons will be repelled by the filament and attracted by the target. The distance between the filament and the target is short, but, in it, electrons achieve speeds approaching the velocity of light (since they are in a vacuum there is no resistance from air molecules).

When the high-speed electrons are suddenly stopped by striking the surface of the target, their kinetic energy (energy of motion) is changed to x rays and heat. (Targets are usually made by imbedding a piece of tungsten in a large bar of copper. Materials [such as tungsten] which have a high atomic number and high melting point [required

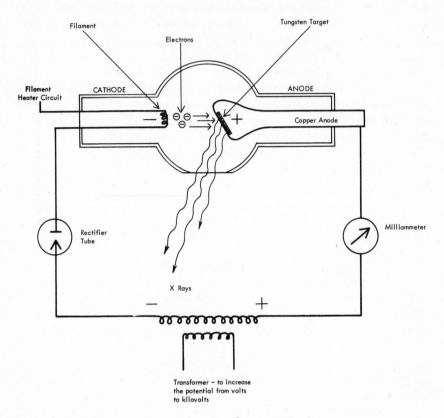

**Figure 2.4.** A diagrammatic representation of an x-ray circuit.

because of great heat production] make ideal targets. The massive copper bar has a high thermal conductivity which can dissipate the heat either to the air or to circulating cooling oil.)

The total amount of x ray produced by a machine may be controlled by two principal means. First, the tube current or the flow of electrons between the filament and the target may be varied. This is controlled by variation of the filament heating circuit; increased heat produces more electrons and therefore more x rays. The variation in x-ray output is proportional to the tube current (if the current is doubled, the output will be doubled). Secondly, variation in the tube high voltage will affect radiation output. Since it is the voltage, the potential across the x-ray tube, which accelerates the electrons to their high velocities before impact, it can be readily seen that if the voltage is increased the velocity (and energy) of the electrons will also be increased. Since the electrons have more energy, an increase in quantity as well as x-ray energy is achieved. The x-ray output varies with voltage as a power function, not as a direct proportionality (as in the case of tube current). Thus a change in tube voltage will have a greater effect on x-ray output than will a proportional change in tube current.

**2.8  Mechanisms of X-Ray Production.**  At the atomic level the process of x-ray production is made up of two major components: (1) the production of a continuous spectrum of x-ray energies from electrons interacting with atomic nuclei (*Bremsstrahlung* or "braking" radiation); and (2) the production of characteristic x rays by the rearrangement of the orbital electrons of an atom after the ejection of one of them by a high-speed electron. The *continuous spectrum* is produced when high-speed electrons encounter nuclei in target atoms.

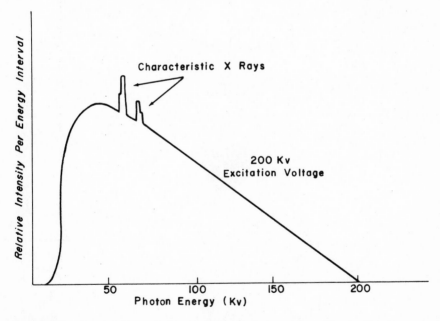

**Figure 2.5.**  The distribution of intensity with photon energy (the continuous x-ray spectrum).

If an electron passes close to the nucleus, it will be attracted by the strong electric field set up by the positively charged nucleus (those nuclei with more protons will produce more intense electric fields) and its direction will be changed. This process will cause a reduction in electron energy; the energy will be irradiated as x rays (*Brems-*

*strahlung*). Maximum x-ray energy is produced when the high-speed electrons occasionally collide with the nucleus. In this case all the electron energy is given up as x ray. Because any amount of energy may be lost by the electron (up to the maximum electron energy) and converted to x ray, the x rays produced are not of a specific energy but are distributed in the form of a continuous spectrum (Figure 2.5). Thus, a machine operating at a peak voltage E would be equivalent to a radiation beam of a single energy (monoenergetic) equal to E/3. A 250 KV x-ray machine, then, produces a radiation beam equivalent to about an 85 Kev gamma ray photon.

The other major mode of x-ray production involves the collision of the accelerated electrons with orbital electrons in the target atoms. If the energy imparted to the orbital electron is greater than the binding energy of the specific electron shell, the orbital electron is ejected. This energy (the binding energy) remains with the atom; the atom is

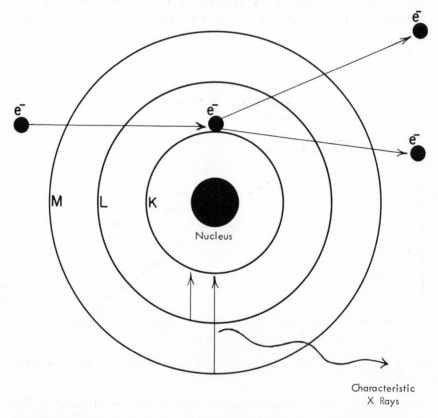

**Figure 2.6** A bombarding electron has ejected an orbital electron from the K shell of an atom. When outer electrons fall back to fill the hole, energy is radiated as characteristic x ray.

left in an excited state. Once an electron is ejected, the "hole" will be filled by an electron from any of the outer shells.

In Figure 2.6 an accelerated electron has ejected a K electron. Energy equal to the binding energy of the K shell has been given to the atom. Electrons from the L or M shells will fall in to fill the space. These transitions of the electrons from the outer to the inner shells result in radiation (characteristic x rays) whose energy is equal to the difference in binding energies of the two shells. After rearrangement of the outer electrons and the filling of all vacancies in the orbits, the total energy given off as x ray will be equal to the initial energy imparted in removing the original ejected electron.

The percentage of the total x ray, contributed by characteristic x ray, is a function of the kilovoltage of the machine. In the region of 50 to 100 Kv the characteristic x rays make up approximately 25 per cent of the total x ray produced, while at energies above 200 Kv their contribution to the total is almost insignificant.

**2.9  Measurement of Radiation Quality (Half-Value Layer).**  The quality of a radiation beam is a description of the distribution of the energies of the photons that make it up. Actual spectral determinations are very difficult to make. However, an estimate of the beam quality (penetrability) can be obtained by determining the degree of attenuation after passing through given thickness of certain materials. X-ray beams composed chiefly of more energetic photons will be less attenuated than beams in which lower energy photons predominate. The basis then of quality measurement is the absorption curve of the x-ray beam in a chosen material. The quantity of radiation, after passing through increasing thicknesses of absorber, will decrease (Figure 2.7). If the radiations were of a single energy (not a continuous spectrum), the plot of reduction in output against added filter (on a semilog scale) would be expected to be a straight line. Since, however, x-radiation is heterogeneous in nature, the curve actually becomes less steep when filtration is added. This is due to the preferential absorption of the less energetic, less penetrating photons as filter is added. The penetration or quality is usually described as the *half-value layer*—that thickness of any substance needed to reduce the radiation intensity to one half its original value.

## SUMMARY

1. *Radioactive decay* is accompanied mainly by emission of alpha, beta, or gamma rays. Alpha decay is characterized by the emission of a highly charged relatively massive particle with quite specific

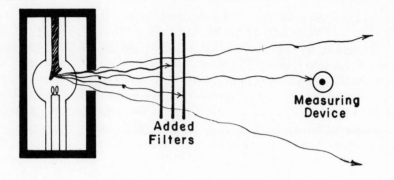

Added
Filters

Measuring
Device

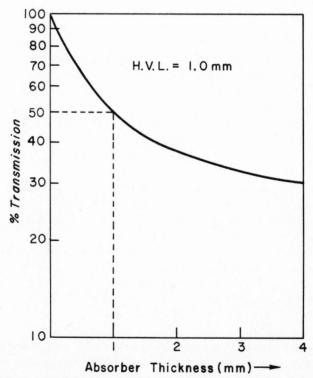

Figure 2.7 The determination of radiation quality, the half-value layer of an x-ray beam.

energies. The very small beta particle is given off in a continuous spectrum in which the energy is shared with the neutrino. In gamma decay there is the emission of pure energy (no change in mass and no change in charge).

2. *X rays* are produced when accelerated electrons strike the target of an x-ray tube. A continuous spectrum of x-ray energies is produced by nuclear interactions, and characteristic x rays are produced by interaction with orbital electrons.

## Text References

1. Johns, H. E.: *The Physics of Radiology*, Charles C Thomas, Springfield, Ill., 1961.
2. Glasser, O., Quimby, E., Taylor, L., Weatherwax, J., and R. Morgan: *Physical Foundations of Radiology*, Harper and Row, New York, 1961.
3. Quimby, E., and Feitelberg, S.: *Radioactive Isotopes in Medicine and Biology*, Lea & Febiger, Philadelphia, 1963.

# 3

# Background Radiation

**3.1 Introduction.** All living things are now and have been throughout the history of life, constantly exposed to ionizing radiations. These radiations, the background radiation, fall generally into three categories: (1) cosmic radiations from outer space; (2) natural radioactivity; and, more recently, (3) artificial radioactivity (usually associated with fallout).

**3.2 Cosmic Radiations.** Primary cosmic rays from outer space which bombard the earth and its atmosphere are composed approximately of: 79 per cent protons, 20 per cent alpha particles, and 1 per cent heavy atomic nuclei.[1] Although these radiations are very energetic, the earth is protected from them by a protective blanket, the atmosphere. Thus the altitude will directly influence the radiation exposure from cosmic rays since the higher altitudes will have less protective-air cover (Figure 3.1).

These high-energy particles interact with the nuclei or atmospheric atoms to produce electrons, neutrons, gamma rays, and mesons (the meson is a particle with a unit positive or negative charge and a mass varying from about 300 times that of an electron to almost that of a proton). At sea level, mesons account for approximately 80 per cent of the total radiations; electrons essentially account for the remainder. Less than 1 per cent of the primary particles reach sea level.[1]

The radiation dose from cosmic rays also varies with the geomagnetic latitude. Because the earth is surrounded by a magnetic field which goes from pole to pole, the primary cosmic rays (being highly charged particles) are deflected by this magnetic field. Cosmic radiation levels (at the same altitude) are therefore lowest at the equator and increase as one moves toward either pole. The more inhabited temperate zones are exposed to intermediate radiation levels.

**3.3 Natural Radioactivity.** When the matter of our universe was first formed, it is safe to assume that there were many more naturally occurring radionuclides than there are now. Many of the radionuclides originally present no longer exist, since the shorter half-lived radioactive forms have disappeared. Those that remain (1) have half lives comparable to the age of the earth or (2) are derived from radioactive decay of very long-lived radionuclides.

Today there are approximately 340 nuclides found in nature; approximately one fifth of these are radioactive. Most of the long-lived radionuclides are to be found within the group of the most heavy elements.

In addition to naturally occurring radionuclides, there are some others, produced by cosmic-ray interaction with nuclides in the

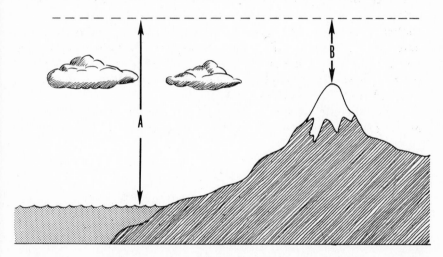

**Figure 3.1.** The variation in the amount of intervening atmosphere between sea level (A) and high altitudes (B). Cosmic radiations will be more completely absorbed in traversing more atmosphere.

atmosphere changing them to radioactive forms. The two major examples of this type are carbon-14 and tritium ($^3$H).

Areas exist throughout the world in which living things are exposed to background radiation levels considerably higher than others. The radioactivity is usually of two sources: (1) mineral springs which contain relatively large amounts of radium, and (2) thorium-bearing minerals such as the nonazete sand of South America.

**3.4 Artificial Radioactivity (Fallout).** Radioactive fallout from the detonation of nuclear devices in the earth's atmosphere is the major source of *artificial radioactivity* which contributes to the background radiations of the earth. These radionuclides are termed "fission" products and are produced by the breaking apart of a heavy atom such as uranium. Briefly, when heavy elements (uranium, plutonium) are bombarded by neutrons, one of these neutrons may enter the heavy atom and produce a combination which is quite unstable. The heavy atom immediately "breaks" into 2 smaller atoms (not necessarily the same size); these atoms produced by the fission are called "fission products."

Fission products have masses varying between 80 and 150. Further, many of them are radioactive. A bomb cloud moves through the upper atmosphere and radioactive debris "falls out" on the earth below.

Further, much less extensive, sources of artificial radioactivity are the areas in the general vicinity of large laboratories using nuclear reactors. Some of these laboratories utilize either air or water as coolants. As the water or air passes through the reactors, it is bombarded by neutrons, and is made radioactive. This material may then be distributed by air currents or by return of water to the adjacent rivers. These areas would be considered as relatively minor and generally not to affect the population at large.

Artificial radioactivity is a recent burden, superimposed on the existing natural background, and is the easiest for man to control.

## SUMMARY

Living things are constantly bombarded by relatively low levels of terrestrial and extraterrestrial ionizing radiations.

## Text Reference

1.   Eisenbud, M.: *Environmental Radioactivity*, McGraw-Hill, New York, 1963.

# 4

# The Interactions of

# Radiation with Matter

**4.1  Introduction.**  Detectable injury or damage to living things as a result of exposure to ionizing radiation is the result of a long, complex chain of events. The first of these is the transfer of energy from an ionizing radiation into the matter of which living things are composed. The *mode* of energy transfer characteristic of ionizing radiation is the production in matter of excited and ionized atoms or molecules. The discussion here will be confined to the biologic results of *ionization;* the contribution of *excitation*, although probably significant, is as yet too poorly understood to permit much to be said about it.

**4.2  The Interaction of X and Gamma Rays.**  X and gamma photons have no mass or charge. In their interactions with matter the energy of the photons is transferred by *collision*, usually with an orbital electron in an atom of the absorbing medium. Following such a collision an electron may either have been moved to an orbit more distant from the nucleus (the atom is excited) or, more commonly, it will have been *ejected* from the atom (ionization) with high energy and at a high speed. The energy given *to* the electron will be dissipated *from* it as it moves through the medium; it will ionize and excite atoms with which *it* interacts.

Since the interaction of x and gamma ray photons with matter depends upon direct collision with orbital electrons (there is no other important mode of interaction), they may penetrate deeply into matter or pass through vast distances in it without having interacted. Atoms are composed chiefly of unoccupied space, and the photon, having no affinity for any of the atomic parts (such as electrical attraction), may pass undeflected through the relatively vast intra- and interatomic spaces. In fact, there is some probability of penetration even through the greatest thickness of the most dense matter without a single interaction ever having taken place.

The probability that a photon *will* interact when it passes through any given thickness of matter will depend on a complex relationship

between (1) the *energy* of the photon, (2) the *density* of the matter, and
(3), in some interactions, on the *physical make-up* of the atoms of
which the matter is composed. Dependent upon photon *energy* there
are two major modes by which the photons give up their energy to a
medium through the ejection of orbital electrons: (1) photoelectric
absorption and (2) compton scattering.

**4.3   Photoelectric Absorption: A Low-Energy Phenomenon.**   When
a *low-energy* photon collides with an orbital electron the most likely
result will be a transfer of *all* of the photon's energy to the electron.
The photon disappears entirely or is "absorbed" by the electron
(Figure 4.1).

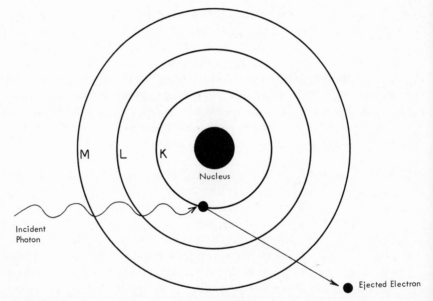

**Figure 4.1.**   In the photoelectric absorption process the bombarding photon gives up
all its energy to the electron with which it interacts. A portion of this energy equal to the
binding energy of the orbit is given to the atom. As the vacancy is filled by outer
electrons this energy is irradiated as characteristic x rays.

The electron itself will be ejected from its orbit and from the atom.
The process is, of course, *ionization* and the result will be an ion pair.
But not all orbital electrons are bound in their orbits by equal
energies; those nearer the nucleus are bound more tightly than those
distant from it. The photon may have enough energy to remove an L or
M electron from a particular absorbing atom but not enough to remove
the atom's K electron. (The process cannot occur with electrons of a
particular orbit if the photon energy is *less* than that of the orbit.)

Photoelectric interaction, then, depends on photon energy; ejection of an electron is most likely to occur when the photon has an energy slightly greater than the binding energy of the orbit. The probability of this interaction increases when the energy of the photon is slightly greater than that of the orbit because *all* electrons of a given shell will be available to undergo photoelectric absorption. The probability of photoelectric interaction decreases with *increasing* photon energy. Higher photon energies will exceed those of the orbits and the interaction becomes less likely to occur.

When an electron is removed from an atom, the atom is, of course, ionized. But the atom will *also* be in an unstable excited state, because an excess of energy, equal to that of the orbital binding energy, was given to it when the electron was removed. This unstable situation is quickly ended when the orbital vacancy is filled. Electrons from orbits more distant than the one in which the vacancy exists are attracted inward, filling the defect. When the defect is filled in this way, characteristic x rays are emitted (Section 2.8). In tissue the binding energy of even the K shell of most of the atoms that make it up averages only about 0.5 Kev. This is so small that nearly all the energy of even low-energy photons is given to the ejected electron; the atom gets essentially none. These electrons, now moving at high speeds, move through tissue, producing ionizations among the atoms through which they traverse. These electrons will be the actual entities responsible for the biologic effects of x or gamma rays. In soft tissue, photoelectric absorption is the predominant energy absorption process for photons up to 100 Kev.

The probability of occurrence of photoelectric absorption depends not only on the energy of the photon, but also on the *atomic number* of the atoms with which it interacts. Since atomic number is an expression of the number of protons in the nucleus (the attractive force of the nucleus on its orbital electrons), elements having high atomic numbers have large positively charged nuclei and bind the electrons of their inner orbits very tightly. In atoms with tightly bound electrons, relatively *higher* energy photons also have a high probability of photoelectric interaction. This is because the highest probability of photoelectric interactions occurs at or about the binding energy of the electron shell. Because of the dependence on atomic number, there is a preferential absorption of photons in materials composed of elements having high atomic numbers (such as are present in bone) when compared to material composed of elements having low atomic numbers (soft tissue) in the energy region in which the photoelectric effect is important. The consequence of this is that, for the *same* exposure dose (with lower-energy photons), bone will absorb more x or gamma radiation than will soft tissue.

**4.4   Compton Scattering: A Median-Energy Phenomenon.**   In contrast to photoelectric absorption, compton scattering (named after its discoverer, H. H. Compton) is a process in which higher energy photons interact with matter (Figure 4.2). In it the photons have only a *portion* of their energy absorbed in interacting with orbital electrons (they are not *totally* absorbed). The process is confined, for the most part, to interactions with outer, loosely bound electrons. Because these electrons *are* loosely bound, nearly *all* the energy exchanged to the electrons will be in the form of electron kinetic energy (the

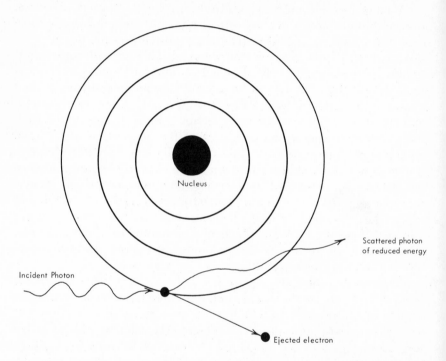

**Figure 4.2**   In compton scattering the incident photon interacts with an orbital electron, but only a portion of its energy is given to the electron (it is ejected from the atom). The photon is changed in its direction and is degraded in energy after the interaction.

binding energy of the orbit is essentially negligible). The photon itself will be deflected in the interaction; its direction will be changed. It is said, then, to have been "scattered." The products of the interaction are: (1) a scattered, less energetic, degraded photon (some of its energy has gone to the electron it ejected); (2) a high-speed electron; and (3) an ionized atom.

The ejected electron, as in photoelectric absorption, will travel some discrete distance in matter, producing ionizations along its track. But in compton interactions, there is also the degraded photon which may undergo two, three, or more *additional* compton collisions before all its energy is finally lost. Thus, photons of this energy range have their energy distributed through repeated compton interactions *over a relatively large volume of matter.* The process is important for photons of median energies but becomes of lesser importance at higher energies.

Since compton interaction principally involves the most loosely bound electrons, it will also differ from photoelectric absorption because it will *not* depend on atomic number (the attractive force of the nucleus). And *because* only the most loosely bound electrons are involved, all of them will absorb about the same amount of energy from the phonton; effectively, none goes to the atom. The compton process is a random process; hence the probability of interaction will depend only on the density of electrons (the number of electrons per gram of material). Most materials have nearly the same number of electrons per gram, so that it follows that compton absorption per gram of matter is almost the same for all materials. This, too, is in contrast to the photoelectric effect where high atomic number materials, such as are present in bone, absorb more energy from the same dose of incident radiation than do materials such as soft tissue. For photons in the range of 100 Kev to 10 Mev, compton interaction is the most important photon interaction process in soft tissue.

**4.5 Pair Production: A High-Energy Phenomenon.** Photon energy may be exchanged into matter by yet another mechanism — which differs from those already described — in two fundamental details: (1) it occurs exclusively with *high*-energy photons, and (2) the interaction is with the *atomic nucleus* and does not involve the ejection of orbital electrons (Figure 4.3).

Photons with energies *greater than 1.02 Mev* may interact with the electric force field of the highly charged nucleus so that their energy is converted to mass. The photon is changed into two particles, a *positive* and a *negative* electron. [The process can occur in reverse; mass can also be converted to energy. Energy (E) and mass (m) are related to each other according to the Einstein formula, $E = mc^2$, where c is the velocity of light.] Pair production cannot occur with photons whose energy is less than the rest mass of *two* electrons (0.51 Mev/electron), a threshold energy of 1.02 Mev. Photon energy in *excess* of the threshold value will be shared as *kinetic energy* between the two newly formed electrons. If there is no excess energy present, the electrons will immediately recombine ("annihilation") and are converted back to energy.

In the instance where threshold energy is exceeded, the electrons will move away from the point of formation. Both will move through matter undergoing interactions with and ionizing other atoms in the

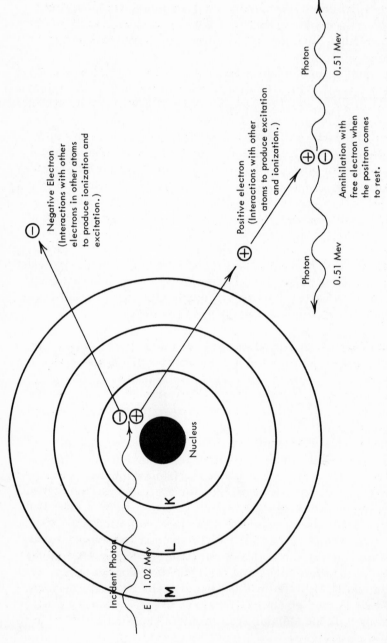

**Figure 4.3.** In pair production the photon interacts with the strong field near the nucleus and a positron and electron are produced. The electron and the positron both give up their kinetic energy to the medium by ionizing and exciting other atoms. When the positron comes to rest, it combines with one of the abundant free electrons annihilating each other, and two equal gamma rays (the energy equivalent of their masses) are given off in opposite directions.

substance until the excess kinetic energy is exhausted. In this way, energy is utimately transferred from the photon to matter.

When the positive electron comes to rest, it will interact with an available negative electron. Annihilation will occur, the electrons will disappear, and the electron masses will be converted to two photons which share the energy.

Pair production is dependent upon atomic number. The initial photon interaction is with the force field of the nucleus. Larger nuclei, having more protons, will have stronger force fields, thus increasing the probability of the occurrence of this process.

**4.6 The Relative Importance of Different Types of Photon Absorption.** Predominance of one or more of these processes will depend upon the energy of the photons and the nature of the absorber. Table 4.1 summarizes the relative *preferential* energy absorption of bone and soft tissue when each of the photon absorption processes is predominant. For example, x-ray tubes operating at voltages up to 150 Kv will produce radiation beams resulting in high bone absorption; most of the interactions are of the photoelectric type. For machines operating between 150 and 250 Kv, the predominance of the photoelectric effect diminishes but bone will still absorb some extra energy. High-energy photons from sources with energies from about 1 to 10 Mev (cobalt-60 gamma rays and high-energy x-ray machines) lose energy exclusively by compton interaction so that there is no preferential bone absorption. With more complex equipment such as betatrons which operate with energies from 10 to 30 Mev, pair production is predominant and preferential absorption by bone again occurs.

**Table 4.1.** Relationship of the Primary Photon Energy Absorption Process to the Energy Absorption in Bone and Soft Tissue

| Primary Absorption Process | Preferential Absorption |
|---|---|
| Photoelectric | Bone will absorb 5 to 6 times as much energy per gram as will soft tissue |
| Compton | Bone and soft tissue absorb essentially the same energy per gram |
| Pair production | Bone absorbs approximately two times as much energy per gram as soft tissue |

**4.7 Interaction of Particulate Radiations with Matter.** The interactions of particulate radiations with matter are distinct from those of electromagnetic radiations (x and gamma radiations) because

particulate radiations may have both mass and charge. These properties make possible interactions with matter not only by *direct* collision
with electrons in the orbits of the atoms in the matter that they
traverse, but also by *interactions* (this can be attraction or repulsion)
*between their charge and that of the orbital electrons*. But, the final
result of the interaction of both electromagnetic and particulate
radiations will be the same; that is, ionization, the production in
matter of high-speed electrons.

**4.8   The Influence of Particle Charge.**   The effect which one
charged body has upon another is related to the *distance between
them* and the *amount of charge* on each. As the distance between
charged bodies increases and/or the quantity of their charge
decreases, the effect they have on each other diminishes. The rate at
which energy is lost along the track of the charged particle depends
upon the *square* of the charge of the particle. Thus, a proton or an
electron moving through matter at the same *velocity* would have the
same rate of energy loss, but an alpha particle (with twice the charge
of either the proton or the electron) with the same velocity would have
a rate of energy loss four times as great. The more highly charged the
particle, the more intense *its* electric force field, and the greater the
likelihood of producing ionization of atoms along its track. The
influence of particle charge is to increase the number of interparticu-
late interactions and hence produce more ion pairs per unit path
length (they would produce a higher "specific ionization").

**4.9   The Influence of Particle Velocity.**   Two particles with the *same*
energy do not necessarily have the same velocity. The kinetic energy
(energy of motion) of any object is equal to $1/2mv^2$, where m is the rest
mass and v is the velocity. For example, protons, because their rest
mass is about 2000 times that of electrons, will be moving much
slower than electrons when the kinetic energies of both are the same.
The influence of particle velocity on interactions between charged
particles lies in the fact that velocity will control the *length of time*
the electric force field of the particle is exerted in any given place.
The effect (attraction or repulsion of orbital electrons) by the force
field of the charged particle will depend on how long the force is
applied. The slower moving charged particles will produce more
ionizations per unit path length (a higher "specific ionization") than
faster moving ones. Two particles having the *same* kinetic energy may
produce vastly different specific ionizations if their masses differ. For
example, even though their kinetic energies are the same, a 1 Mev
proton would have a specific ionization 100 times *greater* than a 1 Mev
electron; the more massive proton would be moving more slowly

than the electron (specific ionization depends inversely on the velocity of the charged particle).

During each interaction, energy is lost by the particle and transferred to the medium (W = 33.7 ev is the *average* energy *required* to produce an ion pair). A loss of kinetic energy will inevitably result in a change in velocity; after each loss the particle will move more slowly. And since the probability of ionization is inversely related to velocity, such a change will mean an increase in specific ionization and an increase in the rate of loss of kinetic energy. The specific ionization of a particle reaches the highest point just before the particle comes to rest.

**4.10  Specific Ionization and Linear Energy Transfer (LET).**  *Specific ionization,* the number of ions formed per unit length of path (track) traversed, takes into consideration the energy transferred to the medium only by means of *ionization.* But energy will also be transferred to the medium by excitation. At present the full biologic significance of excitation is not known, but a substantial amount of energy is transferred to tissue in this way. The process is likely, therefore, to be very important. A unit which has been devised to account for *all* the energy liberated along the path of an ionizing particle, irrespective of the mechanism, is *linear energy transfer* (LET). LET is the energy released (usually in Kev) per micron of medium (tissue) along the track of any ionizing *particle.*

Since *rate of loss of energy* by ionizing particles will be affected by the velocity and the charge on such a particle, a relatively slow-moving highly charged particle will have a high LET. A faster-moving particle and/or one with a lesser charge will have a much smaller LET. Biologic damage is related to LET. In a general way, particles with high LET are *more likely* to produce change in a given volume of living matter, because their ionizations are produced close together in comparison to low LET radiations, whose ionizations are produced relatively far apart.

The increase in biologic damage with increasing LET does not, however, continue indefinitely. With radiations or extremely high LET, *more* energy is transferred to the system than is needed to produce even the maximum biologic effect — death. Such radiations will "overkill," that is, they will deposit more energy in cells or tissues than is required to inactivate them.

**4.11  Particle Tracks in Matter.**  LET is not a static or constant value but will be different even for the same particle over different portions in the track. This is so because, while charge on a particle is a constant factor, the velocity will be continually changing (decreasing) all along the particle track. Each interaction (excitation or ionization) involves a *loss* of energy from the particle and a concomitant deceleration. As a result, LET gradually increases along a particle track with a very dramatic increase occurring just before the particle comes to rest. When a particle does come to rest, it usually acquires electrical neutrality. Positively charged particles will acquire electrons (the proton will become a hydrogen atom; the alpha particle will become a helium atom) and high-speed electrons, when they come to rest, drop into atomic orbits.

Particles with different degrees of charge will produce different tracks. Highly charged particles interact frequently; consequently, they have a high LET, and the ionizations along their tracks are very dense. Particles with lesser degrees of charge are sparsely ionizing; they have a lower LET.

Whether or not the *track* of a particle is altered by its interaction with an orbital electron will depend upon the particle's mass. Large massive particles (such as alpha particles) have straight tracks; they are not deflected in their interactions with the minute electrons. Their direction is changed only when they collide (it will be a chance event) with an atomic nucleus. Electrons, on the other hand, have the direction of their track changed at nearly every interaction. Their tracks, usually described as tortuous, are the result of deflections which come about from the interaction of two bodies of equal mass.

The interaction of any particle in matter is a random affair. This is true because the atoms of all matter are in constant motion and, except for the rigid structure of crystals, are randomly spaced. In addition, the electrons of each atom are also in constant motion. Thus, an ionizing particle traveling through matter will encounter orbital electrons on a change basis. For particles having a very high LET, the *randomness* of interaction will have little biologic importance. The interactions of these particles are so closely spaced that, even when the particles pass through a space as small as the tiniest cellular-compartment, it is highly likely that some energy will have been left there. In contrast to this, sparsely ionizing (low LET) particles interact infrequently enough so that it is even possible for them to pass through cells or their important sub-structures without having interacted at all.

Not every electron ejected by an ionizing particle will have the same kinetic energy; particles do not lose the same amount of energy at each interaction. Some electrons are scarcely removed from their orbits while others are given very large amounts of kinetic energy and move for appreciable distances through matter. Some of these energetic "secondary" electrons may have sufficient energy to produce a track of their own which will appear as a branch from the track of the primary ionizing particle (Figure 4.4).

Such branches or spurs are known as delta rays. They themselves will have an LET which will be different from the primary particle, and in fact will differ sharply in this respect among themselves. Their major importance in radiobiology is in the fact that they distribute the energy of the primary particle to regions *outside* the primary particle track.

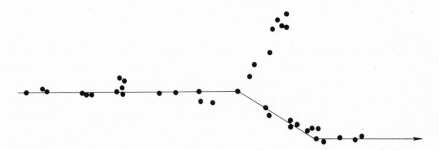

**Figure 4.4.**  Representation of the distribution of ionization along the track of a charged particle. A delta track or "spur" is shown branching from the primary track.

**4.12  Electrons (Beta Rays).**  The loss of energy from high-speed electrons in living systems is of considerable importance. These electrons are, of course, the result of the interaction of high-energy ionizing radiation with matter and are responsible for the distribution of that energy through matter. Beyond this, however, they are a major component of radioactive decay products of biologically important radionuclides (carbon-14, hydrogen-3, and phosphorus-32).

Electrons may interact either with orbital electrons or the atomic nucleus. They may directly collide with or exert their electrical force on orbital electrons (usually displacing them from the orbit), lose some energy, and have a change in the direction of their path. Their interactions with atomic nuclei occur when they pass close enough to a nucleus. The electric force field of the nucleus slows them down and, because they are attracted to the nucleus, their direction is changed. The slowing down represents *loss* of energy from the electron; the energy is irradiated as x-ray photons. The x ray will have a *great* penetration in tissue and can produce biologic damage distant from the track of the electron. This process (*Bremsstrahlung*) is most important with high-speed electrons and absorbers with high atomic numbers (Z). Since soft tissues are made up mainly of low atomic number elements (H, O, N, C) the process in them is not common.

The distribution of ionizations from electrons usually occurs in clusters which have a fairly random distribution. The *number* of ions in a cluster will vary, but *on the average* there will be approximately 3 in each. Assuming the value of $W = 33.7$ ev/ion pair to be approximately correct for soft tissue, an average of 3 ionizations per cluster would mean that approximately 112 ev is deposited at each point of interaction along the track. The effect of decreasing velocity (with increasing LET) is to cause clusters of ions to occur more closely together but not necessarily to increase the number of ions per cluster. Finally, a rough estimate of the distribution of energy from a fast electron (1 Mev) in water has been given by Johns[1]: 20 per cent excitation, 40 per cent ion clusters, and 40 per cent delta rays.

**4.13   Particle Range.**   Because of the tortuous nature of the electron track the actual penetration in matter will be less than the total track length. The distance penetrated is called the *range*. It is a measure of the *linear* distance from the point of origin of a charged particle to its extinction as a charged particle. The *range* is dependent upon energy; the *higher* the energy the *greater* the dependence upon energy; the *higher* the energy the *greater* the distance penetrated. Not all beta particles emitted during radioactive decay have the same energy (Section 2.4), so that no two beta particles from the same radionuclide need necessarily have the same range. There will, however, be a maximum energy of emission of beta particles from any radionuclide and consequently (for any given radionuclide) a maximum beta range. Most of the beta particles from the same radionuclide, however, will have a range *less* than the maximum. Table 4.2 gives examples of the *maximum* ranges of beta particles *in tissue* from some biologically important beta-emitting radionuclides.

**Table 4.2.**   Maximum Range of Beta Particles in Tissue

| Radionuclide | Maximum Energy (Mev) | Approximate Range in Soft Tissue |
|:---:|:---:|:---:|
| $^3$H | 0.018 | 6 $\mu$ |
| $^{14}$C | 0.155 | 300 $\mu$ |
| $^{35}$S | 0.167 | 300 $\mu$ |
| $^{90}$Sr | 0.610 | 0.2 cm |
| $^{32}$P | 1.700 | 0.8 cm |

It should be emphasized that these are *maximum* ranges; most of the beta particles of these radionuclides will have ranges less than these values.

Positrons, the positively charged high-speed electrons, lose their energy in exactly the same type of interactions as do negative electrons and would have the same range. When they come to rest, however, they are not captured by any atom but undergo annihilation by combining with a negative electron (Section 4.5).

**4.14 Protons and Deuterons.** Protons (hydrogen nuclei) and deuterons (heavy hydrogen nuclei) are, in the main, produced artifically by particle accelerators such as cyclotrons and Van de Graaff generators. Their ionizing track is straight; they are undeflected by the less massive electrons with which they interact, but their direction *can* be radically altered by occasional interactions with atomic nuclei. Their ionization density, for equal energies, occupies a place somewhere between that of electrons and alpha particles. Their present practical use is restricted by the elaborate equipment needed to produce them.

**4.15 Alpha Particles.** These are helium nuclei with a mass of 4 and a charge of +2. These particles are the product of radioactive decay of very heavy radionuclides such as radium. Because their charge is twice that of the proton or the electron, and because their great mass makes them relatively slow moving, they give up all their energy in short, straight tracks of exceedingly high ion density. Their range is of the order of microns in soft tissue, and they deposit large amounts of energy over the short distance that they travel. In cells they are highly damaging particles.

**4.16 Heavy Nuclei.** These are the nuclei of ordinary atoms whose electrons have been stripped away yielding a very heavy, very highly charged particle. They are artifically produced and are given high energy in an accelerator. Their large mass confers upon them the capability of colliding with *nuclei* in the absorber, and accelerating those nuclei (a reaction analogous to the production of high-speed electrons).

**4.17 Neutrons.** Neutrons, since they are uncharged particles, are not affected by and cannot themselves affect charged objects (atomic nuclei or electrons). Since their interactions must depend upon chance collisions with atoms, they are able to penetrate great distances in matter of all kinds. Neutrons are classified by their only distinctive property — their energy. Dependent on that factor, they are usually considered as *fast* or *slow*. Fast neutrons lose energy mainly by collision with atomic nuclei. Since carbon, oxygen, nitrogen, and hydrogen are the major components of soft tissue, their interaction with fast neutrons is of importance to radiobiology. Because hydrogen atoms are the most numerous in tissue of average water content (tissues are 70 to 80 per cent water), and since the average energy transferred from a fast neutron to a hydrogen nucleus is much greater than the energy transferred to any other nucleus, for practical purposes the major mode of energy loss of fast neutrons in soft tissue may be considered to be by the *ejection* of high-speed protons (hydrogen nuclei). The protons will have a variety of energies depending upon the neutron energies, but all of them will be highly ionizing particles with a high LET (Section 4.14).

Slow neutrons interact in matter mainly by the process of "capture." The uncharged, slowly moving neutron actually enters the nucleus of an atom in matter and loses its identity. It becomes just another nuclear neutron. The added neutron—and its energy—may put the atom in an unstable state; the atom may become radioactive and itself emit charged particles (protons, electrons, alpha particles) or gamma rays.

## SUMMARY

1. Radiations produce their effect principally by the process of ionization—the ejection of outer orbital electrons from atoms.
2. X and gamma rays lose their energy in matter by three primary processes: (a) *photoelectric absorption* and (b) *compton scattering,* which result in the ejection of an orbital electron, while (c) *pair production* involves a change of the photon energy into mass (a positive and negative electron are formed).
3. Charged particles such as protons, alpha particles, and heavy nuclei also lose the majority of their energy through electron interaction but may also interact with the nuclei of atoms in the medium.
4. High-speed neutrons lose their energy in tissues primarily through the collision with hydrogen atoms. Their nuclei (actually protons) are highly ionizing particles.

### Text References

1. Johns, H. E.: *The Physics of Radiology,* Charles C Thomas, Springfield, Ill., 1961.
2. Glasser, O., Quimby, E., Taylor, L., Weatherwax, J., and Morgan, R.: *Physical Foundations of Radiology,* Harper and Row, New York, 1961.

# 5

## Measurement of Radiation Dose

### Part I: Determination of Amount of Ionization Produced by Radiation within a Specified Air Volume

**5.1 Introduction.** Radiation biology is a study of the effects of ionizing radiations upon living systems. Nearly all radiation effects are dependent upon the amount of energy absorbed (the dose), and this is often most difficult to determine. It is important to be able to measure (or calculate from previous measurements) the amount of radiation delivered to an organism and to record this amount in units that are not ambigious. Units of radiation quantity should be specifically defined and universally accepted so that physical irradiation techniques can be reproduced exactly.

**5.2 Absorbed and Exposure Dose.** Only that energy of a radiation beam which is actually *absorbed* in a biologic system will produce an effect; that which passes through will have no effect. The amount of radiation directed at the biologic system is called the *exposure dose*. It is, as the name implies, the amount of radiation to which the system is "exposed." That portion of the exposure dose which is actually absorbed, the *absorbed dose*, is the biologically effective radiation. *Exposure dose* depends mainly on the properties of the *radiation source* and the *distance* from the source. *Absorbed dose* will depend not only on the exposure dose but also upon the physical properties of the object irradiated. Because x and gamma rays comprise the most widely utilized sources of ionizing radiation, the following sections will be concerned primarily with their measurement, but a consideration of particulate radiations is given in Chapter 7.

**5.3 The Measurement of Exposure Dose.** Exposure dose measurements rely primarily on the measurement of the ionization of gases by radiation. Approximately one year after the discovery of x rays by Wilhelm Roentgen, Perrin, using a charged condenser with air between the plates, demonstrated a loss of charge caused by ionization of the air by x rays. In 1908 Villard proposed a unit of x ray quantity (exposure dose) based on the ionization of air.

Air ionization is now the recognized technique for the measurement of exposure dose. It is rather easily accomplished, reproducible, and controlled. Air is of almost uniform consistency everywhere, and the electricity produced (ionizations) is relatively easily and accurately measured (Figure 5.1).

Since air has an effective atomic number very nearly the same as the soft tissues of the body, the absorption of x-ray energy per gram by

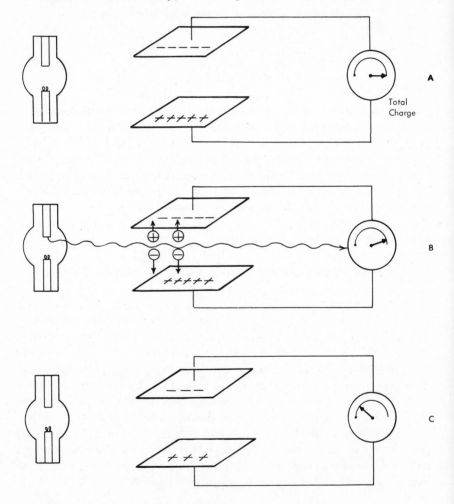

**Figure 5.1.** Measurement of air ionization.
    (a) A parallel plate condenser is charged.
    (b) The air between the plates is irradiated by x rays and ion pairs (positive atoms and negative electrons are produced).
    (c) These ion pairs migrate to the charged plates and discharge them. The radiation exposure is proportional to the measured discharge.

soft tissue, water, and air is almost the same even when x rays of widely varying wavelengths are utilized. This factor makes it possible, with modifications, to extend measurements made in air to absorbed dose in tissue.

**5.4 The Roentgen.** The Second International Congress of Radiology (in 1928) adopted the roentgen as the official unit of radiation quantity. Over the intervening years the wording of the definition has evolved to its present form: "The roentgen shall be the quantity of x- or gamma radiation such that the associated corpuscular emission per 0.001293 gram of air produces, in air, ions carrying 1 electrostatic unit of quantity of electricity of either sign." Actually, 0.001293 gram of air is 1 cc of air at standard conditions of 0° C and 760 mm of mercury pressure. The "associated corpuscular emissions" consist of photoelectrons and compton electrons ejected from the air atoms by the x- or gamma ray photons. Thus the roentgen (R) is a measure of the amount of photon-produced air ionization formed in 1 cc of air at standard conditions. The roentgen, by definition, is a unit of exposure dose for x and gamma rays only; it cannot be used for other types of radiation.

**5.5 Measurement of the Roentgen.** In order to measure roentgens, a known mass of air must be segregated and the ionization produced within this air must be measured. This is accomplished by the use of a device called a *standard free-air chamber*. The chamber is considered a *primary* standard. Primary standards are not routinely utilized but are usually confined to such institutions as the National Bureau of Standards in Washington, D. C. A schematic presentation of a free-air chamber is shown in Figure 5.2. In this instrument an air volume is isolated between collecting electrodes and the charge produced (electricity) is collected by a sensitive electrometer. The charge produced per unit volume of air is by definition the exposure dose in roentgens.

**5.6 Electronic Equilibrium.** An important concept associated with the measurement of exposure dose in roentgens is electronic equilibrium. It can be shown that as the energy of an x-ray beam is increased, maximum ionization occurs at increasingly greater distances from the radiation source. At distances beyond the point of maximum ionization, the measured dose is reduced because of air attenuation. When the number of electrons which is set in motion in a given volume is exactly equal to the number which come to rest in it, electronic equilibrium has been attained. This concept is illustrated in Figure 5.3.

Those secondary corpuscular radiations which originate within but lose a portion of their energy outside the specified volume are balanced by those which originate outside the volume, but contribute ionizations to it. Thus for practical purposes we may consider that all the ions produced within the volume lose all their energy within it. This, of course, is true only when the air volume extends in all

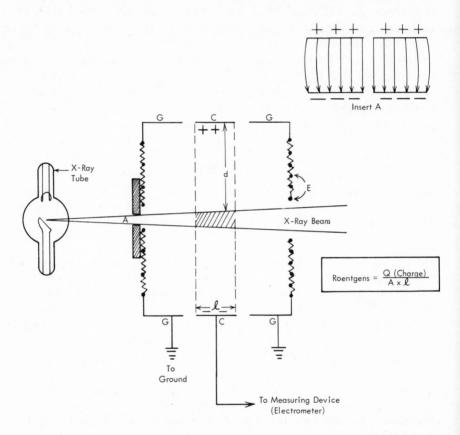

**Figure 5.2.** Diagram of a standard free-air chamber. The radiation beam is collimated by the aperture (A) and passes between the collecting electrodes (C). The shaded area between these electrodes is the volume of air in which the measurement is made. The guard plates (G), which are connected to ground, serve to define the edge of the collecting field. If it were not for these the field would "bulge" as shown in Insert A. The electrodes (E) help to prevent this type of distortion by distributing the voltage down a resistance chain. By multiplying the volume of air in the shaded area by its density (0.001293 gm/cc) one may obtain the mass of air. The distance (d) must be great enough so that the "secondary corpuscular emissions" will expend all their energy in the air volume. They must not hit the guard or the collection plates. The spacing between the plates increases with increasing x-ray kilovoltage: for 200 Kv, d = 6 cm; and for 500 Kv, d = 40 cm. For very high x-ray kilovoltages the chamber may be pressurized with dry air to reduce this distance. If the air pressure is doubled the electrons travel half as far.

directions at least a distance equal to or greater than the maximum range of any secondary corpuscular emission from a photon of a specific energy. This includes, therefore, the distance from the source of radiation to the volume in question. The maximum range of the secondary electrons is reflected in the plate separations in the free-air chamber with varying x-ray energies (Figure 5.2).

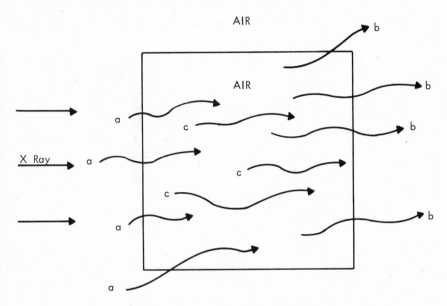

**Figure 5.3.** A unit volume of air is shown, completely surrounded by air, and uniformly irradiated with x rays. There are three groups of secondary corpuscular radiations: (a) those with an origin outside the volume, but which lose a portion of their energy within it; (b) those which originate within the volume and lose a portion of their energy within it *but* produce ionizations outside the volume as well; and (c) those which originate *and* lose all their energy within the specified volume. When electronic equilibrium is attained, the loss from (b) is compensated by the gain from (a).

**5.7  The Thimble Chamber (A Secondary Standard).** This type of measuring device is the most widely used instrument for the measurement of exposure dose (in roentgens). The large free-air chambers do not lend themselves to routine x-ray calibration, and, hence, are found usually in standardization laboratories. They are primary standards against which the light and mobile thimble chambers may be calibrated at intervals. The *thimble chamber* then is a *secondary measuring device*.

Thimble chambers are built to provide electron equilibrium. Consider the air volume in Figure 5.4(a) as being surrounded by air whose pressure can be varied. If the pressure is doubled, secondary electrons can travel only half as far, and the air need extend only half as far in all directions. The process could be "extended" so that the air is condensed to a "solid air wall." The status of the measuring volume itself will not have been changed, only the "air" surrounding it. The thimble chamber (Figure 5.4 [b]) has a solid "air equivalent" wall made of a material which behaves in respect to x rays in the same manner as air.

The effective atomic number of air is $Z = 7.64$. Since x-ray interaction depends on the atomic number of the absorber, thimble chambers can be constructed with walls and electrodes which behave

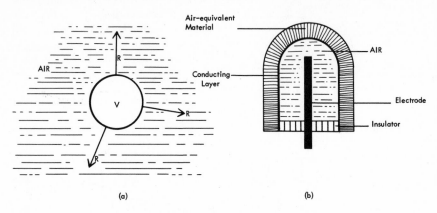

(a)                                                                 (b)

**Figure 5.4.** Schematic diagrams of (a) an air volume surrounded by air in all directions to a distance greater than the range of a secondary electron (R), and (b) an "air wall" thimble chamber shown in cross section.

as if they had a $Z = 7.6$. In actuality, the air wall is usually Bakelite, coated with a thin carbon layer on the interior, and the electrode is usually aluminum.

In the standard free-air chamber the measuring volume of air is surrounded on all sides by an amount of air greater than the range of any secondary electron ejected by a photon (electronic equilibrium). Similarly, the "air wall" of a thimble chamber must be thicker than the maximum range of the electrons ejected in it. For x-ray voltages up to 70 Kev, thin walls such as those composed of nylon are used; for voltages from 70 Kev to several hundred kilovolts the wall is made of Bakelite of 0.5 mm thickness; while for radiations greater than this (cobalt-60 at 1.25 Mev) a wall thickness of 3 to 4 mm must be provided.

**5.8  The Mechanism of the Thimble Chamber.**  The thimble chamber (also called a condenser chamber) uses a condenser system to store and measure electrical discharge produced by air ionization (Figure 5.5).

The Victoreen condenser chamber represents an example of a widely used type of condenser thimble chamber. A diagram is shown in Figure 5.6.

The thimble chamber with its attached condenser is inserted into the electrometer unit. The entire insulated system is then charged by an amber friction mechanism or by a transformer. The deflection of the system is detected by a movement of the platinum wire-quartz fiber assembly as viewed through an optical system and illuminated

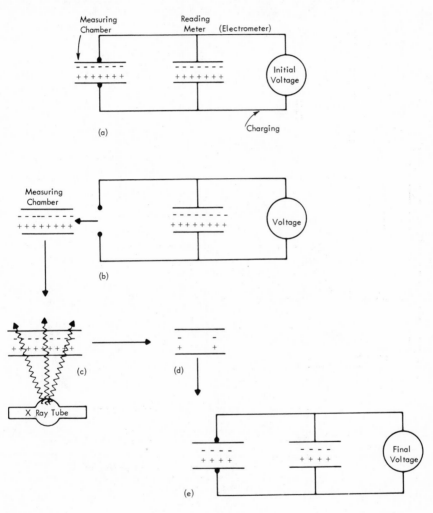

**Figure 5.5.** A schematic diagram of a condenser chamber ionization instrument. (a) The charging mechanism charges the entire system including the measuring condenser and the electrometer portion. The total voltage may be read. (b) The measuring chamber is removed, and (c) it is irradiated by an x-ray beam for a specified time period. (d) The radiation produces ionizations within the measuring chamber and its charge is reduced. (e) When the measuring chamber is reinserted into the system, the charge on the chamber condenser and the electrometer condenser is shared, and a loss in charge (voltage) is measured. This voltage drop is proportional to the amount of radiation to which the chamber has been exposed.

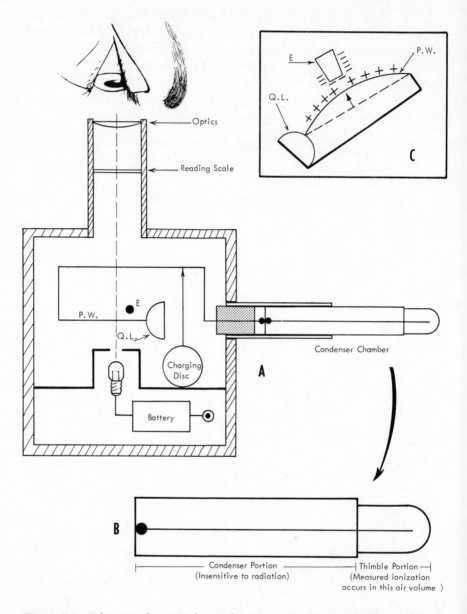

**Figure 5.6.** Schematic diagram of a condenser r-meter (Victoreen). The condenser chamber with its thimble tip is shown: (A) within the socket and electrically connected to the electrometer, and (B) an enlarged representation is shown removed from the electrometer. (C) When fully charged the platinum wire (P.W.) is deflected toward the deflection electrode (E) by movement against the quartz loop (Q.L.). It is the platinum wire which forms the hair-line image which is visualized on the scale. As the instrument is discharged by exposure to radiation the platinum wire moves back toward its uncharged position. The deflection is proportional to the radiation dose.

with a lamp from beneath. When fully charged, the hair line reads zero on the meter scale. The chamber is removed, a protective cap placed over the connector end, and the chamber placed within a radiation beam for a specific interval of time. The cap is then removed and the unit is reinserted into the fully charged electrometer. The loss of charge is indicated by the decrease in deflection of the fiber-wire assembly (the scale is calibrated in roentgens). The sensitivity of the instrument may be varied by using a variety of condenser thimble chambers and one electrometer.

Condenser chambers are secondary standards and should be calibrated against standard air chambers to determine the correction factor required to express the exposure dose in roentgens.

**5.9 The Limitations of the Roentgen.** The definition of the roentgen (Section 5.4) is restrictive in the following ways:
   (a) by definition it can apply only to x and gamma rays (the roentgen unit cannot be used for other radiations such as beta and alpha particles, neutrons, etc.), and
   (b) all of the ionizations produced by the secondary electrons must be collected (electron equilibrium).

Thus, not only is the roentgen restricted to x or gamma rays, but is also restricted to a certain energy range (specifically the roentgen is not defined for x or gamma rays with energies greater than 3 Mev). In order to satisfy the definition of the roentgen, it is necessary for measurements to be carried out under conditions of equilibrium (in each successive layer of air traversed by the primary beam, equal numbers of secondary electrons must be generated and stopped). Scattered photons should also be avoided. As the primary radiation increases in energy, secondary electrons become more energetic (equilibrium is more difficult to obtain) and scattered radiations are unavoidable. At energies greater than 1 Mev, pair production with its energetic annihilation photons becomes important. Thus, for these higher energies, equilibrium conditions break down—the roentgen, as defined, cannot be accurately measured above 3 Mev.

Because of the restrictive nature of the roentgen, a new unit, the rad, was established in 1956.

**5.10 The Rad.** The rad (a unit of *absorbed* dose) is the logical unit for radiobiology. That amount of energy which is actually transferred from a beam of radiation to the system being irradiated is the important portion, not the total energy to which the system is exposed (see Section 5.2—Absorbed and Exposure Dose). One rad is defined as 100 ergs per gram absorbed energy in any medium from any type of ionizing radiation. The rad is less restrictive than the roentgen (the energy absorbed from *any* ionizing radiation in *any* medium) and is a measure of the energy absorbed in a specified volume.

**5.11  Measurement of Absorbed Dose: The Bragg-Gray Theory.**  It is very difficult to directly measure energy absorbed within a given mass of biologic material. Biologic materials and the relatively low doses of radiation normally used in radiobiology do not lend themselves to techniques available for such measurements. However, the absorbed dose in a medium is directly related to the amount of ionization which is produced in that medium. If a small gas-filled chamber is placed within a medium, the ionization produced within it will provide an indirect measure of the energy being lost within the medium.

The Bragg-Gray concept forms the basis for the determination of absorbed dose from gas ionization measurements. If the gas-filled chamber is small enough that its introduction into the medium does not affect the distribution or the numbers of secondary electrons in the medium, then we may define:

$E_m$= Electron energy loss in ergs/gm of the medium.

$J$ = the ionizations produced in the gas cavity by the electrons produced in the medium (ion pairs/gm of gas).

$W$ = average energy to produce one ion pair in the gas = 33.7 ev/ion pair (see Chapter 1).

$E_g$ = the energy imparted per unit mass of the gas by the electrons from the medium (ergs/gm).

Then if J is the number of ion pairs produced per gram of gas and W is the average energy required to produce an ion pair, J and W are related to the energy liberated in the gas Eg as:

$$E_g = J \cdot W \qquad\qquad (5.1)$$

An associated corpuscular emission (an electron) will not lose the same amount of energy in traversing a distance d in the medium that it would in traversing the same distance in the gas. The relative mass stopping power (S) is a ratio of the ability of the medium to absorb the radiation per gram to the ability of the gas to absorb the radiation energy per gram — hence the concept of "stopping power."

Thus if S is the measure of the relative abilities of medium and gas to absorb the radiation energy on a unit mass basis, the energy absorbed per gram of the medium $(E_m)$ is related to the energy absorbed per gram of gas $(E_g)$ as

$$E_m = S \cdot E_g \qquad\qquad (5.2)$$

Substituting for $E_g$ from equation 5.1, we have

$$E_m = S \cdot J \cdot W \tag{5.3}$$

This equation is the famous Bragg-Gray equation which allows one to calculate the absorbed dose in a medium ($E_m$) from the measurement of ionizations produced within a gas-filled chamber. If the charge (J) is measured in esu per unit volume of gas, W is known to equal approximately 33.7 ev/ion pair from gas ionization experiments; the only other quantity required is S (the mass stopping power ratio). The values of S are difficult to give precisely. If the medium and the gas have nearly the same atomic composition, S is nearly equal to 1 and does not vary much with energy. It is beyond the scope of this book to provide the needed tables of S values. Tables which list these values for various mediums, usually against air, are available [1,2] in the literature. These tables are generally limited in that the values listed are given in terms of the energy of the ejected electrons. Since x rays are emitted in a continuous spectrum, the ejected electrons will also have a spectrum of energies; therefore, average values are used to make this approximation.[2]

The utility of this approach is that the data may be used with any energy or any radiation. Although the roentgen has not been defined above 3 Mev, readings made with a small chamber of known composition (for instance, carbon) yield accurate absorbed dose values.

**5.12 The Measurement of Absorbed Dose in a Medium with an Ionization Chamber Calibrated in Roentgens.** A thimble chamber calibrated in roentgens may also be used to obtain absorbed dose in rads.

The medium and the air are exposed to the same radiation but the fraction of the absorbed energy of the incident photons in each will be determined by the relative abilities of the air and the medium to absorb that energy. If the medium is also air, then an exposure of one roentgen will produce an absorbed dose of 0.877 rads in that air (in this instance the absorbed dose is less than the exposure dose). Tissues will absorb different amounts of energy from an exposure dose of one roentgen. The relative abilities of various media to absorb radiation (relative to air) have been determined, and are given as values of f. Thus f is defined as the factor which converts exposure dose in roentgens to absorbed dose in rads (the ratio of rads/roentgens) in a specific medium. Values of f have been calculated for a variety of different energies and are illustrated graphically in Figure 5.7.

The conversion factors from roentgens to rads calculated for potentials between 200 and 300 KV for the most common commercial x-ray

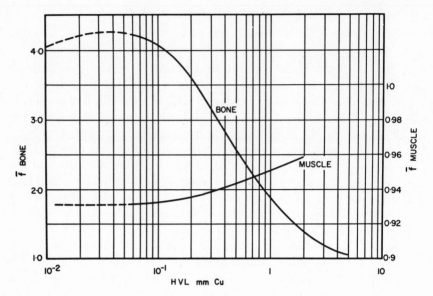

**Figure 5.7.** Conversion factors f̄ to convert from roentgens to rads for bone and muscle. (From International Commission on Radiological Units and Measurements [ICRU], 1956, Handbook 62. U. S. Nat. Bur. Standards.)

machines are compiled by Goodwin[3] and offer a ready reference for this commonly used energy range.

An example will suffice to show the utility of this method.

A small calibrated dosimeter reads air roentgens correctly at half value layer of 0.5 copper. If the chamber is placed in a solid bone and an exposure dose of 100 roentgens is recorded, what will be the absorbed dose?

The f value for radiation HVL = 0.5 mm Cu is 2.6 (Figure 5.7).

Thus the dose to the bone (D Bone) is:

D Bone = f × R rads

D Bone = 2.6 × 100 = 260 rads

**5.13 The Effect of Photon Energy on Absorbed Dose in Biologic Systems.** It has been shown in the previous sections that absorbed dose in a medium may be obtained from measurements with an air- (or other gas) filled chamber. Indeed, in the photon range up to 3 Mev in which the roentgen is defined, a reading with a calibrated chamber may be converted to absorbed dose in the medium by use of the f factor (the ratio of roentgens/rads for the medium and air). This conversion factor is only slightly less than unity for the energy range of 10 Kev to 3 Mev for soft tissue while the conversion factor for bone varies from 4.5 to less than unity in the same energy range (Figure 5.7). The conversion factor from roentgen to rads in air is a constant value (0.877) irrespective of the photon energy. This is because the roentgen is a unit of air ionization and the amount of energy required to produce an ion pair does not vary with the photon energy.

The fact that the relationship of absorbed dose to exposure dose (f) varies as it does is related to the composition of the various absorbing media: air, water (tissue), and bone. All these substances have, for practical purposes, the same number of electrons per gram. However, their effective atomic numbers are: air = 7.64, water = 7.42, and bone = 13.8. At lower energies (less than approximately 60 Kev), the absorption of x- and gamma ray photons is primarily by the photoelectric effect (Section 4.3) which depends on the atomic number of the absorbing medium. Since water and air have essentially the same effective atomic number, they absorb radiation in about the same way. However, because of the higher effective atomic number of bone, the absorbed dose per gram of bone is much higher than air or tissue (Figure 5.7). As the photon energy rises above these lower energies, the compton process becomes more important. Compton scattering (Section 4.4) does not depend on atomic number but upon the number of electrons per gram of the absorbing medium (it is almost the same for air, muscle, and bone). Thus between 60 Kev and 200 Kev bone rapidly becomes less preferential in absorption. For photon energies between 200 Kev and 3 Mev the f factors for bone, water, and air are almost identical — there is no preferential absorption.

### 5.14 Energy Absorption within the Cavities of Bone.

Bone consists of two kinds of material, a non-living matrix of calcium and within it the radiobiologically important portions — the living cells associated with it. Bone may shield soft tissues which lie beyond it and decrease the absorbed dose to them but soft tissues immediately adjacent to or enclosed within bone may have their dose *increased* by the contribution of secondary electrons arising primarily from photoelectrons formed from interactions with the calcium and phosphorus atoms of bone (Figure 5.8).

If the tissue included within the compact bone has dimensions less than 1 $\mu$, the dose received by the soft tissue will be the same as that for bone — the f factor may be applied directly. If, however, the dimension of the soft tissues is greater than 1 $\mu$, the dose will be maximal at the bone-tissue interface, falling to a minimum at the center of the cavity (related to the range of photoelectrons formed in the bone as shown in Figure 5.8 B).

The make-up of bone may be somewhat idealized to facilitate calculations of absorbed dose (Figure 5.9). In this idealized concept the osteocytes are found in small (5 $\mu$) cavities throughout bone. Where the layers of bone are relatively thick, the osteocytes surround

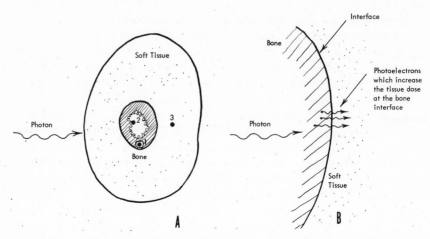

**Figure 5.8.**   A, The tissues of interest are: 1, tissue within small cavities of the bone; 2, tissue within larger bone cavities; and, 3, tissue shielded by bone. B, The dose to soft tissues falls rapidly as one moves from the bone-soft tissue interface because of the short range of the photoelectrons formed in bone. (Redrawn from International Commission of Radiological Units and Measurements. Handbook 85.)

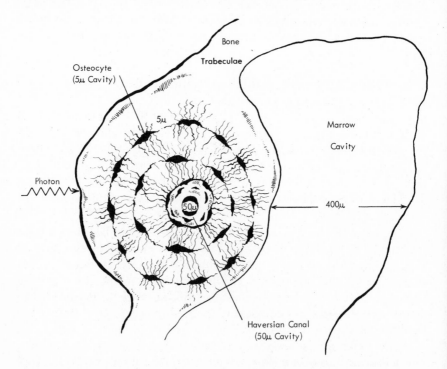

**Figure 5.9**   Diagrammatic representation of the relationship of the soft-tissue components of bone. In regions of marrow the trabeculae are not usually large enough to have Haversian canals although one is shown in the diagram.

an Haversian canal (50 to 100 $\mu$ diameter). These contain capillaries, arterioles, veins, and arteries (as well as blood cells in transit through the vessels). The marrow spaces in trabecular bone (as opposed to compact bone), which contain the red marrow, are larger than the spaces of the Haversian canals. They are on the average about 400 $\mu$ in diameter. In the Haversian canals, osteogenic cells form a lining on the bone approximately 10 microns thick. Table 5.1 shows the difference in energy absorption of these soft-tissue components of bone (this is given as the factor f, the conversion from roentgens to rads).

**Table 5.1.** Mean Dose to Soft-Tissue Components of Bone†
(Mean dose factor f = rads/roentgen)

| Photon Energy (Kev) | Soft Tissue (Muscle) | Compact Bone | Osteocyte 5 $\mu$ Diam. | 10 $\mu$ Lining of Haversian Canal (50 $\mu$) | Mean Marrow Dose for a 400 $\mu$ Marrow Space | Average Soft-Tissue Dose in Bone†* |
|---|---|---|---|---|---|---|
| 25 | 0.914 | 4.31 | 2.80 | 1.50 | 0.960 | 1.73 |
| 35 | 0.915 | 4.26 | 3.12 | 1.76 | 0.989 | 2.05 |
| 50 | 0.926 | 3.58 | 3.25 | 1.89 | 1.05 | 2.27 |
| 75 | 0.936 | 2.20 | 2.40 | 1.60 | 1.04 | 1.85 |
| 100 | 0.949 | 1.46 | 1.52 | 1.26 | 1.01 | 1.36 |
| 200 | 0.963 | 0.979 | 1.05 | 1.02 | 0.973 | 1.03 |

†This is an average value for osteocytes, cells in the Haversian canals and the bone marrow.
*ICRU Report NBS Handbooks 85 and 87 from data adopted from Spiers.

It is evident that there is a maximum radiation dose to soft tissues irradiated in small bone cavities by photons of energies between 50 and 60 Kev. Further, the smaller the bone cavity, the higher the radiation dose to the tissue within it. The osteocytes within their 5 $\mu$ cavities are affected the most, the 10 $\mu$ cell lining of Haversian canals to a lesser extent, and finally the red marrow cells of the bone marrow cavities (400 $\mu$) the least.

## SUMMARY

1. The amount of radiation directed at an object being irradiated is called the exposure dose. X- or gamma-ray exposure dose is measured in roentgens.
2. That portion of the exposure dose which is absorbed by the biologic system, the absorbed dose, is the biologically effective radiation. The unit of absorbed dose is the rad.

3. Absorbed dose may be obtained at a point within an irradiated medium by use of appropriate gas-filled chamber ionization measurements at that point.
4. At lower photon energies, high preferential energy absorption occurs within bone as compared to soft tissue.
5. At median photon energies there is no preferential bone absorption.
6. At higher photon energies, preferential bone absorption again occurs.
7. The living cells within bone are the radiobiologically important portions; their dose will depend upon the size of the cavity within the bone.

## Text References

1. International Commission on Radiological Units and Measurements. Handbook 85. *Physical Aspects of Irradiation.* U. S. National Bureau of Standards.
2. Johns, H. E.: *The Physics of Radiology,* Charles C Thomas, Springfield, Ill., 1961, pp. 272-299.
3. Goodwin, P. N.: Spectral measurements of 200 to 300 KVp x-rays, Radiology 87, 205-213 (1966).

# 6

## Measurement of Radiation Dose

### Part II: Other Methods

**6.1 Introduction.** The most important physical technique for measuring radiation is the determination of the amount of ionization produced by radiation within a specified air volume (Chapter 5). Air is readily available; its ionization is rather easily measured; and the techniques are generally reproducible. Other methods for the determination of radiation dose, although of lesser importance in radiobiology, may have special application.

**6.2 Biologic Dosimeters.** In the early days of radiotherapy a widely used biologic indicator of radiation dose was the threshold erythema dose. This is the amount of radiation required to produce a mild reddening of the skin, and it provided a gross measure of the total absorbed dose. Other biologic indicators have included the dose that kills bacteria, phages, and tissue culture cells. These latter systems, as is the erythema method, are relatively unreliable because of biologic variability in response to radiation.

**6.3 Chemical Dosimetry.** Chemical dosimetry is based on the observation that quantitative oxidation and reduction reactions take place upon irradiation of certain chemical systems, and that the quantity of the reaction is directly proportional to the radiation dose. Bacq and Alexander[1] have enumerated four practical criteria which must be satisfied in such a system. The reaction
   (1) must be independent of the dose-rate over a wide range;
   (2) must be little influenced by changes in ion density over a wide range;
   (3) must be carried out in dilute solutions such as -water or benzene where the absorption is largely independent of photon wavelength;
   (4) and must be relatively insensitive to the presence of impurities.

5

Of all chemical systems available for routine use, the ferrous sulfate system is the most reliable and the most widely used.

The ferrous sulfate or Fricke dosimeter (named after the chemist who first described the reaction) usually is made up of a dilute solution which contains ferrous sulfate, sulfuric acid, and sodium chloride (which counteracts the effect of organic impurities in the water).

In the radiation reaction, ferric ions are produced from the ferrous ions. After irradiation, the amount of ferric ions produced may be determined directly in an ultraviolet spectrophotometer; the yield of ferric ions depends directly on the dose absorbed. The reaction proceeds only in the presence of dissolved oxygen. The amount of oxygen normally present in an aerated solution is usually completely exhausted after about 50,000 rads, but this upper limit may be extended if oxygen is supplied. Since the G value (the number of molecules changed per 100 ev in a chemical reaction) is quite precisely known, this aerated solution makes an excellent dosimeter because it is a tissue equivalent absorber (water) and the absorbed dose in rads may be quite precisely calculated. Its G value is quite constant for beta particles and x and gamma rays in the energies normally employed in radiobiologic and medical experimentation, but the yield does fall off as the ionization density (LET) is increased.

The *cerric sulfate* dosimeter has been utilized for dosage levels higher than 50,000 rads (the practical upper limit for aerated ferrous sulfate solutions). The use of this system extends the limits of useful dosimetry to $10^8$ rads (but little radiobiologic work goes on in this dose range).

**6.4  Calorimetric Methods.**   From an over-all point of view, the most satisfactory type of dosimeter would be one which would directly measure absorbed dose or absorbed energy per gram of material irradiated. For most absorbing materials all but a small percentage of the energy absorbed from radiation ultimately appears in the form of *heat*. Thus a calorimeter which measures heat directly is, in principle, a very direct approach to the measurement of radiation dose. But it requires elaborate, refined equipment in its operation.

Calorimetric systems operate by absorbing energy from the radiation field, retaining the energy until it is degraded to thermal energies, and measuring the temperature rise of the system. The major problem in their use is the small amount of heat actually produced by even high doses of radiation. Acute lethal effects in mammals are seen with whole body doses of 500 rads. A simple calculation shows that a dose of this magnitude would produce a temperature rise of only $1/1000°C$ in water.

Today, sensitive calorimeters capable of precisely detecting very minute rises in temperature are in use. They usually consist of a small thermally insulated mass of material centered in an extended medium. Thermal sensors to measure the temperature change and electrical heaters for calibration are included. The loss of absorbed energy to forms other than heat (chemical energy) is a fundamental difficulty.

**6.5 Photographic Dosimeter.** The photographic emulsion is one of the oldest measuring detectors of ionizing radiations. On a comparative basis, the accuracy of photographic emulsion as a radiation dosimeter is relatively low (a minimum error of 5 to 10 per cent may be expected). It still must, however, rank as a valuable technique for measurement of dose to occupationally exposed personnel, mapping intensity of high-energy radiation fields, and in other areas where ruggedness and low cost are important.

**6.6 Optical Density Methods.** Some types of plastics and glass undergo a radiation-induced change. There is an increase in their optical density (the opaqueness to light) which is directly related to the radiation dose.

(a) *Glass.* The two types of glass used most widely for dosimetry are silver-activated phosphate glass and cobalt-activated borosilicate glass. These are useful in dose range from $10^3$ to $10^6$ rads. With care, 2 per cent precision is attainable, and the response is independent of dose-rate up to high levels ($> 10^8$ rads/hr). The silver-activated glass is troubled by loss in radiation-induced opacity over the initial 24-hour post-irradiation period, but this is not a problem with cobalt-activated glass. In addition, cobalt-activated borosilicate glass is probably less energy dependent than silver-activated glass.

(b) *Plastics.* Many transparent plastics can be utilized as dosimeters because they undergo radiation-induced changes in optical density in the ultraviolet or visible spectrum ranges. The useful dose range is $10^5$ to $10^8$ rads, and these plastics are relatively photon-energy independent (except for those, such as polyvinylchloride with high atomic numbers). The main drawback of plastic is the instability of the radiation-induced change.

**6.7 Photoluminescence.** The effect is seen in certain materials which will show an increase in the ability of the material to fluoresce under ultraviolet light after irradiation by ionizing radiations. The most widely used dosimeter system of this type is based on radiation-induced photoluminescence of silver-activated phosphate glass. When irradiated with ionizing rays and subsequently exposed to ultraviolet light, centers develop within the glass which not only absorb ultraviolet light but then emit orange fluorescent light continuously. The intensity of the fluorescent light, as monitored by a calibrated phototube, is a measure of the absorbed dose in the glass for a given type of radiation. Reproducibility is well within ± 5 per cent,

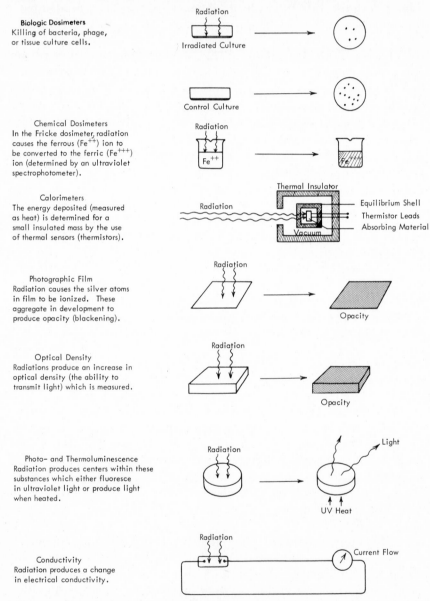

**Biologic Dosimeters**
Killing of bacteria, phage, or tissue culture cells.

Chemical Dosimeters
In the Fricke dosimeter, radiation causes the ferrous ($Fe^{++}$) ion to be converted to the ferric ($Fe^{+++}$) ion (determined by an ultraviolet spectrophotometer).

Calorimeters
The energy deposited (measured as heat) is determined for a small insulated mass by the use of thermal sensors (thermistors).

Photographic Film
Radiation causes the silver atoms in film to be ionized. These aggregate in development to produce opacity (blackening).

Optical Density
Radiations produce an increase in optical density (the ability to transmit light) which is measured.

Photo- and Thermoluminescence
Radiation produces centers within these substances which either fluoresce in ultraviolet light or produce light when heated.

Conductivity
Radiation produces a change in electrical conductivity.

**Figure 6.1**

and the dose response is linear from about 10 rads to 10,000 rads. The photoluminescence appears to be stable over extended periods of time. A difference in response to the same exposure dose of low- and high-energy radiations is regarded as its main hindrance, but with the use of metal shields the energy dependence is reduced.

**6.8 Radiation-Induced Thermoluminescence.** When certain crystalline solid materials are exposed to ionizing radiations, the process of ionization produces free electrons which are subsequently trapped in imperfections in the crystal lattice. At normal room temperatures the electrons remain trapped on a relatively permanent basis. Upon heating, thermal agitation will release them, and they will recombine with opposite-charge carriers and emit light in the process. The light emitted is directly related to the absorbed radiation dose. Lithium fluoride (LiF), the most widely used, is little affected by the atmosphere, stores the signal with little fading, and, because of its low atomic number, is nearly air and tissue equivalent.

**6.9 Measurement by Conductivity Changes.** The following devices are based on a temporary increase in electrical conductivity during exposure to ionizing radiations.

(a) *Semiconductor junction devices.* These devices have a small volume (0.1 cm³ or less) and are many times denser than air (x 1850). Because their low W (the energy required to produce an ion pair) is 1/10 that of air, their sensitivity per volume is about 18,000 times that of air. Semiconductor probes are ideally suited for measurement in tight places, particularly *in vivo.*

(b) *Cadmium sulfate devices.* These are of limited use because the crystals vary greatly in their "sensitivity."

## SUMMARY

Systems other than air ionization types may provide suitable methods of dosimetry in special circumstances. They are summarized in Figure 6.1.

### Text References

1. Bacq, Z. M., and Alexander, P.: *Fundamentals of Radiobiology,* Pergamon Press, New York, 1961.
2. Recommendations of the International Commission of Radiological Units and Measurements. Physical Aspects of Irradiation. National Bureau of Standards Handbook 85.

# 7

# The Dosimetry of Internally

# Administered Radionuclides

**7.1 Introduction.** The factors which determine the amount of radiation delivered by an external source of radiation are more easily controlled than those affecting radiation delivered by internally administered radionuclides. The dose delivered by the latter will depend upon:

(1)  the physical half-life of the radionuclide,

(2)  the energy and the types of radiations emitted in radioactive decay,

(3)  the volume of tissue in which the radionuclide is distributed,

(4)  the homogeneity (or lack of it) in the radionuclide's distribution, and

(5)  the biologic elimination of the radionuclide.

The physical factors (items 1 and 2 above) are usually rather well known and can be measured with good precision. However, the biologic factors are more difficult to measure, and, since simplifying assumptions must be made to facilitate calculations, the radiation doses from internally administered radionuclides cannot be as accurately determined as those from external exposure.

**7.2 The Influence of the Type of Radiation.** Radiations emitted by radioactive nuclides during their decay are either particulate (alpha, electrons, positrons, and conversion electrons) or non-particulate (characteristic x rays and gamma rays). Of the particulate radiations, the electrons (beta) are the most penetrating, but even their range in tissue is only in the order of millimeters (Section 4.13). Thus, when particle emitting radionuclides are distributed *uniformly* within a tissue, their energy will be lost essentially within that tissue volume (except for very small volumes and high-energy radiations). Gamma rays, on the other hand, may be so penetrating that most of their energy is lost outside the tissue region in which the radionuclide is deposited. As opposed to particulate radiations which give up their energy close to where they originate, the size and shape of the mass of tissue become important. With uniform distribution of the radionuclide, the calculation of beta dose is relatively simple while the calculation of gamma dose is relatively more complex.

**7.3 Physical and Biologic Half-Life.** When a radionuclide is present in an organ (or an organism), the radiation dose to that organ will depend upon (1) the fraction of the material lost per unit time from physical decay of the radionuclide ($R_p$), and (2) the fraction eliminated per unit time by biologic processes ($R_b$). The effective removal rate ($R_{eff}$) is the sum of the two rates:

$$R_{eff} = R_p + R_b \qquad (7\text{-}1)$$

The removal rate, the rate of loss, will be characterized by its own half-life (the time required for half the material to be lost). A short half-life implies fast removal. The length of the half-life and the rate of loss are inversely proportional to each other.

$$\text{Removal rate } (R) \propto \frac{1}{T_{1/2}} \qquad (7\text{-}2)$$

If $T_{eff}$ is the effective half-life, $T_p$ is the physical half-life, and $T_b$ is the biologic half-life, they are related by combining equations 7-1 and 7-2 as

$$\frac{1}{T_{eff}} = \frac{1}{T_p} + \frac{1}{T_b} \qquad (7\text{-}3)$$

or

$$T_{eff} = \frac{T_p \cdot T_b}{T_p + T_b} \qquad (7\text{-}4)$$

Thus, if the rate of radioactive decay and the rate of biologic removal are known, the effective rate of removal can be calculated from Equation 7-4.

**7.4 Internal Dosimetry of Alpha Emitters.** Since the alpha particle is a large charged particle, its range in tissue is quite small (the range does not exceed 70 $\mu$). For practical purposes all the energy carried by an alpha particle will be absorbed where it is emitted. If there is uniform tissue distribution there will be uniform absorbed dose.

One microcurie ($\mu$Ci) is defined as that amount of a radionuclide in which $3.7 \times 10^4$ atoms are undergoing radioactive decay per second. If, for each atomic decay process, one alpha particle is emitted, then 1 $\mu$Ci emits $3.7 \times 10^4$ particles. Further, alpha particles which are emitted during radioactive decay have specific energies (Section 2.2), which do not vary. If an alpha-emitting radionuclide is uniformly distributed within a tissue volume and the concentration is C $\mu$Ci/gram, and the alpha particle of the radionuclide has an energy of E Mev, the following follows logically:

The number of disintegrations per second per gram of tissue = $3.7 \times 10^4 \times C$.

Since each disintegration produces an alpha particle with an energy E Mev, the energy absorbed in Mev/sec/gram = $3.7 \times 10^4 \times C \times E$.

Since 1 rad is defined as an absorbed dose of 100 ergs/gram and there are $1.6 \times 10^{-6}$ ergs/Mev, it follows that 1 rad = $6.24 \times 10^7$ Mev/gram. Thus, the dose per second is

$$\frac{D_\alpha}{\sec} = \frac{3.7 \times 10^4 \times C \times E}{6.24 \times 10^7} \text{ rads} \tag{7-5}$$

$$\frac{D_\alpha}{\sec} = 5.92 \times 10^{-4} \times E \times C \text{ rads} \tag{7-6}$$

This can be converted to dose per day by multiplying by the number of seconds per day:

$$\frac{D_\alpha}{\text{day}} = 51.2 \times E \times C \text{ rads,} \tag{7-7}$$

and holds if the half-life is long compared to one day. Most alpha emitters have very long physical half-lives so that physical decay is of little importance even for extended periods of time. Further, most alpha emitters are bone-seekers (radium, plutonium) with little biologic removal after deposition. Thus their effective half-lives ($T_{eff}$) in living organisms are usually very long, even compared to the lifetime of the organism.

*Example:* Assume that a man has incorporated within the bones of his body 10 $\mu$Ci of the alpha emitter, radium-226. The physical half-life of radium-226 is 1622 years; since radium is a bone seeker, little is excreted, and it will produce intense radiation doses to the soft tissues in and adjacent to bone. The energy of the primary alpha ray is 4.79 Mev and homogeneous distribution of the radionuclide in 7000 grams of bone is assumed. The dose per day from the alpha particles emitted by radium-226, using Equation 7-7, would be:

$$\frac{D_\alpha}{\text{day}} = 51.2 \times E \times C = 51.2 \times 4.79 \times \frac{10}{7000}$$

$$\frac{D_\alpha}{\text{day}} = 0.348 \text{ rads}$$

Because of the long physical half-life and limited excretion, the dose per year would be:

$$\frac{D_\alpha}{\text{year}} = 0.348 \times 365 = 127 \text{ rads}$$

The calculated result represents *only* the dose from the primary alpha from radium-226. There will be further radiation dose from the radioactive daughter products of radium-226. In addition, radium is not uniformly distributed in bone. There will be "hot-spot" areas which will receive doses much in excess of these calculated values.

**7.5   Internal Dosimetry of Beta Emitters.**   The radiation dose from internally administered beta emitters (as with alpha emitters) is essentially confined to the tissue region containing the radionuclide. The range of beta particles in tissue, although greater than the range of alpha particles is, nonetheless, small (of the order of a few millimeters). In most organisms, the organs are quite large in relation to the range of the beta particle (Table 4.1). There will be escape of energy, however, when high-energy beta rays are irradiating very small organs.

Beta radiations are emitted from the atoms of a radionuclide with energies varying from nearly zero to the maximum decay energy (Section 2.3); that is, in a spectrum of energies. For the purposes of internal dose calculations it would be improper to use the maximum decay energy. The average energy $(\overline{E}_\beta)$ is more representative of the average beta particle emitted by a particular radionuclide.

The same logical derivation of the equations used in calculating internal dose may be used for beta as were used for alpha emitters (Section 7.4). The dose per day from a uniformly distributed beta emitter, whose concentration in the tissue is C $\mu$Ci/gram, whose average energy is $\overline{E}_\beta$, would be

$$\frac{D_\beta}{\text{day}} = 51.2 \times \overset{\bullet}{C} \times \overline{E}_\beta \text{ rads} \qquad (7\text{-}8)$$

if the half-life is long compared to one day. The concept of average life (Section 2.2) is useful in internal dose calculations. The total dose from complete decay of the radionuclide is given by the product of the dose per day (Equation 7-8) and the average life in days. The average life is 1.44 times the half-life (T). Thus the total dose from complete decay is obtained by multiplying Equation 7-8 (the dose per day) by 1.44 T. The result is

$$D_\beta = 73.8 \times C \times \overline{E}_\beta \times T \text{ rads} \qquad (7\text{-}9)$$

If data are available, the half-life used should be the effective half-life ($T_{eff}$). Since this is not always known, the physical half-life ($T_p$) may also be used, but since it neglects biologic removal, use of $T_p$ will give maximal dosage values. Equation 7-9 gives the dose for complete decay. The dose may be calculated with the same equation for time intervals less than that required for complete decay; that is to say,

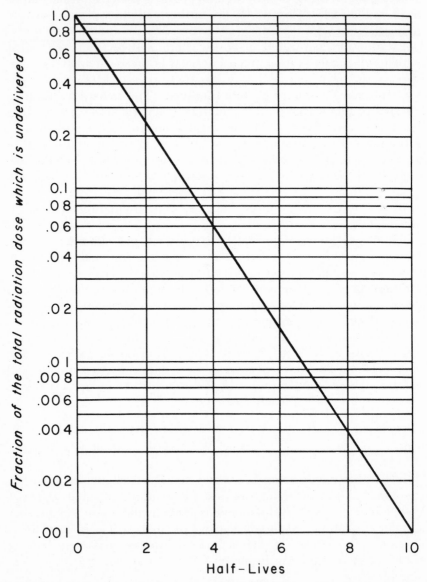

**Figure 7.1.** The determination of the percentage of the dose undelivered in a specific time. As the time increases the percentage of the undelivered dose diminishes.

one half the dose would be delivered in the first half-life, three fourths by the end of the second half-life, etc. The dose delivered may be calculated for time intervals other than even multiples of half-lives by use of appropriate equations, or *more simply* by plotting the fraction of the dose not yet delivered on a log scale against time (Figure 7.1). The relationship is exponential and is expressed as a straight line.

**7.6   Internal Dosimetry of Gamma Emitters.**   It can be stated generally that when gamma rays are emitted within an organ or organism, there is rarely *complete* energy absorption within the tissue of interest. In a tissue mass with a uniformly distributed gamma emitter, the dose is greatest at the center and falls off to the periphery. And, the radiation dose to the tissue mass will depend upon:

(1)   The energy of the gamma ray and the average number of gamma rays given off per disintegration. This value is designated $\Gamma$ and is the R/hr at 1 cm from 1 mCi. Since the amount of the radionuclide is given in $\mu$Ci, $(10^{-3}\Gamma)$ is the R/hr at 1 cm from 1 $\mu$Ci. Values of $\Gamma$ are listed in Table 7.1.

(2)   The concentration of the radionuclide ($\mu$Ci/gram) in the tissue.

(3)   The size and shape of the tissue in question. The quantity which takes into consideration the size and shape of the tissue mass is called the geometric factor (g). Since it will vary throughout the tissue, Hine and Brownell[1] have tabulated *average* values, $\bar{g}$, for the human body and for various

**Table 7.1.**   Physical Factors for the Decay of Radionuclides†

| Element | Symbol | Half-Life | Radiation | Average Beta Energy $E_\beta$ (Mev) | $\Gamma$ R/mc-hr at 1 cm |
|---------|--------|-----------|-----------|-------------------------------------|--------------------------|
| Carbon | $^{14}$C | 5570 yr | B$^-$ | 0.050 | — |
| Cesium | $^{137}$Cs | 30 yr | B$^-$, $\gamma$ | 0.242 | 3.0 |
| Chromium | $^{51}$Cr | 27.8 d | EC°, $\gamma$ | 0.005° | 0.18 |
| Cobalt | $^{60}$Co | 5.2 yr | B$^-$, $\gamma$ | 0.093 | 12.9 |
| Gold | $^{198}$Au | 2.7 d | B$^-$, $\gamma$ | 0.328 | 2.27 |
| Hydrogen | $^{3}$H | 12.26 yr | B$^-$ | 0.006 | — |
| Iodine | $^{131}$I | 8.1 d | B$^-$, $\gamma$ | 0.188 | 2.20 |
| Iron | $^{59}$Fe | 45 d | B$^-$, $\gamma$ | 0.118 | 6.8 |
| Phosphorus | $^{32}$P | 14.3 d | B$^-$ | 0.70 | — |
| Potassium | $^{42}$K | 12.5 hr | B$^-$, $\gamma$ | 1.45 | 1.4 |
| Sodium | $^{24}$Na | 15 hr | B$^-$, $\gamma$ | 0.56 | 18.7 |
| Strontium | $^{90}$Sr | 28 yr | B$^-$ | 0.20 | — |
| Sulfur | $^{35}$S | 87 d | B$^-$ | 0.049 | — |
| Yttrium | $^{90}$Y | 2.7 d | B$^-$ | 0.93 | — |

°EC (electron capture) produces low-energy x rays which are included as a "beta-like" radiation.

†Compiled from Quimby and Feitelberg.[2]

cylinders (Tables 7.2 and 7.3). For spheres of tissue of less than 10 cm radius, the value of $\bar{g}$ can be calculated directly:

$$\bar{g} = 3\pi R$$

where R is the radius in cm. Use of the average geometric factor, $\bar{g}$, will give the average dose to the tissue in the sphere. The maximum dose is 25 per cent greater than the average and is at the center of the sphere. Values of $\bar{g}$ for spheres are listed in Table 7.4.

**Table 7.2**   Average Geometrical Factor, $\bar{g}$, for a Gamma Ray Emitter Uniformly Distributed in Average Human Body*

| Weight of Individual (Kg) | Height of Individual (Cm) | | | | | | |
|---|---|---|---|---|---|---|---|
| | 200 | 190 | 180 | 170 | 160 | 150 | 140 |
| | | | Values of $\bar{g}$ | | | | |
| 100 | 138 | 139 | 142 | 145 | 147 | 150 | 154 |
| 90 | 134 | 136 | 138 | 140 | 143 | 146 | 148 |
| 80 | 129 | 130 | 131 | 134 | 136 | 139 | 141 |
| 70 | 123 | 124 | 125 | 126 | 129 | 131 | 135 |
| 60 | 117 | 118 | 119 | 120 | 122 | 125 | 128 |
| 50 | 112 | 113 | 114 | 116 | 117 | 119 | 122 |
| 40 | 102 | 104 | 105 | 106 | 108 | 109 | 110 |

*From Hine and Brownell.[1]

Thus, the gamma ray dose to any tissue volume which has within it a uniformly distributed gamma emitter is dependent upon: $10^{-3}\Gamma$ (the radiation dose rate in R/hr at a distance of one centimeter from one microcurie), the concentration (C) in $\mu$Ci/gram, and the geometric configuration $(\bar{g})$ of the tissue mass.

$$\frac{D_\gamma}{hr} = 10^{-3}\Gamma \times C \times \bar{g} \text{ roentgens} \qquad (7\text{-}10)$$

The number of rads per roentgen varies with the energy of the gamma ray and the atomic number of the absorbing material. Since, however, most gamma-ray energies lie in the range of 0.2 to 3 Mev where the conversion factor (f) from rads to roentgens varies from 0.96 to 0.98, this correction is of little consequence and the results of Equation 7-10 may be expressed directly in rads with small error. For energies other than these, the dose must be multiplied by the appropriate f factor. Thus the absorbed dose is

$$\frac{D_\gamma}{hr} = 10^{-3}\Gamma \times C \times \bar{g} \text{ rads} \qquad (7\text{-}11)$$

**Table 7.3.** Average Geometrical Factor, $\bar{g}$, for Cylinders Containing a Uniformly Distributed Gamma-Ray Emitter

| Length of Cylinder (cm) | Radius of Cylinder (cm) | | | | | | | | | | |
|---|---|---|---|---|---|---|---|---|---|---|---|
| | 1 | 2 | 3 | 5 | 7 | 10 | 15 | 20 | 25 | 30 | 35 |
| 1 | 3.8 | 7.5 | 10.2 | 13.0 | 13.5 | 13.8 | 15.1 | 16.0 | 17.5 | 18.0 | 19.0 |
| 2 | 6.5 | 11.7 | 15.7 | 21.6 | 23.2 | 25.2 | 28.1 | 30.5 | 32.8 | 35.4 | 37.3 |
| 3 | 8.4 | 14.7 | 19.8 | 27.7 | 31.0 | 34.5 | 39.2 | 42.9 | 46.5 | 49.5 | 52.5 |
| 5 | 10.6 | 18.8 | 25.6 | 36.0 | 42.4 | 48.5 | 56.1 | 62.6 | 68.2 | 73.0 | 77.2 |
| 7 | 11.6 | 21.4 | 29.3 | 41.4 | 50.0 | 59.0 | 68.7 | 77.8 | 84.7 | 90.2 | 93.8 |
| 10 | 12.7 | 23.6 | 33.0 | 47.1 | 57.8 | 70.2 | 83.2 | 94.0 | 103 | 109 | 113 |
| 15 | 13.7 | 25.6 | 36.4 | 53.2 | 66.1 | 81.4 | 99.7 | 113 | 123 | 130 | 135 |
| 20 | 14.2 | 26.7 | 38.0 | 56.3 | 72.2 | 89.6 | 111 | 127 | 139 | 147 | 152 |
| 30 | 14.5 | 27.6 | 39.7 | 59.9 | 76.8 | 98.8 | 124 | 144 | 159 | 172 | 179 |
| 40 | 14.8 | 28.2 | 40.7 | 62.4 | 80.0 | 103 | 133 | 156 | 175 | 187 | 197 |
| 50 | 14.8 | 28.4 | 41.3 | 64.1 | 82.2 | 106 | 139 | 165 | 185 | 199 | 208 |
| 60 | 14.8 | 28.7 | 41.7 | 65.5 | 84.0 | 109 | 143 | 171 | 193 | 206 | 216 |
| 70 | 14.8 | 28.8 | 41.9 | 65.6 | 85.3 | 111 | 146 | 174 | 196 | 212 | 222 |
| 80 | 14.8 | 28.8 | 42.1 | 65.8 | 86.0 | 112 | 148 | 176 | 198 | 214 | 226 |
| 90 | 14.8 | 28.9 | 42.3 | 66.0 | 86.5 | 113 | 149 | 177 | 199 | 216 | 228 |
| 100 | 14.8 | 29.2 | 42.5 | 66.2 | 86.8 | 114 | 150 | 179 | 201 | 218 | 230 |

°From Focht, Quimby, and Gershowitz.[4]

The dose per day may be obtained by multiplying by twenty-four hours per day. The total gamma ray dose when there is complete decay is simply the dose per day multiplied by the average life in days (1.44 T where T is the half life in days).

$$D_\gamma = 0.0346\Gamma \times C \times \bar{g} \times T \text{ rads} \qquad (7\text{-}12)$$

**Table 7.4** Approximate Values of $\bar{g}$, the Geometric Factor, for Gamma Ray Dose Calculations°
(These are for a sphere of radius R)

| Radius of Sphere, R (cm) | Volume cm³ | Maximum Geometric Factor at Center of Sphere g max | Average Geometric Factor for Sphere $\bar{g}$ |
|---|---|---|---|
| 1 | 4.2 | 12.6 | 9.5 |
| 2 | 33.5 | 25.2 | 18.9 |
| 3 | 103 | 37.8 | 28.4 |
| 4 | 278 | 50.4 | 37.8 |
| 6 | 905 | 75.6 | 56.7 |
| 8 | 2140 | 101 | 75.8 |
| 10 | 4180 | 126 | 94.5 |

°Adapted from Hine and Brownell.[1]

Again, one half of the total dose would be delivered in one half-life, three quarters in two half-lives, etc.

These formulas are applicable for gamma energies between 0.1 and 3.0 Mev where the absorption of radiation in tissue is nearly constant. For gamma-ray energies between 15 and 100 Kev, special techniques of calculation are needed.[1] Radiations such as the soft characteristic x rays which occur after electron capture penetrate in tissue less than a centimeter. Since they behave as beta particles, these low-energy radiations (less than 0.015 Mev) are best handled as "beta particles" and added into the total dose by the use of the equations in Section 7.5.

### 7.7 Examples of Internal Dose Calculations for Uniformly Distributed Beta and Gamma Emitters.

The relative contribution of beta and gamma emitters to absorbed dose depends upon their respective energies and the configuration of the tissue mass. As a general rule when both types of radiations are present, the absorbed dose from beta radiation is higher than from gamma, since most of the beta energy is absorbed locally. (It should also be pointed out that since gamma rays are more penetrating than beta rays, the gamma dose is much less affected by non-uniform distribution of the radionuclide than is the beta ray dose.)

*Example:* The application of these concepts can be seen in the calculation of the radiation dose after the administration of radioactive iodine-131 to a patient with an overactive thyroid gland. (Since radioactive iodine is concentrated by the thyroid gland for use in hormone production, it will locally irradiate the gland and destroy a portion of it.) Almost all of the radionuclide not deposited within the gland will be excreted within twenty-four hours. It will be assumed that biologic removal from the gland has a longer half-time than physical decay so that $T_{eff} = T_p = 8.1$ days. Further,

$$\left.\begin{array}{l} \overline{E}_\beta = 0.188 \text{ Mev} \\ \Gamma = 2.2 \text{ R/hr} \end{array}\right\} \qquad \text{(Table 7.1)}$$

The thyroid gland is assumed to be a 33 gram gland and to contain 3 millicuries of $^{131}$I. Thus the concentration (C) of the radionuclide is 3000 $\mu$Ci/33 grams. For a 33 gram sphere, $\overline{g} = 18.9$. Therefore using the formulas for complete decay:

$$\begin{aligned} D_\beta &= 73.8 \times \overline{E}_\beta \times C \times T \text{ rads} \\ &= 73.8 \times 0.188 \times \frac{3000}{33} \times 8.1 \\ &= 73.8 \times 0.188 \times 90.9 \times 8.1 \\ &= 10{,}217 \text{ rads} \end{aligned}$$

$$D_\gamma = 0.0346 \times \Gamma \times C \times \bar{g} \times T \text{ rads}$$
$$= 0.0346 \times 2.2 \times \frac{3000}{33} \times 18.9 \times 8.1$$
$$= 1059 \text{ rads}$$

Thus $D_\beta + D_\gamma = 11{,}276$ rads, about 90 per cent of which is contributed by the beta radiation. These doses are for complete decay, half (5,638 rads) would be delivered during the first half-life (8.1 days) and at 16.2 days, three quarters (8,457 rads) would have been delivered. The dose delivered at the end of *any* time interval can be calculated by the use of Figure 7.1. The dose at thirty days $(30/8.1 = 3.7$ half-lives) can be determined from the graph. In 3.7 half-lives, 8 per cent of the dose is undelivered; 92 per cent has been delivered. Thus the dose at thirty days would be:

$$0.92 \times 11{,}276 \text{ rads} = 10{,}374 \text{ rads}$$

*Example:* A 200 gram rat is given an intravenous dose of 200 $\mu$Ci of radioactive $^{198}$Au colloid. This colloid is rapidly taken up by the reticuloendothelial cells of the animal. We shall assume that 85 per cent is taken up by the liver and the remaining 15 per cent divided evenly between the spleen and the red bone marrow. Since the radiocolloid is not lost through biologic processes, $T_{eff} = T_p = 2.7$ days. The liver is assumed to weigh 6.7 grams. Determination of the dose to the liver of the rat is to be made. The following are the constants of irradiation:

$$
\begin{array}{ll}
T_{eff} = T_p = 2.7 \text{ days} & \text{(Table 7.1)} \\
\overline{E}_\beta = 0.328 \text{ Mev} & \text{(Table 7.1)} \\
\underline{\Gamma} = 2.27 \text{ R/hr} & \text{(Table 7.1)} \\
\overline{g} \text{ for 6.7 gram sphere} = 11 & \text{(Table 7.4)} \\
C = 0.85 \ (200 \ \mu\text{Ci}/6.7 \text{ grams}) = 25.4 &
\end{array}
$$

For complete decay:

$$D_\beta = 73.8 \times \overline{E}_\beta \times C \times T \text{ rads}$$
$$= 73.8 \times 0.328 \times 25.4 \times 2.7$$
$$= 1660 \text{ rads}$$
$$D_\gamma = 0.0346 \times \Gamma \times C \times \bar{g} \times T \text{ rads}$$
$$= 0.0346 \times 2.27 \times 25.4 \times 11 \times 2.7$$
$$= 59.3 \text{ rads}$$

Again most of the dose to the rat liver comes from the high-energy beta particles.

*Example:* A patient is suspected of having hemolytic anemia. A diagnostic test of red blood cell life is carried out using $^{51}$Cr, a radionuclide with a physical half-life of 26.6 days. In the procedure, a sample of the patient's blood is withdrawn, incubated with 50 $\mu$Ci of the radionuclide which fixes to his red blood cells. The tagged cells are then reinjected, permitted to mix, and a blood sample withdrawn. Blood samples are obtained several times over a period of two to three weeks and the radioactivity of these samples and that withdrawn on the first day are determined. Since the blood samples are counted at the same time as the initial blood sample, loss of radioactivity due to radioactive decay is accounted for. Thus, the disappearance of radioactivity from the blood is due to biologic elimination (hemolysis). The half time of the disappearance of red blood cells in this patient was twelve days (normally it is thirty days). What will be the whole body dose?

The effective half-life ($T_{eff}$) is calculated.

$$T_p = 26.6 \text{ days}$$
$$T_{eff} = \frac{T_p \cdot T_b}{T_p + T_b} = \frac{26.6 \times 12}{26.6 + 12} = 8.3 \text{ d}$$
$$T_b = 12 \text{ days}$$

All of the radioactive decay of $^{51}Cr$ is by electron capture with the emission of K-characteristic x rays (E = 0.005 Mev). A 0.323 Mev gamma ray is also emitted in 9 per cent of the disintegrations, with a $\Gamma$ of 0.18 R/hr at 1 cm. from 1 mCi. For a 70 kg man 180 cm tall, $\bar{g} = 125$ (Table 7.2), the absorbed dose from the gamma is

$$D_\gamma = 0.0346 \times \Gamma \times C \times \bar{g} \times T$$
$$= 0.0346 \times 0.18 \times \frac{50}{70,000} \times 125 \times 8.3$$
$$= 0.0046 \text{ rads}$$

Since the characteristic x ray is less than 15 Kev it is regarded as "beta dose" where $\bar{E}_\beta = 0.005$ Mev.

$$D_\beta = 73.8 \times \bar{E}_\beta \times C \times T \text{ rads}$$
$$= 73.8 \times 0.005 \times \frac{50}{70,000} \times 8.3$$
$$= 0.0022 \text{ rads}$$

Thus the total whole body absorbed dose is simply the sum of the individual doses, 0.0068 rads.

## SUMMARY

Radiation dose from internally administered radionuclides will depend upon:

1. The physical half-life of the radionuclides and how rapidly radionuclides are eliminated by biologic processes.

2. The type and energy of the radiation. Specifically, particulate radiations such as alpha and beta radiations lose their energy in the immediate tissue area in which the radiations originate; with gamma rays much energy is lost to areas remote from the origin.
3. Homogeneity of distribution. This is rarely attained in biologic systems; it is of lesser importance for gamma rays.

## Text References

1. Hine, G., and Brownell, G.: *Radiation Dosimetry*, Academic Press, New York, 1956.
2. Quimby, E., and Feitelberg, S.: *Radioactive Isotopes in Medicine and Biology*, Lea & Febiger, Philadelphia, 1963.
3. Johns, H. E.: *The Physics of Radiology*, Charles C Thomas, Springfield, Ill., 1961.
4. Focht, E. F., Quimby, E. H., and Gershowitz, M.: Revised average geometric factors for cylinders in isotope dosage, Radiology *85*, 151-152 (1965).

# 8

## Irradiation Techniques with

## External Sources of X or

## Gamma Rays

**8.1 Introduction.** The care in the determination of the radiation dose may vary from an estimate of a general level to a very precise measurement. An experiment should be designed so that the dosimetry is sufficiently accurate and reported in such a way that all pertinent information is given. The primary approach of this chapter will be to describe the radiation techniques utilized with x and gamma rays, although many of the principles apply to other radiations.

**8.2 The Uniformity of Absorbed Dose.** Usually in an experiment in radiobiology it is desirable to irradiate as uniformly as possible some well-defined tissue volume (in many instances this may be whole-body exposure). Even when only a portion of an organism is to be irradiated, uniformity of radiation dose is desirable, with as little radiation as possible given to surrounding tissue.

It has seemed useful to classify radiation conditions according to the degree of uniformity of absorbed dose.[1] These classifications are as follows:

A. *Uniform irradiation* is defined as conditions under which variations in absorbed dose throughout the tissue volume are not large enough to have a significant effect on the biologic response. A ratio of less than 1.15 between the maximum and the minimum doses is considered "uniform irradiation."

B. *Non-uniformity of irradiation due to absorption.* When radiations with limited penetrations are used to irradiate comparatively large animals, non-uniformity of absorbed dose is likely to occur. If the ratio between maximum and minimum dose does not exceed 1.30, this is called "moderately uniform." If, however, the ratio exceeds this value, the conditions are said to be *"non-uniform."*

C. *Non-uniformity in dose due to particle equilibrium.* When high-energy radiations such as cobalt-60 gamma rays are used, the dose rises rapidly and reaches a maximum at a depth of 3 to 5 mm in tissue (equilibrium depth). The tissues in the buildup region would be non-uniformly irradiated (see Class B). Thus the amount of incomplete dose due to unestablished equilibrium will depend on the thickness of the object and the energy of the radiation. For microorganisms exposed in air, considerable non-uniformity of dose may occur due to lack of equilibrium even with conventional x-ray energies.

It is usually desirable to have uniform irradiation (Class A). If this *is* attainable, one value will closely represent absorbed dose at any point within the tissue. If the dose is not uniform it is the custom to express it as the "dose to the midline or the center" of the irradiated object or tissue volume.

**8.3   The Effect of the Radiation Source.**   When the results of irradiations of groups of specimens are to be compared, it is important that radiation output be closely reproducible. Modern x-ray machines are normally fairly well regulated with respect to tube current and potential (voltage). Small changes in tube current will produce proportionately small changes in output, but small changes in voltage may have a greater effect on the radiation output. Gamma-ray sources can be expected to be very constant except for decay; errors may occur if the source is partially shielded or they may be due to the presence of shorter lived radio-impurities.

When conventional x-ray machines are utilized to provide a large area of irradiation, the dose within this area may vary considerably from point to point. This type of non-uniformity may be averaged out by placing the objects to be irradiated upon a rotating turntable. However, the average dose should be determined by measurement with a dosimeter on the same rotating turntable.

**8.4   The Effect of Distance from the Source.**   It may be practically necessary at times to place an object (or animal) close to the source of radiation to obtain high dose-rates. If, however, the dimensions of the object are comparable to the source-object distance, considerable non-uniformity in absorbed dose will result. This is because:

A.   the lateral extensions of the object will be further from the source and receive less dose, and,

B.   if the thickness of the object is significant, its proximal surface will be closer to the source than the distal surface.

Tabulation of these variations may be found elsewhere.[1]

**8.5 The Effect of Scattered Radiations.** X and gamma radiations may lose all their energy in an encounter with an orbital electron (photoelectric absorption) or undergo a scattering process in which their direction is changed. Radiations may be scattered into a tissue volume by material between the specimen and the radiation source, beside the specimen, or beneath the specimen (the latter is called backscatter).

These scattered and backscattered radiations can add materially to the absorbed dose in an object. The absorbed dose will rapidly rise as radiation scattering material (such as exposure supports, other animals, etc.) are brought close by. The addition of the *first* extraneous scattering material has the greatest effect on the absorbed dose. Additional scattering material contributes relatively *less* to absorbed dose. It usually facilitates irradiation to use conditions of *maximum* scatter (a condition in which the addition of further materials does not increase the absorbed dose). In addition, it facilitates the use of tables which give the reduction in dose with depth of absorber (depth-dose tables) and curves which show the distribution of dose in an absorber (isodose curves)[2,3] since these curves are determined with maximum scattering conditions. For photon irradiation it can be taken as a general rule that maximum scatter is obtained with substantial backing of materials whose density is equivalent to tissue (water, Masonite, are good examples). The backing should be approximately 7.5 cm thick and exceed the width of the primary beam by 5 cm on all sides.[1] When irradiating groups of animals, there should be the *same* number of animals in each irradiated group each time the animals are irradiated. The animals should also be spaced uniformly. If equal groups of equal numbers are not to be used each time, *simulated* animals ("phantoms") should be added to make up the required number; dead or unwanted animals may also be used in this way.

**8.6 Irradiation of Microorganisms.** Although absorbed dose may be estimated and measured on the *macroscopic level* and clearly shown to be uniform, variations in absorbed dose may still occur if very small organisms are being irradiated (unestablished equilibrium during irradiation). Tissue culture cells which are attached to a glass surface may experience non-uniform irradiation because of photoelectrons ejected from glass which has a relatively high atomic number. Such variations are exceedingly difficult to detect and measure, because they may extend only over a fraction of a millimeter. But they may seriously influence the outcome of a biologic study. Some of these problems may be overcome by placing such organisms within a container inside a large block of scattering material. When *low-energy* x-ray exposure is to be made of a thin layer of cells, the cells should be spread on something other than glass so as to reduce the effect of photoelectrons. Plastic dishes are available, but not all are useful; some may produce volatile, noxious compounds upon being irradiated. Plastics containing constituents of higher atomic number (polytetrafluoroethylene, vinyl-chloride, etc.) should be avoided.[1]

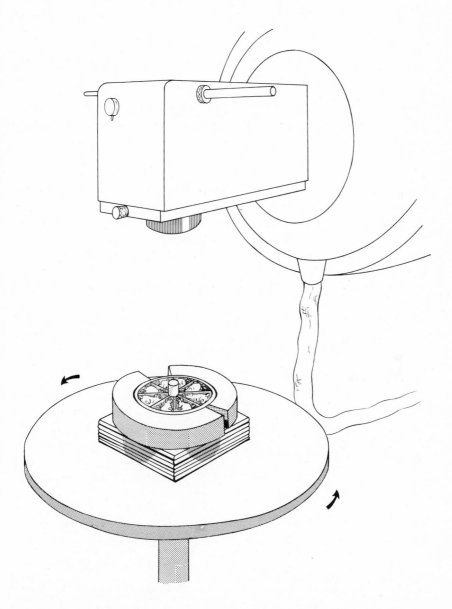

**Figure 8.1.** Irradiation of small animals (mice) on a rotating turntable to improve dose uniformity. (Adapted from International Commission on Radiological Units and Measurements, Handbook 88.).

**8.7 Irradiation of Small Animals (Less than 250 Grams).** When incident radiation is substantially absorbed within the volume being irradiated, non-uniformity of absorbed dose throughout the volume will occur. The portion of the irradiated volume *nearer* the source of radiation will absorb more radiation. This may be improved in two ways: (1) selecting a more penetrating radiation, and (2) irradiation by several sources at once or the same source from several directions (*multilateral* exposure). The most important step in the achievement of uniformity of absorbed dose is the progression from unilateral to *bilateral exposure.* Further extension will achieve increased dose uniformity, but each of them will add only a small additional improvement. The kilovoltage required to moderately uniformly irradiate animals will depend on beam penetration and the size of the animal; however, the larger the animal the more necessary is bilateral irradiation.

Most therapeutic x-ray machines designed for clinical work are suitable for the irradiation of small animals. For x rays with a half-value layer greater than 1.5 mm of copper, the radiation is sufficiently penetrating to ensure at least moderately uniform whole-body exposure of unilaterally irradiated animals as large as rats or medium-sized guinea pigs. However, for x-ray machines of less than 150 KV, bilateral exposure may be necessary even for these animals to achieve moderate uniformity of dose[1] (unless the beam is highly filtered).

In any case, with x rays, uniformity of dose is improved by placing the animals in something like a Lucite irradiation cage and putting them on a rotating turntable (Figure 8.1).

**8.8 Irradiation of Medium-Sized Animals (250 Grams to 2.5 Kilograms).** Medium-sized animals (rabbits, monkeys, large guinea pigs) usually require bilateral irradiation with x rays of at least 200 KV in order to obtain "moderate" uniformity of dose (Class B). Unilateral radiation may be acceptable for x-ray energies greater than 300 KV.[1] Medium-sized animals are best irradiated singly (in snug Lucite boxes) with adjacent material to yield maximum scatter conditions.

**8.9 Irradiation of Larger Animals (Larger than 2.5 Kilograms).** In the case of larger animals such as dogs, swine, etc., bilateral exposure to x rays with energy greater than 250 KV may be adequate for moderate uniformity of dose, but bilateral exposure to supervoltage radiations or gamma rays is preferred.[1] Larger animals are best irradiated if they are "molded" so that the body is essentially circular with a minimum diameter. This is best accomplished by anesthetizing the animal and placing it in a circular container (Figure 8.2).

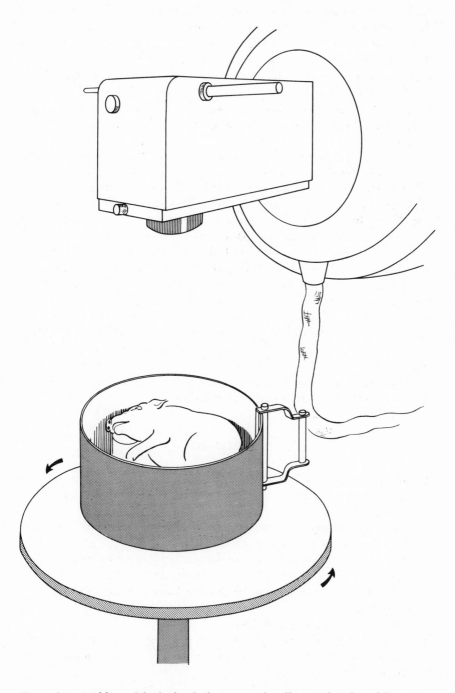

**Figure 8.2.** Molding of the body of a large animal is illustrated. (Adapted from International Commission on Radiological Units and Measurements, Handbook 88.)

**8.10   The Recommended Exposure Technique and the Report of the Irradiation.**   The previous sections have described techniques which are useful in obtaining relatively uniform absorbed doses in tissue volumes. In reporting the data of an experiment in radiobiology it is useful to describe the irradiation technique in complete detail so that the distribution of the absorbed dose and the technique are completely understood. An example of such a report is taken from ICRU Handbook 88 which describes a Class A (uniform) exposure of mice.[1]

"A constant potential x-ray machine was used to irradiate the mice, using the following exposure factors: 250 KV; added filtration of 0.5 mm copper, 1 mm aluminum; HVL, 1.2 mm copper; 30 ma; source distance (to center of animal): 100 cm. The mice were exposed, 10 at one time, in a circular container measuring 20 cm in diameter, divided into sectors, and placed on top of a block of wood measuring $25 \times 25 \times 7$ cm. The exposure with scatter was measured by placing a _____ (give make) dosimeter in the center of a phantom placed at a point corresponding to that of a representative animal, and the exposure rate thus determined, with the apparatus rotating, at approximately 3 revolutions per minute, was found to be 24R per minute. The absorbed doses reported were derived by applying the factor 0.95. A diagram of the exposure arrangement used is shown in Figure _____."

This type of presentation is complete throughout and is an ideal model for other reports of animal exposure.

## SUMMARY

1.   Radiation is usually delivered to an organism or a tissue volume in such a way as to yield a relatively uniform distribution of absorbed dose. This uniformity may be influenced by:
     (a)   The dimensions and thickness of the object with respect to the distance to the source,
     (b)   Whether equilibrium conditions have been established, and
     (c)   The effect of extraneous scattering materials.
2.   Particularly for larger objects, bilateral irradiation, and irradiation with higher-energy x rays (or gamma rays), will markedly improve the homogeneity of the dose.
3.   Examples of radiation techniques for small, medium-sized, and large animals are detailed with reference to recommendations by the ICRU.

## Text References

1. Recommendations of the International Commission on Radiological Units and Measurements. Radiobiological Dosimetry. National Bureau of Standards, Handbook 88, Washington, D. C. (1963).
2. Johns, H. E.: *The Physics of Radiology*, Charles C Thomas, Springfield, Ill., 1961, pp. 704-744.
3. Glasser, O., Quimby, E. H., Taylor, L. S., Weatherwax, J. L., and Morgan, R. H.: *Physical Foundations of Radiology*, Harper and Rowe, New York, 1961, pp. 437-479.

# PART II

## Interactions of Radiations

## with Living Systems

# 9

## Direct and Indirect Action: Action of

## Radiations in Aqueous Systems

**9.1  Ionization Is Random.**  Ionization produced by radiation is a random process; ordinarily, an ionizing particle will have sufficient energy to remove an orbital electron from any atom with which it chances to interact. Any atom, without preference, may lose an electron in this way and is, itself, ionized. The randomness – the non-selectivity of the process – is in sharp contrast to the action of radiations of lower energy (ultraviolet) which are absorbed selectively by certain molecules and have no effect on others. The transfer of energy from lower-energy radiations, unlike that of ionizing radiation, is not random and will occur only with certain atoms or molecules, even at times, with a small portion of a molecule.

**9.2  Energy Transfer in Complex Systems.**  If a complex system (one consisting of more than one kind of molecule) is irradiated with any of the ionizing radiations, then, because the nature of the energy exchange is random, ionization is most likely to occur in those kinds of molecules that are present in the largest number. This is not to say that the other kinds of molecules in the mixture will be unaffected by the radiation. They will be ionized in the proportion in which they are present. The total amount of radiation given a mixture will, of course, determine the precise status of the mixture in the instant after irradiation, but, unless a dose so large as to ionize every molecule in the mixture is given, the following situation will result. Some molecules of every type will have been ionized (the greatest number of *ionized* molecules will be found among those that are present in the greatest number), and some of every type will be left intact. The precise ratio of ionized to intact molecules is determined by the total dose of radiation. But, unless the dose was large enough to ionize all molecules, some molecules of every type will escape this kind of change.

However, this does not mean that *all* the intact molecules will escape *radiation-related* change. Changes (although not necessarily ionizations) may be brought about in them by the *irradiation products* of a molecule which has, itself, been ionized. The energy of an ionizing particle can be transferred to one of the intact, un-ionized molecules from a molecule that has been "hit" (ionized).

There are, then, two, quite different mechanisms by which chemical changes in molecules may be brought about by ionizing radiation. One is *direct action*, i.e., a molecule is ionized or excited (see Chapter 1) by the passage through it of either an electron (secondary to electromagnetic radiation) or another ionizing particle. The other is *indirect action*. The changed molecule has not itself been ionized or excited by a particle; no ionizing radiation passes through it. It is changed, however, because it received the energy of an ionizing particle by transfer from another molecule which *has* been ionized through the direct action of radiation.

**9.3  Observations in Solutions.**  The difference between the two modes of action — direct and indirect — is especially striking when the irradiation of solutions is studied. A solution, which is a type of mixture, will contain molecules of solvent and solute (more than one kind of solute can, of course, be present in a single solution). Inevitably, the molecules of solvent will far out-number those of the solute and, if the solution is irradiated, because energy exchange from ionizing radiation is random, most of the energy will be transferred in the solvent. Although more molecules of solvent than of solute are present, solute molecules will also be ionized, but, compared to the energy exchange in the solvent, in lesser proportion. The majority of changes made in the molecules of solute will be due to energy transferred to these molecules by the irradiation products of directly ionized solvent molecules.

**9.4  The Analogy of the Cell to a Solution.**  It should be kept in mind that cells (and, therefore, living things which are composed of cells) are extremely complex mixtures or solutions. Water is the solvent, and the chemical reactions which make up the process called "metabolism" take place in it. There is, of course, some variation, depending upon the tissue, but, on the average, cells consist of about 70 to 80 per cent water. The cell molecules (proteins, carbohydrates, nucleic acids, inorganic substances) are myriad, but they are either dissolved in or suspended in a watery medium. When cells or tissues are irradiated, most of the energy transfer goes on in water, because the water presents the largest number of "targets" for the radiation. Solute molecules, because they are *relatively* scarce, will be directly acted upon infrequently. Chemical changes, however, can be brought about in them if the energy of the ionizing particles is transferred to them from the ionized water. It is obvious then, with respect to changes brought about in the molecules of which cellular constituents are composed, that the interaction of ionizing radiation and water, and the chemistry (the reactions possible) of irradiated water, will be very important. The degree of change, brought about by radiation, in the constituents of the cell depends upon that brought about in the molecules of which the cell is composed. The number of alterations, for example, in the structure or function of chromosomes, of mitochondria, or of any organelle, depends upon how many molecules within the organelle have been changed. The changes in these molecules following irradiation are dependent primarily upon their interaction with the products of irradiated water, and, to a lesser but by no means insignificant extent, upon the direct interaction of the molecules with radiation.

**9.5   The Interaction of Ionizing Radiation and Water.**   When irradiated, water, like any other material, is ionized. An electron is removed from the molecule leaving behind an ionized water molecule.

$$1. \quad H_2O \xrightarrow{\text{radiation}} H_2O^+ + e^- \text{ (electron)}$$
$$2. \quad e^- + H_2O \longrightarrow H_2O^-$$

Equation 1 depicts the ejection of an electron form an orbit of a water molecule. The molecule is now positively charged and the electron which has been ejected is traveling with some discrete energy through the medium.

The reaction in Equation 2 typically follows that in Equation 1. An un-ionized or intact water molecule captures an electron (one perhaps set free in a reaction such as that in Equation 1). The result is another ion — a water molecule now endowed with a negative charge. A pair of ions ($H_2O^+$ and $H_2O^-$) has been formed.

The above reactions can, however, represent only a first step in a series of reactions, because, when water is irradiated, it has been shown that the final products include H, OH, $H_2O_2$ and $HO_2$, none of which is formed as an *immediate* result of the passage of an ionizing particle through a water molecule. They must in some way have been formed from the two ions which are produced by irradiation ($H_2O^+$ and $H_2O^-$).

**9.6   The Further Reactions of Ionized Water.**   The ions $H_2O^+$ and $H_2O^-$ are not stable; they are not believed to persist in this form for more than a small fraction of a second before undergoing some change. They are said to dissociate almost immediately ($10^{-16}$ seconds) into entities which are called *free radicals*.

**9.7   Free Radicals.**   Free radicals are distinguished by the presence of a single, unpaired orbital electron, unpaired from the point of view of direction of spin on the electron's own axis. Electrons, in addition to moving about the nucleus of an atom in an orbit, also rotate upon their own axes; the direction of this rotation may, however, differ.

Within any orbit, electrons are paired with respect to spin so that for each electron spinning in one direction there will be another spinning in the opposite direction (this is known as Pauli's Exclusion Principle). If, for some reason, there is an odd number of electrons in an orbit, pairing cannot occur, and there will be *one electron* rotating upon its axis for which there is none spinning in opposition. An atom or molecule having such an unpaired electron is a free radical. Free radicals are exceedingly important in the study of radiation effects, for it is through them that the *indirect action* of radiation occurs.

**9.8   The Formation of Free Radicals from Ionized Water.**   The outer electron orbits of $H_2O^+$ and $H_2O^-$ may be represented in the following manner:

$$H_2O^+ = H\cdot \ \cdot \ddot{O}\cdot \ \cdot H$$

$$H_2O^- = H\cdot \ :\ddot{O}: \ \cdot H$$

There are seven and nine electrons respectively. These ions almost immediately dissociate into two subunits:

$$H_2O^+ \longrightarrow H^+ + OH\cdot$$
$$H_2O^- \longrightarrow H\cdot \ + OH^-$$

Each water ion will yield one smaller ion ($H_2O^+$ gives $H^+$ and $H_2O^-$ gives $OH^-$) and one free radical (there is no way that either seven or nine electrons may be split between the two subunits so that both will have an even number). These are $H\cdot$ and $OH\cdot$ (the dot symbolizes the unpaired electron). The free radicals thus formed are responsible for the indirect action of radiation. They are extremely reactive; in pure water they ordinarily react within $10^{-5}$ second. If a solute is present, their reaction will usually have been accomplished in even less time.

**9.9   Reactions of the Free Radicals.**   The energy exchanged into water from the ionizing particle ionizes the water. The water ions formed this way dissociate, yielding free radicals. The free radicals, then, will diffuse through the irradiated system, reacting with and producing chemical changes in anything with which they interact. In this way the energy of an ionizing particle is exchanged into water and, from water, to another, possibly an intact, molecule.

The reactions of free radicals are reasonably indiscriminate; a free radical may interact with another free radical, with a molecule already damaged by radiation, or, most important, with an intact molecule, possibly a solute molecule—one previously unchanged by radiation.

The reactions of the free radicals can be subdivided into five general categories.

A.  Commonly, there will be a number of reactions among the free radicals themselves.

    1.  $H \cdot + OH \cdot \longrightarrow H_2O$      Water is reconstituted.
    2.  $H \cdot + H \cdot \longrightarrow H_2$      Molecular hydrogen is formed.
    3.  $OH \cdot + OH \cdot \longrightarrow H_2O_2$   Hydrogen peroxide is formed.

B.  Free radicals may react with the water in which they are formed:

    $H \cdot + H_2O \longrightarrow H_2O + OH \cdot$

C.  They may react with their own reactions products.

    1.  $H_2 + OH \cdot \longrightarrow H_2O + H \cdot$   Molecular hydrogen is a reaction product in A.2 above.
    2.  $H_2O_2 + OH \cdot \longrightarrow HO_2 \cdot + H_2O$   Hydrogen peroxide is a reaction product in A.3 above.
    3.  $HO_2 \cdot + HO_2 \cdot \longrightarrow H_2O_2 + O_2$ ⎫ $HO_2 \cdot$ is a product of the
    4.  $HO_2 \cdot + OH \cdot \longrightarrow H_2O + O_2$ ⎬ reaction between $H \cdot$ and molecular oxygen, $O_2$.

D.  Free radicals may react with oxygen. This reaction if of considerable importance and is treated in detail in Chapter 11. It will not be discussed here save to state that it does occur and that it enhances the effects of radiation.

E.  Finally, and very important, free radicals may interact with organic molecules—the molecules of which cells and tissues are built—and change them. When this takes place the *indirect action* of radiation has occurred. The first step in the process is the exchange of energy in water (the solvent) from an ionizing particle. But the last step is a change in one of the molecules of *solute*, one of the molecules of which the cell is built.

    The following equations illustrate how this may come about.

    1.  $HO_2 \cdot + RH \longrightarrow R \cdot + H_2O_2$
    2.  $RH + HO_2 \cdot \longrightarrow RO \cdot$ (an organic free radical) $+ H_2O$

If RH in either of these cases is a fundamental organic molecule—one important in the metabolism of the cell, either as a
building block or as a finished product—an upset in the
chemistry or the metabolism of the cell can be expected. In
addition, $H_2O_2$ (hydrogen peroxide) is a cell poison and if
present in sufficient quantities can materially interfere with
metabolism.

**9.10  Products of Interactions with Free Radicals.**  Not all the products of free-radical interactions are harmful to living systems. Water
is a product; so is molecular hydrogen. And, after a free radical has
interacted, it is, itself, extinguished; it no longer exists. But this does
not mean that all danger is past for the remaining cellular constituents.
Some of the products of such reactions are poisons; still others are
free radicals themselves, capable of further reaction and, consequently,
further transfer of the energy of the ionizing particle. Organic free
radicals may represent not only changed molecular constituents of the
cell, but also substances that are free to attack other such constituents
and spread molecular change still further.

**9.11  Sources of Radiation-Produced Free Radicals.**  It must not be
imagined that free radicals will be formed only from irradiated water.
The ionization of nearly any cellular component (fats, in particular)
can result in free-radical formation which, in turn, will contribute to
the indirect action of radiation. Water constitutes, however, the most
abundant species of molecules in cells and, consequently, will play
the largest role in this phenomenon. But, direct action upon any molecule which results in its ionization may also result in the formation of
free radicals from the ion. Indirect action primarily, but not exclusively, occurs from water-derived free radicals.

**9.12  The Influence of Ion Density on Free-Radical Interactions.**
The interactions of free radicals both among themselves and with
their own reaction products is dependent primarily on how closely
together the free radicals have been formed. After they are formed,
they must diffuse through the medium in which they find themselves
until they encounter something with which they may interact. Densely
ionizing radiations (alpha particles, protons, electrons) produce clusters of ions that are very close together. These ions may subsequently
dissociate into free radicals which also will be in close association
with one another. Since free radicals can and do interact with each
other, and since, after exposure to densely ionizing radiation and the
dissociation of those ions, *they* are very close to each other, they need
not diffuse far before encountering something with which they can
interact. This something will be another free radical. Consequently,

there will be a high probability of interactions between free radicals and of free radicals with the products of previous radical-radical interactions.

If ionization, on the other hand, is brought about by sparsely ionizing radiation, the clusters of ions formed are more widely separated than those produced by densely ionizing radiation. The probability of interaction between the resultant free radicals is much smaller than that following irradiation with densely ionizing particles. As the energy transfer from ionizing radiation within a given volume increases, there is an increase in free-radical interactions and an increase in the number of products of these reactions. The products are, in themselves, at least potentially harmful so that, as the density of ionization increases (increasing LET), there is likely to be an increase in the number of changed molecules—an increase of radiation effect—in the cell.

**9.13  The Role of Oxygen.**  The presence of oxygen during irradiation enhances the magnitude of radiation effects. These effects are of sufficient importance to merit special treatment (see Chapter 11). It is enough to state here that oxygen reacts with the free radicals produced by radiation and draws them into further destructive reactions with the molecules of the cell.

**9.14  Influence of Hydration on Radiosensitivity.**  If the formation of free radicals from ionized water is the major mechanism through which the indirect action of radiation proceeds, then the degree of hydration of a living system should influence its radiosensitivity. The more water there is, the greater the number of interactions with ionizing radiation that can go on in it, and a greater number of free radicals that will be formed from it.

A solution in which water is the solvent may be considered more or less "hydrated" if it is more or less concentrated. The greater the concentration of solute, the "dryer" the solution may be said to be. More dilute solutions can be regarded as "hydrated" or "wetter." By testing the effects of radiation on solute molecules in solutions of differing concentrations, an appreciation for the part played in changing these molecules by water-derived free radicals can be gained.

**9.15  The Influence of Hydration on Radiosensitivity: Observations in Solutions: The Dilution Effect.**  In solutions a fixed number of free radicals is produced by any given dose of radiation. Hypothetically, if the action of radiation in a solution, that is, the number of *solute* molecules chemically changed as a result of irradiation, were to occur only through the mechanism of indirect action (only by free radicals), the number of these molecules actually changed would be *independent* of their concentration (except at extremely low concentrations). This is so because the number of free radicals which will bring about the changes from any given dose of radiation is limited. This number of free radicals can react only with a certain, fixed number of solute molecules. The availability of more or less *solute* molecules, then, will have no bearing on the total number of these molecules that are changed. If, for example, at a given dose of radiation, sufficient free radicals to change ten solute molecules are produced, it will make no difference whether ten, twenty, thirty or more such molecules are present. Ten and only ten will actually be changed. If indirect action were the sole mechanism by which solute molecules in solution are changed, then the dose of radiation and the number of free radicals it produces will be the limiting factor and the only factor determining the number of solute molecules that actually are affected.

On the other hand, if, hypothetically, the action of radiation is exclusively direct (that is, direct ionization of solute *or* solvent molecules, but no transfer of energy from one to the other is possible), the number of *solute* molecules chemically changed will depend upon (in fact, is proportional to) their concentration. Since, in this instance, chemical change can be brought about only by direct ionization, the more solute molecules present, the greater the probability that some of them will be in the path of an ionizing particle and will be changed. The actual number "hit," then, will be proportional to concentration.

Of course, while it is true that both direct and indirect action actually go on in any solution, observations made in more or less concentrated solutions can give a good idea of the importance of hydration, and, consequently, the importance of *indirect* action. Such observations are made by irradiating solutions of different concentrations and comparing the *actual* results with those expected or predicted from the two hypothetical cases just described. Stated another way, if solutions of varying concentrations are irradiated with given doses of ionizing radiation, will the number of solute molecules changed depend upon the concentration of the solute molecules, or will the number be essentially independent of the concentration?

Experimental evidence has shown that, in dilute enzyme solutions of varying concentrations,[1,2] inactivation of enzyme (chemical change) produced by radiation is independent of concentration. Figure 9.1 shows schematically the results of a typical experiment. These give strong evidence that enzyme inactivation has come about primarily through the action of free radicals (indirect action) and that direct action upon the enzyme molecules has played a small, if not insignificant, role.

In extremely dilute solutions (those closest to zero in Figure 9.1) the relatively constant relationship between dose and inactivation no longer holds. The solutions are so dilute—there are so few solute molecules—that the free radicals which have been formed react with

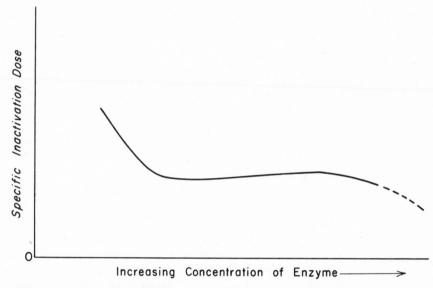

**Figure 9.1.**   Figure 9.1 shows the relationship of dilution upon enzyme inactivation (chemical change) by ionizing radiation. Except for the most dilute solutions, there is a very constant relationship between dose and inactivation which appears to be independent of concentration.

each other and not with enzyme. The free radicals interact and, in so doing, extinguish themselves, rather than inactivating (bring about change in) enzyme.

**9.16   Observations in Living Systems.**   As a general rule, living systems containing little water are much less sensitive to radiation than organisms which exist in highly hydrated states.[3,4,5] It must be borne in mind that this is a generalization, and that not every experiment comparing the radiosensitivity of the same organism in both the dry and wet state has shown unequivocally that radiosensitivity is greatest when irradiation is carried out in the hydrated condition. (Viruses; the seeds of higher plants; *Artemia*, the brine shrimp; and bacterial spores are examples of living systems in which such comparisons may be made.) However, dessication and hydration are perhaps more complex biologic processes than the mere addition or subtraction of water would imply. Changes in rate or even in the mode of metabolism may accompany dessication and hydration and these might affect radiosensitivity. It is possible that such changes could mask or even reverse the expected influence of water upon radiosensitivity.

**9.17   Proof of the Existence of Radiation-Produced Free Radicals in Biologic Systems.**   While it is true that free radicals are formed subsequent to the ionization of water by radiation, and while it is true that it is reasonable to assume that the interactions of radiation and cellular water would also produce free radicals, experimental demonstration of such free radicals in tissue (that is, those formed from *ionized water*) after irradiation has not always been possible. At the usual metabolic temperature the life of water-derived free radicals is extremely short.

The length of time that free radicals exist as free radicals (their "life") is dependent primarily upon their rate of diffusion through the medium in which they are formed. They are formed, and then they move (diffuse) until they encounter something with which they interact. After interacting, they, as entities, become extinct, for they will now exist in combination with whatever underwent the reaction with them. (This is not to say that the product will not be another free radical, which is, of course, possible. It means only that the interaction of a given free radical brings about its own extinction. At the same time it may give rise to something new.) The rate of diffusion, then, determines how long a time will elapse between free-radical formation and an encounter which results in reaction and extinction. Efforts to demonstrate the existence of free radicals in living things have been hamstrung by the exceedingly brief period between the time of the formation of the free radicals and that of their extinction as a species.

It can be supposed that indirect action will be inhibited in living systems which are irradiated in the frozen state (bacterial spores can be used in such instances) and that this inhibition can be taken as evidence for radiation effects being brought about by free radicals. These suppositions are made because the diffusion of free radicals through solid water will be greatly impeded. The impedance should make the degree of change at any given time following radiation less than that observed in non-frozen systems. Methods and the results of such experiments are not directly applicable nor, unfortunately, extrapolatable to living systems of high normal body temperatures.

**9.18   Significance of Changes in the Molecules of Which Cells Are Composed.**   Any change brought about by ionizing radiation in the molecules of which cells are composed is, potentially at least, detrimental to the viability of the cell. It can be said that, because radiation brings about chemical changes, *any* exposure in *any* amount will be a potential hazard to living things. This is true, because living things and the material of which they are composed, through millenia of selection and development, are in precise, harmonious balance with their various environments. Each molecule in every cell is part of a delicate system of checks and balances with every other molecule. Similarly, the cells in each tissue are in balance with each other; the tissues within the body function in coordination with each other, and organisms themselves are balanced with each other and with the physical environment. Within the cell, the balance between molecules is so finely adjusted that deviations from it produce flaws in essential cellular activity and work to the detriment of the cell as a whole. If the status quo within cells is changed, serious imbalances or errors in metabolism and function, even some that are lethal, can be the result.

Ionizing radiation, by depositing energy in cells through the ejection of electrons, upsets this status quo—this finely attuned balance. The total amount of energy in the cell is changed. But, more then that, the products of irradiation—the products of interaction between ionizing particles and the atom with which they chance to interact (ions, excited atoms or molecules, and free radicals)—may be of a kind foreign to the cell or, under normal circumstances, of a kind present only in smaller quantities. Reactions may go on between these radiation products and the remaining normal cellular constituents that usually do not or cannot occur. Thus, because any dosage of ionizing radiation, regardless of how small, has some probability of exchanging some of its energy within any cell which it traverses, there is no dose of radiation too small to be without any hazard at all.

**9.19   The Relative Importance of Direct and Indirect Action in Biologic Systems.**   In a certain sense it is meaningless to speak of the relative importance of direct and indirect action. Whether molecules are changed by direct interaction with radiation or by interaction with the products of an exchange of energy with another molecule will be of little importance to a biologic system. A changed molecule —a deviation from the status quo—is the result. Yet, in another sense the two modes of action will have a relative importance, for, although it is true that any energy exchanged to the molecules of the cell is potentially dangerous to the cell, changes brought about in certain molecules will be more certain to damage the cell than others. That is, not every molecule is of equal importance to the cell although every *species* or kind of molecule is indispensible. Some species of molecules of which living things are composed are, themselves, made up of a very large number  of individual molecules. Often, more are present at any given time than are necessary or essential. Although these are present within cells, each and every one of them will not enter into the cell's metabolism or become part of the structure of the cell. Enzymes are a good example of such a species; water itself is another example. Both are present in an excess. Changes brought about in certain kinds of enzyme molecules may do no harm to the cell at all if the changed molecule is one of those that never enters into metabolism. If that particular molecule never functions, that particular radiation effect is disarmed. On the other hand, one can never be certain which of the large, even excessive number of enzyme molecules will or will not become functional. At present, there is no way to tell. Whenever an enzyme molecule is changed, then, the change is *potentially* harmful to the cell. This is true because any enzyme molecule has the *potential* to become functional. If the radia-tion-changed enzyme molecule is one which is called upon to function, the change in its structure may very well have brought about a change in its function or impaired its ability to function in the cellular situation in which it is needed. The metabolism of this cell will be, for that enzyme and for that function, impaired. There will have been a deviation from the status quo; the system of intra-molecular checks and balances will have been upset. The cell may or may not be able to overcome this difficulty and restore the proper balance. If it can overcome it, the radiation effect will have been temporary and it may be thought of as reversible, possibly even as "repairable." If it cannot, the cell will be permanently damaged; within the cell the molecular environment will be out of balance. Further, the cell itself will now be out of balance with the others in the tissue of which it is a part.

Other species of molecules, on the other hand, are composed of only a few members. The members are not present in excess, and each of them takes an active, often critical role in metabolism. The nucleic acids exemplify this type. Changes brought about in nucleic acid molecules, in particular in deoxyribonucleic acid molecules (all metabolism is under the direction of these molecules), will almost certainly bring about a defect or derangement of normal metabolism, because each of the molecules is intimately involved in cellular, even intracellular, activity. (See Chapter 13 for a discussion of the role of nucleic acids.) Each of the molecules of deoxyribonucleic acid may be said to constitute a critical or vital target for radiation. At the same time, however, the number of such molecules is small. Therefore, the likelihood of *direct* interaction of *randomly* interacting radiation with one of these molecules is also small. By direct action of radiation, changes brought about in these critical or *key* molecules are rare. It is in this case that the indirect action of radiation assumes its greatest importance. The irradiation products of more common but less vital molecules can transfer energy to and bring about changes in one of these key molecules. By indirect action, then, changes in the vital, key molecules become rather more common, and serious, usually irreversible deviations from normal metabolism are brought about. From the point of view of changes in key molecules, from the point of view of serious deviations from the status quo, indirect action is more important than direct action.

## SUMMARY

1. The action of ionizing radiation (excitation, ionization) is random; any atom with which it interacts is likely to be ionized.
2. In mixtures the substance present in the greatest amount has the greatest probability of interaction with radiation; those present in lesser quantities are involved less often.
3. Ions produced during irradiation can dissociate into free radicals.
4. Free radicals can interact with and bring about changes in molecules not themselves directly changed by radiation. This is called the *indirect* action of radiation. It is the process by which energy from ionizing radiation is transferred from a directly ionized molecule to one not directly ionized.
5. No amount of radiation is too small to produce no potential deviation from normal cellular metabolism.
6. Indirect action is the most important mode of change of key cellular molecules and in the production of sharp deviations from the cellular status quo.

## Text References

1. Dale, W. M., Gray, L. H., and Meredith, W.: Phil. Trans. A. *242*, 33 (1949).
2. Dale, W. M.: The Effect of x-rays on the conjugated protein d-amino-acid oxidase. Biochemical Journal *36*, 80-85 (1942).
3. Hollaender, A.: *Symposium on Radiobiology*, John Wiley, New York, 1952, p. 285.
4. Hutchinson, A.: Rad. Res. 7, 468 (1957).
5. Engel, D. W., and Fluke, D. J.: Radiation Research *16*, 173-181 (1962).

# 10

# Target Theory and the Interpretation of

# Survival Data

**10.1 Introduction.** The various molecular species of which cells are composed (water, proteins, amino acids, fats, the nucleic acids, to name a few general categories) have specific functions. This is not to say that each of them has only one function, or that all the functions of every molecular species are known. It is to say that the labors of the cell as a whole are divided among its various components, and that the components function, in cellular activity, in harmony with each other. Every component of the cell – each of its molecular species – is important, perhaps even indispensable, for the maintenance of normal metabolism and for viability, because each has its special rôle to play in normal metabolism. However, the *number* of molecules that makes up each type or species varies. Some molecules (enzymes, water, for example) are present in an excess. In species having excess molecules, not every molecule (not every water or enzyme molecule) actually takes part in metabolism; there are more present than are needed. Further, the scope of metabolic activity of such molecular species is circumscribed. The role they play, while important, is not all-encompassing.

On the other hand, in certain other molecular species (nucleic acids) the number of members present is limited – often so limited that the loss or change of one of them seriously affects metabolism. Among the nucleic acids, deoxyribonucleic acid (DNA) is the most important in this respect; it is the rarest species of molecule in the cell, and it plays the widest, most critical role in metabolism (Chapter 13).

The existence of such a hierarchy of functions, and of the molecules which perform them, has led to the supposition that there may be critical or "key" molecules, the alteration of which can result in the loss of vital functions and, eventually, death of the cells of which these molecules are components. Changes made in other kinds of molecules, those present in an excess and having a more limited function, are not as likely to have the same effect. The "key" molecules would present an important "target," or, at least, occupy a sensitive volume in which an exchange of energy from radiation may easily exert far-reaching effects in the activity of a cell. The supposition has been that changes brought about within such a critical target or the volume it occupies, can be seriously, permanently damaging, even lethal.

**10.2   Target Theory.**   The above supposition has led to the evolution of a concept known as the "target theory"—a theory that has been used to interpret radiation results in both living and non-living systems. This theory demands that, for serious change in function of an organism or a molecule to be brought about by radiation, the initial transfer of energy (ionization) must occur within a limited vital or sensitive volume. Consequently, its application must be *restricted to cases* in which *direct action* is the sole or, at least the predominant, mechanism for producing molecular changes. But it should be remembered (Section 9.19) that nearly all biologic systems are composed of large amounts of water and that indirect action is by far the predominant mode through which changes in the molecules which comprise a cell, regardless of the importance of these individual molecules to the cell, are brought about.

Target theory, in fact, has had its greatest success when its use has been restricted to experimental systems in which indirect action is ruled out. Dried, crystallized viruses have constituted, so far, the best test system.

**10.3   Application of the Target Theory.**   In order to apply the target theory, the following requirements must be met:

1. Survival of function following varying dosages of radiation must be exponentially related to increasing dose (the supposition is that the radiation effect is the result of a single hit or ionization and that the resulting chemical reaction that occurs does so within a discrete volume). Sections 10.7 and 10.8 give a fuller explanation of this single hit relationship.

2. The process must be independent of dose-rate. It is true that, whether a given dosage of radiation is delivered in seconds, minutes or hours, continuously or in fractions, the same total number of ionizations will be produced. However, to apply target theory, the number of targets *irrevocably* inactivated

by *any* dose, given in *any* manner, should be the same. That is, if the same total dose given at two dose-rates does *not* produce the same end-point or the same *degree* of change the target theory cannot be applied.

3. The dose of different types of radiations required to produce a given biologic effect must increase in the order of gamma rays, hard x rays, soft x rays, neutrons, beta and, finally, alpha particles (an order of increasing ionization density). Because of differences in the number of ionizations per unit path length traveled by an ionizing particle or ray (LET), heavily ionizing particles may produce many ionizations in volumes the size of biologically important molecules. Since one "hit" is supposed, by the target theory, as sufficient for inactivation of a target, additional ionization ("hits") in a target or sensitive volume adds nothing to the biologic effect. It does, however, contribute to the total dose. Thus, in the view of target theory, heavily ionizing particles are less efficient for producing biologic effect than are sparsely ionizing ones since the yield of inactivation per ionization with heavily ionizing particles is smaller than with sparsely ionizing ones.

**10.4 Estimation of Target Size.** In order to calculate target size (to apply target theory) *all* of the conditions listed in Section 10.3 must be met. But in most biologic material, all of these conditions cannot be met. The target theory rests upon the idea that the biologic end-point of radiation damage is directly related to the initial transfer of energy (the primary ionization). Anatomic changes—changes in structure and function—brought about by radiation must occur at the exact site where the primary ionization has occurred. But, in biologic systems, this is rarely the case. Changes in molecules and anatomic lesions related to them may occur distant from the site of ionization if radiation-produced free radicals diffuse widely before interacting. Where it is possible, as in small viruses and isolated macromolecules, the experimental findings correspond quite closely to the measured size of what are believed to be the key molecules of the viruses or the sensitive volume of the macromolecule.

**10.5 The Existence of Key Molecules.** The fact that the target theory cannot be directly applied to all living systems does not destroy the concept of the key molecule.

If there are such sensitive targets, in order to identify them it will be necessary first to inactivate all of them. By so doing the function or functions they control and the relationship of energy transfer (either by direct *or* indirect action) in molecules to functions controlled by these molecules can be ascertained.

Second, the dose of radiation required to change (inactivate) the key molecules must be determined.

From these data, an approximation of the number of key molecules can be derived.

The characterization thus obtained can then be compared to that of known cellular constituents or, in the case of irradiation of non-living solutions, to solute molecules in the solution. Then a determination of which of these is most likely to have been the key or sensitive molecule can be made.

**10.6  Single and Multi-Hit Effects.**  Some functions will be sensitive to inactivation by smaller amounts of radiation energy than others. This will be due in the main to a difference in the number of agents which control the function. For example, a change in one molecule can result in the loss of function (inactivation) of some viruses. But life (vital function) in more complex structures such as cells is not dependent upon one molecule but upon many, so that several, at the least, must be changed before inactivation (death) occurs.

In the simplest case there will be a single, controlling entity; it can be thought of as occupying a specific volume. If a change related to an exposure to radiation (changes can, of course, be brought about by diffusing free radicals as well as by direct ionization) occurs within it and inactivation is the result, inactivation is spoken of as having occurred as a result of a single hit.

On the other hand, if the control of a function is exerted by more than a single entity, changes must be brought about in all of those that control it before the function ceases to exist (inactivation). Inactivation here is the result of more than a single hit; it is a multi-hit phenomenon.

**10.7  Single-Hit or Single-Change Phenomena.**  Survival of function in enzymes following increasing dosages of radiation well illustrates the single-hit phenomenon. One hit or change in an enzyme molecule is all that is thought necessary to influence such molecules in such a way as to inactivate them. Thus, in a typical enzyme-inactivation experiment, the relationship of inactivation of enzyme in solution and increasing dose is expected to lie on a straight line if, indeed, a single ionization or change taking place within an enzyme molecule inactivates that molecule. The number of expected interactions of radiation, or the free radicals it produces, with enzyme (consequently, the number of enzyme molecules inactivated, since one hit inactivates one molecule) is proportional to the total number of ionizations produced by radiation (assuming that the ionizations are distributed randomly), which is, in turn, proportional to the total dose of radiation delivered.

But neither ionizing radiation nor the free radicals it brings about react *exclusively* with intact enzyme molecules. It is as likely that a molecule which has been ionized or which has interacted with a free radical will suffer a second such interaction as it is that an intact molecule will interact for the first time. Thus, as a solution is irradiated, the total number of intact molecules decreases, so that the number of intact enzyme molecules *per unit volume* is reduced. Because the number of these intact molecules is decreased, the remaining intact molecules now present a smaller target for radiation than did the initial volume, and the probability of interaction with radiation, on this basis alone, is decreased. At the same time the number of inactivated molecules increases with increasing dose. These can and do react directly with radiation and indirectly with the free radicals which the radiation generates. The radiations and the free radicals that interact in this way are "wasted," for it is impossible for them then to change intact molecules. The remaining intact enzyme molecules, as dose of radiation is increased, may be said to be "protected," for their number diminishes, presenting a smaller target, and the number of already inactivated molecules, which may suffer a second interaction but which cannot be "inactivated" again, becomes quite significant.

At low doses of radiation a small proportion of enzyme molecules are hit. Few are inactivated, and their number, compared to the total present, will be infinitesimal. In a practical sense, at very low doses of radiation the inactivated molecules are non-existent and do not offer measurable protection to intact molecules. In low dose ranges, then, inactivation of enzymes *will* vary with dose in a linear way, because protection is not a factor. As the total dose increases, however, the number of targets inactivated represents a considerable proportion of the enzymes present. Thus, the number of observed inactivations at higher doses will be less than the number expected (based upon a linear relationship throughout) since previously inactivated molecules will offer a significant protection to the remaining intact ones. With respect to enzyme inactivation, then, a deviation from the straight line relationship in the higher dose range is expected.

Analysis of experimentally obtained data on the survival of enzyme function (inactivation) shows that this is actually what happens. The *inactivation efficiency* decreases with increasing dose and inactivation expressed as a function of increasing dose falls off as a geometric progression, that is, exponentially. Simply stated, in high dose ranges, each increment of dose fails to inactivate as many enzyme molecules as any preceding like increment (Figure 10.1).

A curve of the type shown in Figure 10.1 is termed an exponential function and describes a relationship between two variables which is specific but not linear. The relationship is written $y = e^x$ where $e = 2.718$ (the base of the natural logarithm). For the example

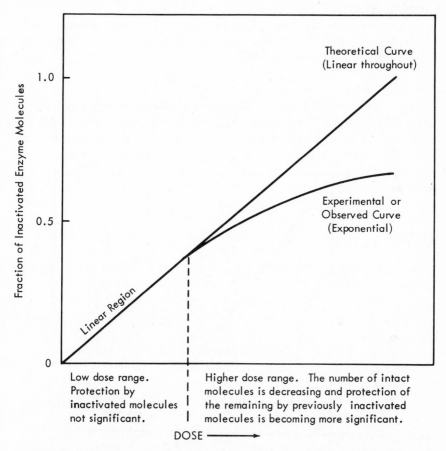

Figure 10.1. The general relationship between survival of a function following increasing dosages of ionizing radiation *when a single* change or interaction brings about loss of that function (single-hit response curve) is shown. In the figure, the general relationship is applied to enzyme inactivation.

shown in Figure 10.1, y (the ordinate) is the fraction inactivated and x (the abcissa) is the total dose. Because of this relationship to the natural logarithm, a *logarithmic* plot of such a function is a straight line (Figure 10.2).

Simply stated, this relationship implies that the dose of radiation sufficient to inactivate *all* of the available molecules (where one interaction equals inactivation) actually inactivates only a fraction of them; the remaining escape damage. There is enough radiation given to inactivate all, but, because some are "inactivated" more than once, and some not at all, incomplete inactivation occurs. In actual fact, when enough radiation is given to inactivate all molecules present, 63 per cent are inactivated; 37 per cent are protected and remain intact.

Such observed survival data and their dependence on the natural logarithm have made possible the concept of the $D_{37}$ dose, based on the following simple relationship:

$$y = e^{-x} = e^{-D/D_0} = e^{-1} = 0.37$$

Here, D represents the dose given and $D_0$ the dose required to score one hit per target. Thus, in this instance $D = D_0$ and the ratio is 1.

It must be stated that these concepts apply only to experiments which measure damage *at a molecular level* (whether it be *in vivo* or

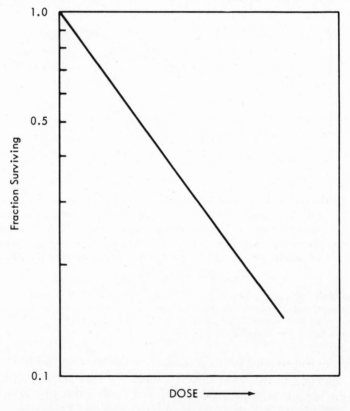

**Figure 10.2.** The experimental, observed curve, the exponential or geometric progression given in Figure 10.1, is shown as it would appear on a plot in which the y axis fraction enzyme surviving in Figure 10.1) is a logarithm. The resultant line is straight.

*in vitro*). The 37 per cent dose has no meaning in complex mechanisms such as whole body irradiation of mammals. A dose of radiation sufficient to kill 63 per cent of a group of animals releases an equal amount of energy in the other animals. Any difference in survival, in this case, will be related to biologic variability.

**10.8  Multi-Hit Survival Curves.**  All of the foregoing is based on the supposition that a single hit (an ionization or a reaction with a free radical) within a specific sensitive volume is all that is required for inactivation of a given function. Such phenomena are expressed as exponential curves when plotted against dose. These curves are characteristic of some viruses where one target or sensitive volume per organism appears to exist.

Higher on the scale of life, however, organisms become increasingly complex. There are often several different structures which may control the same function. This multiplicity of "targets" makes inactivation of the organisms as a whole, by a single hit, highly unlikely.

Since more than one target must be changed to inactivate vital function or cause death in most living things, this, in its turn, will require that several hits or interactions will have to occur within an organism in order to inactivate that organism. This is not to say that one hit is now insufficient to inactivate any one of the targets, merely that sufficient active targets will remain to carry on the function of the inactivated ones, so that the organism as a whole *appears* unaffected.

In Figure 10.1 a survival curve is shown illustrating inactivation following a single hit. In contrast to this, organisms with more than one "target" controlling a specific vital function do not initially respond to increasing dose in a linear fashion (Figure 10.3).

Where there is one target per organism $(N = 1)$, any amount of radiation, however small, will inactivate some organisms (the curve intersects at zero dose). But, where the number of targets is more than one, there are doses of radiation which produce no measurable inactivation at all (see arrows in Figure 10.3; the curves do not intersect at zero dose). As the number of targets per organism increases, the dose at which inactivation becomes apparent is higher $(N = 2, N = 4)$. Since more than one target controls the vital function, at low doses it is unlikely that all of the targets within the same organism will be inactivated. Further, the greater the number of targets within the organism the less likely it becomes that all will be inactivated with a low dose of radiation. Some of the targets or key molecules, of course, *are* inactivated (a single hit *within a molecule* is still all that is required to inactivate it), but the vital functions of the organism survive. The survival curve, then, is S-shaped (sigmoid)

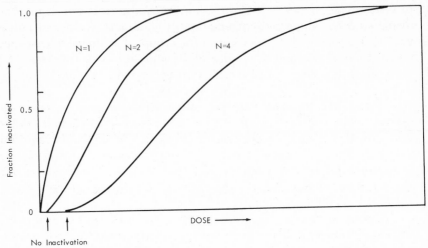

**Figure 10.3.** The survival of organisms as related to dose when (1) the organism has only one key molecule – loss of function occurs after a single-hit (N = 1); (2) the organism has two such molecules – loss of function occurs after a single hit in *each* (N = 2); and (3) an organism has four key molecules – loss of function occurs after a single-hit in *each* (N = 4). Inactivation of organisms in *all* cases is the result of inactivation of *all* key molecules. Thus, inactivation of N = 2 and N = 4 will have to be the result of more than one hit (multi-hit phenomenon).

when the number of targets is greater than one. At the dose at which measurable inactivation is detected in a multi-target organism (Figure 10.3, the arrows) many of the organisms will have sustained from one to several interactions and, as well, several key molecules will have been inactivated, without apparent functional change. Increases in dose beyond the first sign of inactivated organisms lead to a very steep rise in organism inactivation, because there is a good chance that any further hits incurred will occur in organisms which have sustained several previous hits. These further hits have a good chance of inactivating all the remaining key molecules. Thus, organism inactivation, on a large scale, occurs.

The more targets there are per organism the less efficient any given dose of radiation will be for inactivating them (compare slopes of N = 2 and N = 4). The more targets there are per organism the less likely it is that all will be inactivated at once. And, further, a greater total dose will be required to inactivate all of the organisms.

When these survival data are expressed as the logarithm of survival related to dose, the result for a single target organism is a straight line (Figure 10.2). If survival data from "multi-hit" organisms are expressed in the same fashion, the initial portion of the curve is non-linear, but the response at higher doses becomes linear (Figure 10.4).

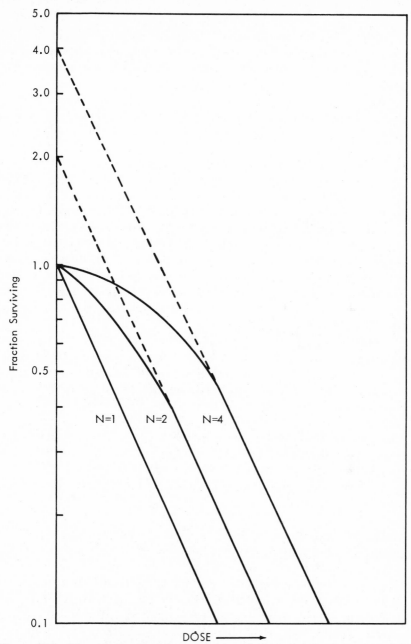

**Figure 10.4.** The relationship between increasing dose and the logarithm of the fraction of organisms, having different numbers of key molecules, that *survive* a given dose of radiation. For those having a single target (N = 1) the relationship is a straight line. But for those having more than one such target (N = 2, N = 4) the relationship is not initially linear although at higher doses it becomes so. The linear portion of both the curves (in these portions each increment of dose results in the killing of the same number of organisms and, therefore, the inactivation of all the targets in them) is extrapolated in such a manner that the entire process is seen as linearly related.

When the linear part of the curve is extrapolated beyond the initial threshold value to zero dose, the point of intercept on the y axis is said to be numerically related to the *average number* of targets or key molecules per organism. That is, the intercept at zero for $N = 1$ is taken to mean that only one key molecule exists in these organisms. On the same basis, then, an interception of the y axis at points greater than one is taken to indicate more than one target per organism.

**10.9  Survival Data.**  The concept of *survival* has implicit in it the notion that a function or characteristic has remained intact ("lived-through") after a particular life-threatening experience. This concept applies not only to living things but equally to non-living things and even to particular functions of these things. For example, the function of an enzyme may depend upon a given structural arrangement of the atoms of which it is made up. If forces come into play that can change that arrangement, but fail to do so, it may be said that the function has survived. If, however, that arrangement *is* changed, the function will have failed to survive, and, for that function, the enzyme will have been inactivated.

The ability to survive a given "insult" or life-threatening experience will depend upon a constellation of factors. Among these will be an innate sensitivity (or vulnerability) toward the insult in question (is a portion of an enzyme easily re-arranged?), the ability, if any, of the changed entity to restore itself (repair), the presence of substances or factors which may "shield" the particular arrangement, mitigating vulnerability (protectors), the presence of substances or factors which enhance the detrimental effect (potentiation), and, finally, the manner in which the insult occurs or is delivered.

An exposure to ionizing radiation is, for both living and non-living things, just such a life-threatening experience.

**10.10  Interpretation of Survival Data.**  Analysis of survival data following increasing doses of radiation does provide a means for the determination of the number of key molecules governing the various functions of living systems (including vital functions). But, knowledge of the number of such molecules does not, in itself, say *what* they are. At present, no cellular entity can be pointed to with absolute certainty as *the* structure which, if changed, causes death or loss of the vital function of the cell. Much evidence does, however, support the idea that chromosomes and the DNA are key targets. Their role in metabolism will be discussed in Chapters 13 and 14.

**10.11  Factors Which May Influence Survival Following Irradiation.**  Survival of function following irradiation is not dependent solely upon the dose of radiation and the number of key molecules governing or responsible for the function. As earlier stated, it will also be dependent upon innate sensitivity, repair processes, protective agents, potentiating agents, and manner of delivery (dose-rate) of insult.

In the chapter that follows, one of the most important potentiating agents (oxygen) and the manner in which it modifies survival following irradiation will be discussed. Later, the remaining modifiers will be described in detail.

## SUMMARY

1. Certain molecules, rare in number but highly important in function, are regarded as key targets for radiation in cells.
2. The "target theory" has been proposed as an apparatus to explain survival following irradiation.
3. The relationship of survival of function to increasing dose of radiation can indicate the number of molecules controlling the function.

### General Reference

1. Lea, D. E.: *Actions of Radiations on Living Cells*, Cambridge University Press, New York, 1956.

# 11

# The Oxygen Effect

## Part I: Description

**11.1 General Statement.** The presence of oxygen in cells and tissues at the time of irradiation increases the magnitude of the effects of radiation, irrespective of the end-point under observation. This interaction between oxygen and radiation is known generally as "the oxygen effect."

**11.2 Conditions under Which There Is an Oxygen Effect.** *Presence of Oxygen at the Time of Irradiation.* Numerous experiments have demonstrated that oxygen's enhancement of the radiation effect occurs only if it is present at cellular or tissue levels at the time of irradiation. The presence of oxygen before or after irradiation contributes only to the rate of development of the lesion by its effect on metabolic rates within the cell.

The importance of the presence of oxygen at the time of irradiation is dramatically demonstrated in an experiment of Howard-Flanders and Moore,[1] in which dysentery bacilli were exposed to oxygen and/or nitrogen and irradiated, all within 1/50th of a second. This experiment was performed by moving a metal carrier containing the bacteria through a chamber filled with either oxygen or nitrogen and breaking through a foil into a second chamber filled with either gas. Mica windows were provided in both chambers through which irradiation might be carried out either immediately before or after breaking through the foil (Figure 11.1). The survival data (Figure 11.2) demonstrate that the important factor is the presence of oxygen at the time of irradiation, for only those organisms *irradiated* in oxygen, regardless of their immediate pre- or post-treatment, showed shortened survival times.

Hollaender and associates[2] have also tested this point. Using *Escherichia coli*, they set up four experimental conditions. Figure 11.3 lists these conditions and presents the results.

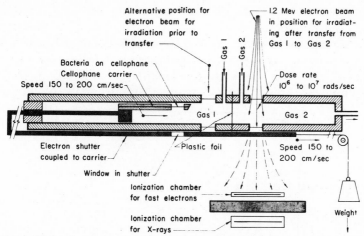

**Figure 11.1.**  Apparatus for the irradiation of bacteria immediately before or immediately after the transfer from one gas to another. The time taken by the irradiation and the transfer is less than 20 msec. (From Howard-Flanders, P., and Moore, D.: Radiation Research 9: 424, 1958.)

The difference in sensitivity between bacilli cultivated and irradiated in air and bacilli cultivated and irradiated in the absence of oxygen (in $N_2$) is so great that ten times as much energy is needed to inactivate the same porportion of non-oxygenated as of well-oxygenated bacilli. For a given dose of x rays, the proportion of oxygenated bacteria inactivated can be as much as 100,000 times greater than that of non-oxygenated organisms (Figure 11.3). In-

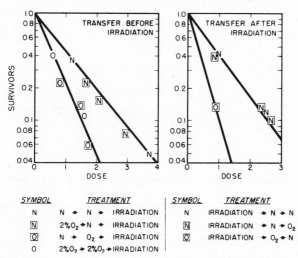

**Figure 11.2.**  Survival curves for bacteria (*left*) irradiated after transfer from one gas to another, and (*right*) irradiated after the transfer. (From Howard-Flanders, P., and Moore, D.: Radiation Research 9: 427, 1958.)

creased sensitivity, then, depends upon the presence of oxygen during the irradiation.

Extremely rapid exhaustion of oxygen and change to the anoxic state by cells is not restricted to bacteria. Wright and Howard-Flanders,[3] with the use of short-duration, high-intensity electron irradiation, were able to show that, after clamping off the blood supply

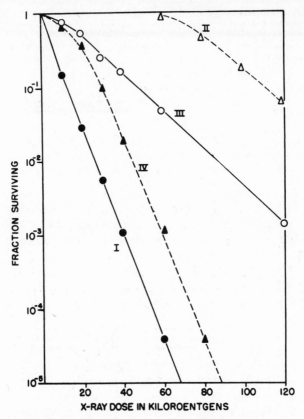

**Figure 11.3.** E. coli B/r irradiated in buffer solution with 250 kv x rays. I, Aerobically grown and irradiated. II, Anaerobically grown and irradiated. III, Aerobically grown and anaerobically irradiated. IV, Anaerobically grown and aerobically irradiated. (From Hollaender, Stapleton and Martin: Nature, London 167: 103-104, 1951.)

to tails of young mice, maximum radioresistance (reflecting tissue hypoxia) was obtained within four seconds. Oxygen, then, must be very quickly used up and radioresistance quickly acquired.

*Oxygen Concentration within a Definite Range.* Air consists of about 20 per cent $O_2$, 0.1 per cent $CO_2$, and 80 per cent $N_2$. In air, as in any mixture of gases, each gas exerts its own partial pressure.

The pressure of air at sea level is 760 mm Hg. Therefore, the pressure of oxygen in air is $760 \times 0.20 = 150$ mm Hg. This is known as *the partial pressure* of oxygen.

But the critical factor in the oxygen effect is the oxygen tension at the tissue or cellular level. Oxygen tension depends directly upon the partial pressure of oxygen ($pO_2$) in the inspired or environmental gas. It is usually defined as the pressure of dry oxygen gas with which dissolved oxygen in the blood is in equilibrium. If either the pressure of the inspired gas is changed, or the composition of the gas is changed (as we seen above in determining the $pO_2$ in air at sea level, both pressure on the total gas and the relative amounts of each gas in the mixture determine the partial pressure of any gas in it), there will be a change in the pressure of undissolved oxygen in the blood with a consequent change in tension.

Oxygen tensions in most tissues are at levels similar to that of venous blood or lymph—approximately 20 to 40 mm Hg. Tissues which have tensions below this are probably hypoxic. It should be immediately pointed out, however, that some tissues are hypoxic when considered with relation to others, but that this is, for them, normal. Nevertheless, normal or not, hypoxic cells or tissues (those that are at low oxygen tensions and, if oxygen tensions in the blood are raised, will acquire a greater oxygen tension) will be radio-resistant when compared to normal cells or tissues, or even to themselves at higher oxygen tensions.

It is interesting to note that increases in the magnitude of radiation effects do not indefinitely grow larger as the tensions of oxygen are brought ever higher. When the oxygen tension reaches that conferred by air at sea level (20 to 40 mm Hg), no appreciable further increase in radiosensitivity has been observed. The oxygen effect will occur, then, between oxygen tensions of 0 and 20 mm Hg (each increment in oxygen tension giving rise to an increase in radiation effect) but, above 20 mm of Hg, it is nearly evanescent (Figure 11.4).

The remaining gases of which air is composed have no effect on radiosensitivity at normal atmospheric pressures. But at increased pressures, gases in mixtures containing oxygen have been shown to reverse the oxygen effect; that is, gases such as hydrogen, nitrogen, argon, krypton, and xenon in a high pressure mixture can protect against oxygen's enhancement of radiation damage. At high pressures these gases are more likely to enter into cells and may compete with oxygen (which enters easily at atmosperic pressure) for senstive sites within the cell. As pointed out by Ebert and Hornsey,[4] it is possible that the sensitive site (at which oxygen might react to produce the radiation lesion) is protected by a layer of inert gas. An exception to this apparent "pressure phenomenon" is nitrous oxide which partially reverses the oxygen effect even at atmospheric pressure.

**11.3   Universal Effect of Oxygen.**   The effect on radiosensitivity of
different oxygen concentrations has been demonstrated in all classes
of organisms. The dependence on oxygen has been shown in all plant
and animal cells.

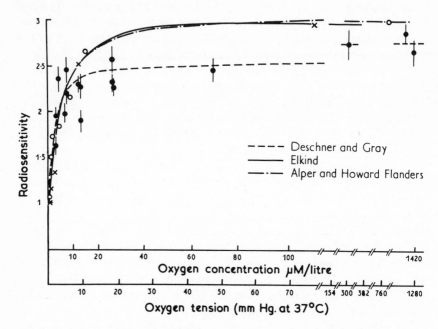

**Figure 11.4**   Curves of radiosensitivity as a function of oxygen tension at the time of
irradiation. Alper and Howard-Flanders, 1956; Deschner and Gray, 1959; Elkind,
Swain, Alescio, Sutton and Moses, 1965. (Note: Elkind's curve drawn by Alper from
his data. The three curves redrawn and superimposed by Thomlinson.) (From
Churchill-Davidson, I.: The Oxygen Effect in Radiotherapy, Oncologia *20*, Suppl.
18-29, 1966.)

In mammals the data of Graievskii and Konstantinova[5] typify the
results of many investigators (Table 11.1).

**Table 11.1.**   Oxygen Concentration: Survival of Irradiated Mice*

| Dose of Radiation | Experimental Conditions | Content of $O_2$ in Atmosphere (%) | Survival Number | % | Mean Life Span in Days |
|---|---|---|---|---|---|
| 900r | Control | 21 | 1/36 | 0 | 5.1±0.4 |
| | Hypoxia | 8.2 | 14/29 | 48.4 | 10.2±1.3 |
| 1200r | Control | 21 | 0/43 | 0 | 4.5±0.3 |
| | Hypoxia | 8.2 | 8/58 | 13.7 | 8.8±0.7 |
| | Hypoxia | 6.5 | 15/47 | 31.9 | 14.1±1.4 |

*From Graievskii and Konstantinova.[5]

**11.4   Adaptation.**   There is some evidence that animals may adapt to environments of low oxygen concentrations after certain periods of time. One of the ways in which they may do this is through the increase in the number of red blood corpuscles. In effect, by increasing the number of cells competent to carry oxygen to tissues, they have restored the normal tissue oxygen level and would not demonstrate increased resistance to radiation. The length of time for adaptation, however, is long, of the order of several days to weeks.

**11.5   Dependence on LET.**   The magnitude of the oxygen effect is greatly reduced with radiations of high LET (alpha particles, protons, etc.) when compared to sparsely ionizing radiations (x rays). It is believed that the ion density produced by radiations of high specific ionization is so great that there would occur several ionizations within the same target molecule. Such extensive damage probably could not be restored, and consequently, no oxygen enhancement of the lesion would be possible. Figure 11.5 illustrates the effect of oxygen on the survival of ascites cells irradiated with radiations of increasing LET.

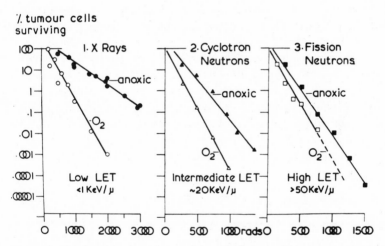

**Figure 11.5.**   Reproductive survival of mouse P-388 ascites leukemia cells, irradiated and assayed in vivo with various different radiations, under *oxygenated* and *anoxic* conditions. I, X rays, oxygen enhancement ratio (OER) = 2.5. 2, Cyclotron-produced fast neurons (6 Mev), OER = 1.7. 3, Fission-spectrum fast neutrons, OER = 1.2. (From Berry, R. J.: The Radiologic Clinics of North America, Vol. 3, No. 2, August 1965, p. 250.)

**11.6   Mechanisms through Which the Effect Occurs.**   Several mechanisms have been proposed to explain the enhancement of the magnitude of radiation effects when radiation is given in the presence of oxygen.

*Toxicity of Oxygen.*   Oxygen itself, for example, is not without toxic properties. Under certain circumstances (high pressure, high concentrations) it is a potent damaging agent, producing effects which closely mimic those of ionizing radiation. Conger and Fairchild[6] observed as many changes in the chromosomes of *Tradescantia* microspores when the pollen was kept for one hour in pure oxygen as occurred following a dose of 1200r of x rays.

It appears, further, that some types of damage from radiation and the toxicity of oxygen have a common mechanism; that is, the same free-radical mechanisms are responsible for both. Oxygen may interact with radiation-produced short-lived free radicals. Such radicals exist for extremely short periods (in the order of $10^{-5}$ sec.) so that it is this interaction which accounts for the occurrence of the effect only if oxygen is present at the time of irradiation. It must be present at the time of radical formation in order to interact with the free radicals.

*Properties of Oxygen.*   Oxygen, as a molecule ($O_2$), has certain singular properties which result from its unusual electronic configuration (Figure 11.6).

There are two unpaired electrons, indicated by arrows at Py and Pz in Figure 11.6. This configuration gives oxygen its high oxidizing potential from which are derived its property as an excellent oxidizing agent for maintaining life as well as its capacity for destroying it (toxicity). Atomic oxygen, because it has only one unpaired electron, is a free radical. Since energy is required to raise molecular oxygen to atomic oxygen, this energy probably presents a barrier against molecular oxygen being raised to atomic oxygen indiscriminately. Once it

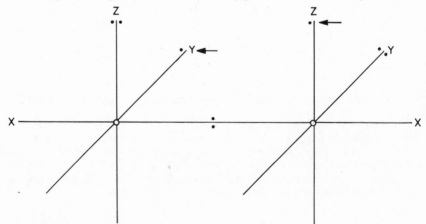

**Figure 11.6.**   Electronic configuration of molecular oxygen ($O_2$) at the P orbital.

is in its free-radical form, oxygen can react with many cellular components.

*Generation of Free Radicals.*   Free radicals are generated by metabolic processes as well as by ionizing radiation. While it appears that some defense exists in cells against normal numbers of free radicals generated by normal oxidative processes (although these defenses are, as yet, incompletely understood), large numbers of free radicals can start destructive chain reactions which are typified by auto-oxidation. Such auto-oxidative chain processes are illustrated below. In the illustration, RH is a normal, carbon-hydrogen bonded molecule, a typical compound to be found in any cell. In this example, RH is the target molecule for radiation damage. Damage to RH is damage to the target molecule. R· is a normal, active biologic free radical. RSH is a normal sulfhydryl compound to be found in any cell.

*Auto-oxidative Chain Reactions.*   The chain reaction may be initiated by ionizing radiation, by biologic reduction of oxygen, or by the oxidation of R·, the normal active biologic free radical.

If ionizing radiation is the initiating agent, its action may be direct, i.e., it interacts with a biologic molecule (in this case, RH), or indirect, through water.

*Direct Action.*

1.   $RH \xrightarrow[\text{quantum}]{\text{energy}} R· + H·$, both of which are free radicals.

*Indirect Action.*

2.   $H_2O \xrightarrow[\text{quantum}]{\text{energy}} H_2O^+ + e^-$

3.   $H_2O^+ + H_2O \longrightarrow H_3O^+ + OH·$

4.   $e^- + H_2O \longrightarrow OH^- + H·$

Thus, in equations 2, 3, and 4, energy is exchanged from an ionizing radiation to water by the ejection of an electron ($e^-$). The resulting positive ion reacts with un-ionized water to yield yet another species of charged water molecule and the free radical, OH· (the hydroxyl radical). The ejected electron can react with un-ionized water to give an $OH^-$ ion and a hydrogen free radical. In this way, and, directly, as in equation 1, free radicals are provided with which the chain reactions may start.

*Biologic Reduction of Oxygen.*

5.   $O_2 \xrightarrow{H\cdot} HO_2\cdot \xrightarrow{H\cdot} H_2O_2 \longrightarrow OH\cdot + H_2O \xrightarrow{H\cdot} 2H_2O.$

Here the hydrogen free radical reacts with oxygen to give $HO_2\cdot$, the hyperoxal radical. This is a very important product, because it is this radical which can react (as in equation 5) to give the potent poison, hydrogen peroxide ($H_2O_2$). Later in this discussion the role of the hyperoxal radical in some of the damaging steps of the chain reaction will be discussed. The steps in equation 5, including the formation of this important free radical, can be illustrated as in Figure 11.7.

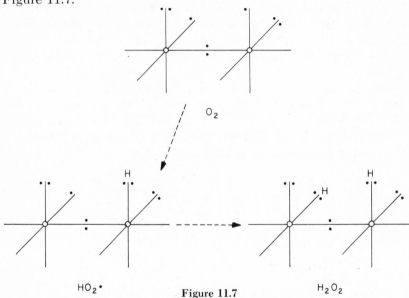

HO$_2$·                          **Figure 11.7**                          H$_2$O$_2$

*Oxidation of Normal Biologic Free Radicals by Oxygen.*

6.   $R\cdot + O_2 \longrightarrow RO_2\cdot$

Each of the six interactions described above, then, results in the formation of one or more free radicals and all are initiating events for the chain reactions.

*Chain Reactions.*

1.   $RH + HO_2\cdot \longrightarrow R\cdot + H_2O_2$

The radical $R\cdot$ may then enter into reaction as in equation 6 and the chain reaction may be continued with the radical $RO_2\cdot$. In addition, hydrogen peroxide is formed.

2.   $RO_2\cdot + RH \longrightarrow RO_2H + R\cdot$

The result here can be a chain reaction if R· enters into reaction as in equation 6.

3.   $RSH + HO_2· \longrightarrow RS· + H_2O_2$

Again, if equation 6 interposes here, a chain reaction results.

**11.7   Oxygen Enhances the Magnitude of the Radiation Effect.**   It is clear from the foregoing, then, that oxygen can enhance the effects of radiation by interacting with radiation-produced free radicals, whether they are produced from water or from some other molecular species, and, by so doing, draws these free radicals into destructive, auto-oxidative chain reactions. It is also very possible that oxygen can block restoration of an intact molecule by interacting with a radiation-produced organic free radical which might have been restored to its normal state. Thus, the effect of radiation can also be enhanced by prevention of some fraction of the expected restoration.

1.   $RH \xrightarrow[\text{quantum}]{\text{energy}} R· + H·$

2.   $R· + H· \longrightarrow RH$ Restoration.

3.   $R· + O_2 \longrightarrow RO_2·$ Restoration blocked.

Chain reaction and damage result. If oxygen is absent or present in small amounts, reaction 3 above is not so likely to occur.

*Formation of Peroxide.*   Finally, the presence of oxygen at irradiation will greatly promote the formation of hydrogen peroxide and organic peroxides.

*Magnitude of the Effect.*   There is some variation in the change in sensitivity resulting from the oxygen effect. In Table 11.2 are representative values. The table includes a variety of biologic systems and shows that the effect is an important one.

**11.8   Protection against Radiation: The Oxygen Effect**

*Antioxidants.*   Compounds which are active reducing agents are capable of terminating the chain reactions and, by so doing, sparing molecules within cells which might otherwise have been damaged by one of the free radicals generated or perpetuated in the chain reaction.

*Sulfhydryl Compounds.*   These compounds, many of which are naturally occurring, are organic compounds which have active thiol groups (RSH). Many of them (glutathione, cysteine, cystamine, ami-

**Table 11.2.** Relative Magnitudes of the Oxygen Effect

| System | Action Measured | Experimental Conditions at Irradiations | Relative Change in Radiosensitivity | References |
|---|---|---|---|---|
| E. coli | Survival | O₂ Saturated media vs. N₂ saturated media | X10 | Hollaender, A., et al.: Cold Spring Harbor Symp., Quant. Biol. 16, 103 (1951) |
| Microspores of Tradescantia | Number of interchanges produced on chromosomes | Oxygen vs. vacuum | X5.8 | Giles, N. H., and Riley, H. P.: Proc. Nat. Acad. Sci., US, 36, 337 (1950) |
| Plants and insects | Survival | 0% Oxygen vs. 20% oxygen | X2.5 | Bacq and Alexander: Fundamentals of Radiobiology, 1961, p.287 |
| Ascites tumor cells | Chromosomal abnormalities | 1 Atm of air vs. absence of oxygen | X3.0 | Gray, L. H.: Brit. J. Radiol. 30, 403 (1957) |
| Small lymphocyte of rat lymph gland | Production of pyknosis | 1 Atm pure O₂ & 1 atm pure N₂ | X12 | Trowel, O. A.: Brit. J. Rad. 26, 302 (1953) |
| Tail of 7 day old mouse | Growth of tail after irradiation | Tissue anoxia after clamping the tail | X1.8 | Howard-Flanders, P., and Moore, D.: Rad. Res. 9, 422 (1958) |
| Mammary carcinoma | Survival of cells | Cold (0°C) and cyanide vs. O₂ atmosphere | X2 | Hall, B. V., et al.: Ca Res. (abs) 12, 268 (1952) |
| Mouse | Survival | 8.2% O₂ vs. 21% O₂ at 1 atm | X2 | Graievskii, E. I. A., and Konstantinova, M. M.: Akad. Nauk. SSSR Dokl. 140, 705 (1961) |

noethylisothiuronium, for example) are capable of terminating chain reactions because their radical forms may interact to produce a stable, naturally occurring biologic compound.

$$RSH + HO_2\cdot \longrightarrow RS\cdot + H_2O_2$$

$$RS\cdot + RS\cdot \longrightarrow RSSR$$

For the RS· radical, the chain is terminated. At normal concentrations of tissue oxygen, sulfhydryl compounds are good radioprotectors, but at lower oxygen concentrations they may enhance the oxygen effect; in all likelihood, they present the cell with a thiol compound which is converted in the following way by oxygen to two radicals.

$$RSH \xrightarrow{O_2} RS\cdot + HO_2\cdot$$

*Vitamin E.* Vitamin E and the alpha-tocopherols are antioxidants. Deficiency of vitamin E can result in oxygen toxicity at normal sea-level concentrations. Vitamin E deficient animals are quite sensitive to high oxygen environments.

*Other Protective Agents.* Antioxidants are not the only substances which can confer radiation protection nor do they represent the only mechanism by which protection is conferred.

*Cobalt.* Cobalt, which can destroy hydrogen peroxide,[7] protects against ionizing radiation.[8]

*Chelating Agents.* These agents (ethylene diaminetetraacetic acid and diethyldithiocarbamic acid, EDTA and DEDTC, respectively), which can chelate (remove from solution) heavy metals such as copper, protect against radiation,[9,10] possibly by removing metals which can catalyze peroxy free-radical reactions.

*Other Sources of Free Radicals.* Indirect action through water may not be the sole source of radicals produced by radiation. Irradiation of lipids produces peroxides which may be responsible for some of the effects of radiation.

## Part II: Application of the Oxygen Effect to Radiotherapy

**11.9 Basic Premise.** The basic concept under which there is an application of the oxygen effect in radiotherapy rests on the premise that certain tumors have hypoxic (radioresistant) regions when compared to normal tissue and even to other regions of the same tumor. Even though tumors, with their large numbers of dividing cells, are, in many cases, more sensitive to radiation than the more static normal tissues that surround them (Chapters 12, 13, 14, 15), regions of poor oxygenation within tumors might make some of the cells quite insensitive to radiation—insensitive enough to survive the usual forms of radiotherapy.

*Tumors Have Hypoxic Regions.* Oxygenation of cells of tumors depends upon blood carried to them by vessels in the stroma. However, there is considerable variation among tumors in the spatial relationship of tumor cells and vascular stroma. In some, nearly every cell will be very near or adjacent to a capillary. Such cells, of course, will be well oxygenated or, at least, have complete access to oxygen. Others, however, are different; they grow in masses or cords which are surrounded by capillaries but are not penetrated by them. Oxygen will reach these cells by diffusion, and, as a result, the concentration of oxygen around any given cell in a cord will depend on (1) the coefficient of diffusion of oxygen in a tumor cord, a factor that takes into consideration all those things that both promote and inhibit diffusion; (2) the oxygen tension in the capillary that feeds the cell in question; (3) the distance from the cell to the capillary; and (4) the respiratory rate of intervening tumor cells.

Many tumors, although by no means all, do grow in such solid cords. This pattern is, for example, common in the structure of many squamous cell carcinomas taken from many parts of the body. Characteristically, there is a zone of living, intact tumor cells and a necrotic interior (Figure 11.8). The mass of cells grows outward from its interior. However, the width of the zone of living cells remains quite constant[11]; it is the necrotic center that becomes larger.

In considering the factors influencing oxygenation of any given cell in this zone of living cells of a tumor, (2) and (3) are probably the most important. Although the coefficient of diffusion of oxygen probably varies little from tumor to tumor, the respiratory rate may vary considerably. Yet, when this is compared to the differences of oxygen tensions in the sources of oxygen (the capillaries) and to the distance that a cell may be away from a capillary (perhaps better expressed as the number of cells between it and the capillary which are consuming oxygen), it is a minor consideration.

Oxygen concentration diminishes as the distance from the capillary increases. Cells near the necrotic center may actually be anoxic. Calculations based on values obtained by Warburg[12] and by Krogh[13] have indicated that oxygen concentration will fall to zero 150 microns from capillaries; cells more distant than this will be anoxic. This anoxia may underlie the observation that the zone of living cells is rather constant in width. Diffusion of oxygen across the zone, and its eventual exhaustion by the cells in it, may determine how many cells can live as the tumor mass increases. The source of oxygen and nutrients may be pushed too far away from the cells at the center and

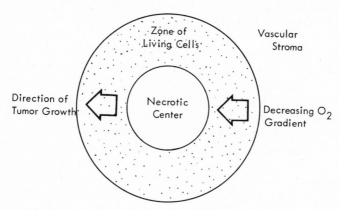

**Figure 11.8.** Schematic representative of solid tumor cord.

many of the cells may die. Such hypoxic or anoxic cells would be quite radioresistant when compared to normally oxygenated ones adjacent to the stroma. It may well be that, in the usual course of events, they die and become part of necrotic center of the tumor, but, because they are extremely hypoxic they may survive a normal course of radiotherapy. They may account, then, for the recurrence of tumor after irradiation. Well-oxygenated tumor cells are killed by the radiation and carried off, greatly diminishing the number of cells in the zone of living cells and, more important, the number of cells between the source of oxygen and the radioresistant, surviving cells. The blood supply to them is, in effect, improved. They may not then die but, in fact, may begin to divide and give rise to recurrence of the tumor.

*Experimental Evidence.* Not every link in the hypothesis outlined above rests upon solid, direct evidence or proof. However, many of its parts are supported by good experimental evidence.

Mottram[14] noted that, in the irradiation of tar warts of mice, cells close to the vascular stroma were more damaged than those distant from it, in spite of the fact that the latter received a larger dose of radiation. It seemed from this that a relationship might exist between proximity to the vascular stroma and radiosensitivity. Such a relationship has been tested. On the assumption that it would actually be based upon a falling gradient of oxygen across a solid tumor from a high point near the vascular stroma to lower points at a distance from it, Thomlinson and Gray[11] considered the histologic structure of some human lung tumors. They noted that, in examining cross sections, solid tumor cords were seen which were surrounded by vascular stroma, but no capillaries were seen in the tumors. Further, all cords greater than 180 microns in radius had necrotic centers. Those cords which had large necrotic centers had zones of living cells of only about 100 microns in width. They saw no tumor cord more than 200 microns in radius that was without necrosis. On the other hand, no central necrosis was seen in any tumor cord less than 160 microns in radius. Finally, and most important, however great the radius of the necrotic center, the zone of living cells was never greater than 180 microns; that is, no apparently intact tumor cell was seen more than 180 microns away from the stroma. These observations are important because they indicate that *distance* from the vascular stroma appears a critical factor in whether a tumor cell lives or becomes part of the necrotic tumor center. It appears from this work that the zone of living cells is very constant in width, never more than 180 microns nor, evidently, less than 160 microns. If these figures are considered in light of the four factors earlier listed governing the concentration of oxygen around tumor cells in such a solid cord, it would appear that 160 to 180 microns is the critical distance from the source of oxygen for these tumor cells. Implied in it is the conclusion that something in the stroma supports the life of the tumor cells. Whatever this is will be depleted when a mass of cells 180 microns in thickness has taken it up. While the life-supporting substance may be either nutrient or oxygen, the calculations of Thomlinson and Gray show that the scale of the observed histologic pattern is of the order to be expected if the supply of oxygen *alone* is the limiting factor which determines the onset of necrosis. It should be pointed out that while these authors have recognized this, they have not advanced it as an argument that the cells do, in fact, die from the lack of oxygen. For the purpose of this hypothesis it is enough to say that those distant cells will be anoxic; whether this accounts for the central necrosis or not is not strictly to the point.

There is one further point of interest in this connection. Oxygen values, based upon data of Warburg and Krogh presented earlier, indicated that cells more distant than 150 microns from stroma would be anoxic. This is in good agreement with the findings and calculations of Thomlinson and Gray.

*Model Experiments.* Scott[15] has set up model experiments, based upon the tumor structure under discussion, in which an attempt was made to determine whether layers of non-vascularized tumor cells actually do become hypoxic as the distance from the oxygen source is increased and, in addition, whether this hypoxia protects, from radiation, the ability of these cells to divide and proliferate. The test system involved the use of transplantable mouse ascites tumor cells. Scott took advantage of the fact that heavily irradiated cells continue to respire normally for some hours after irradiation, although they cannot any longer reproduce. He could, then, either centrifuge a layer of intact, unirradiated ascites cells and add directly above it a layer of blood or, alternatively, centrifuge one or more layers of normally respiring, but heavily irradiated cells (no longer capable of reproduction) over the intact cells (between them and the blood). Thus, by increasing or decreasing the number of irradiated cells between the layer of normal cells and blood, he could bring the normal ones closer or farther away from the blood supply—much the same situation as would exist in a solid core of cells. All the cells were then irradiated with experimental doses and inoculated in the peritoneum of host mice. Observations of consequent tumor growth were made. It should be re-emphasized that only those cells irradiated with *experimental* doses (those placed nearer or farther from the oxygen source) could contribute to any tumor growth at all; the others could not. Scott's results showed that there is a marked gradient of oxygen tension through the tumor mass. Further, an increase by a fraction of a millimeter of the tumor mass did give rise to a layer of hypoxic cells. These cells were rendered less sensitive to radiation damage by the respiring cells between them and the blood. Finally, when placed in the peritoneum of mice, they could proliferate, indicating that hypoxia alone cannot destroy this ability.

*In Vivo Measurements.*   Cater and Silver,[16] using platinum electrodes, measured oxygen tensions in human tumors and surrounding normal tissues, *in situ.* As can be seen from Table 11.3, the mean oxygen tension of the tumor before treatment with x ray (subject breathing air) is 17.7 while the tension in the tissue near the tumor under the same circumstances was 23.0 (a difference of 29.9 per cent). While this difference may not at first seem great, if it is considered in the light of Figure 11.4 where it is shown that relatively small differences in oxygen tension, provided that cells are at tensions below what is normal for them (that of venous blood or lymph), are reflected by rather larger differences in radiosensitivity, it takes on considerable importance.

This study, to which we will refer later, has shown differences in oxygen tension between tumors and normal surrounding tissue, but has not demonstrated that tumors have hypoxic regions from which, provided an improved oxygen supply is given them, proliferation can occur. In fact, while many studies of tumor structure make almost inescapable the conclusion that such regions actually exist, to date none has brought out direct evidence of them.

**Table 11.3.**   Relative Oxygen Tensions in Tumor and Normal
Tissue before and after Irradiation[*]

| | Mean $O_2$ Tension Breathing Air | Mean $O_2$ Tension Breathing $O_2$ | Mean Ratio of Tissue $O_2$ Tension When Breathing $O_2$/Air |
|---|---|---|---|
| Muscle | 14.3 | 27.5 | 2.07 |
| Subcutaneous | 42.0 | 78.3 | 2.28 |
| Tumor before x ray | 17.7 | 34.7 | 2.06 |
| Tumor after x ray | 27.3 | 65.1 | 2.93 |
| Tissue near tumor before x ray | 23.0 | 52.5 | 2.27 |
| Tissue near tumor after x ray | 39.9 | 81.8 | 2.26 |
| Normal bone marrow | 15.5 | 17.9 | 1.33 |

[*]From Cater and Silver.[16]

However, Powers and Tolmach,[17] using a transplantable lymphosarcoma in mice, have recently been able to show that this tumor
is composed of cells not all of which have the same sensitivity to
radiation. The difference in sensitivities seems to depend upon the
cellular environment—in all likelihood, the oxygen environment.
Previous to the publication of these results, survival studies following irradiation indicated that tumors were composed of cells all of
which had the same radiosensitivity (this is not to say that all tumors
have the same radiosensitivity, only that all cells in a given tumor
appear equally sensitive). If there were anoxic regions in tumors,
expected differences in radiosensitivity did not appear to demonstrate them. It has been suggested, however, that anoxic cells may
exist in extremely small numbers in tumors (a reasonable assumption
in view of the fact that anoxic cells probably do not live long and
large numbers of them are not likely to exist) and that their presence
goes undetected.

Powers and Tolmach irradiated the lymphosarcoma with varying
doses of x ray, under four experimental conditions,

1.  *In situ,* in mice breathing air (control group).
2.  *In situ,* in dead mice. This condition produces hypoxia in
    all tumor cells.
3.  *In situ,* in mice breathing pure oxygen under high pressure.
    This condition increases the oxygenation of hypoxic cells.
    More oxygen is in the capillaries and more should be avail-
    able for diffusion across the solid cord of tumor.

4. *In vitro,* in ice-cold fetal calf serum. This condition brings about hypoxia.

Those tumors irradiated *in situ* were removed after irradiation, minced, and made into a suspension in ice-cold calf serum. Then, serial ten-fold dilutions were made of the suspension. As a result each dilution had ten times more suspending medium, or one tenth the number of cells as the one before it. Those irradiated *in vitro* were minced, suspended, and diluted as above, but were, of course, removed from the animal before irradiation. Each of the dilutions was then injected into host mice. The end-point observed was the number of cells required to produce a tumor in 50 per cent of the host animals. Obviously, at high doses of radiation, few cells will survive, and the suspensions with the greatest number of cells would be required to achieve this end, while, at low doses, a dilute suspension would achieve the same end.

Powers and Tolmach found that in tumors of the control group there is a radioresistant group of cells. This component of the total tumor population comprised only 1 per cent of the cells. If these cells represent anoxic cells, they are, indeed, present in very small numbers. In the tumor irradiated *in situ* in dead mice (2) and *in vitro* in ice-cold serum (4), the number of resistant cells greatly increased. Since, except for environment, these tumors are the same as those in group (1), and there is nothing inherently different about them, it must be concluded that the change in environment, probably in the oxygen environment, brought about the change in the number of sensitive cells. Finally, those tumors irradiated *in situ* while the animals were breathing oxygen at high pressure (3) had a smaller population of resistant cells compared to those in the control group (0.1 per cent).

The authors conclude that the cell population is heterogeneous with respect to degree of oxygenation, which accounts for heterogeneity in radiosensitivity.

Hewitt and Wilson[18] have calculated the dose of radiation that will be required to obtain a 90 per cent chance of "cure" of a tumor if all cells are fully oxygenated, if 1 per cent are anoxic, and if all are anoxic (Figure 11.9). It is clear that, if these figures are correct, even if only 1 per cent of cells in a tumor are anoxic (as in the case of the lymphosarcoma described above) the chance of "cure" is drastically reduced at conventional radiotherapeutic doses.

If such differences in oxygen tensions within tumors or between tumors and surrounding normal tissues do indeed exist, any technique which increases oxygen tension in the anoxic tumor regions while decreasing the oxygen tension in surrounding normal tissue will be of potential benefit to radiotherapy, for it will either render equally sensitive all the cells of the tumor (by increasing tumor oxygenation) so that none may escape radiation death, or increase the radiation tolerance of normal tissues (by making them hypoxic) so that higher tumor doses may be given.

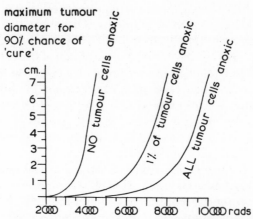

**Figure 11.9.** Single x-ray doses required to cure tumors of various sizes containing different percentages of anoxic cells. This application of mouse leukemia cell survival curves to predict response of human tumors assumes that all tumor cells have similar intrinsic radiosensitivities. Note that the presence of only a minute proportion of anoxic cells drastically reduces the chance of tumor "cure." (From Berry, R. J.: The Radiologic Clinics of North America, Vol. 3, No. 2, August 1965, p. 250.)

**11.10   Methods of Increasing Tumor Oxygen Tension.**   As noted earlier the important factor in the oxygen effect is the partial pressure of oxygen at the tissue and cellular level. Oxygen is transported to the tissues and cells chemically bound to hemoglobin as well as physically dissolved in the blood. Normally, for oxygen transport, only the former is important. However, the amount of physically dissolved oxygen is directly proportional to the percentage of oxygen in inspired gas and to the pressure on the gas. When breathing air at atmospheric pressure, the $pO_2$ *in arterial blood* is 100 mm Hg. When breathing 100 per cent oxygen at the same pressure, however, the $pO_2$ becomes 675 mm Hg. If 100 per cent oxygen is breathed at a pressure of 3 atmospheres absolute, the arterial pressure becomes 2195 mm Hg, approximately a twenty-fold increase over that of breathing air at normal pressure.

Thus, if regions of tumors can, in fact, be said to be hypoxic or even anoxic, the breathing of pure oxygen at atmospheric pressure or at high pressures (hyperbaric oxygenation, hyperbaria) will increase the amount of oxygen available to them by raising the arterial pressure. This, in its turn, should greatly reduce the number of anoxic (radioresistant) cells and greatly increase the efficiency of a course of radiotherapy for destroying the cells of the tumor (it will be remembered that, in the experience of Powers and Tolmach, the number of resistant tumor cells decreased by a factor of ten when the tumor-bearing animals were breathing oxygen at high pressure during radiation).

*Inhalation of Pure Oxygen at Atmospheric Pressure.* Cater and Silver, in the study referred to previously, compared the oxygen tensions of human tumors and surrounding tissues when air at atmospheric pressure and oxygen at atmospheric pressure are breathed before, during and after a course of radiation therapy. Table 11.3 represents a summary of their data. It can be seen that, if oxygen is breathed before the course of x ray, the increase in the oxygen tension in the tumor and normal tissues (over that observed while breathing air) is comparable. After irradiation, if oxygen is breathed, the change, relative to air, in tumor oxygen tension is far greater than that in irradiated normal tissues. At the onset of radiation therapy in which inhalation of pure oxygen is used as a means of increasing tumor oxygen tension, there would appear to be no difference in the increase of oxygen in tumor and in normal surrounding tissues. However, Cater and Silver state that after the first few daily treatments, when tumor cells are damaged and the inflammatory phase of the radiation reaction has begun, there is an increase in the oxygen tension exactly where it is most important, namely, in those parts of tumor that are hypoxic, and relatively radioresistant. No such change in oxygen tension of the normal tissue was observed.

*Hyperbaria: Oxygen at High Pressure.* Oxygen at high pressure (hyperbaric oxygenation) does increase the arterial tension of oxygen. But, as has been previously noted (Figure 11.3), increases in oxygen tensions over a critical level produce only minor increases in radiation sensitivity. Therefore, the primary effect is to increase radiosensitivity of hypoxic cells, among them tumor cells, because these are the only ones that can respond to increases in oxygen.

**11.11  Clinical Experience.** Certain non-cancerous tissues are hypoxic as a normal state of affairs. These will occasionally be affected where hyperbaric oxygenation is used. Churchill-Davidson[19] has reported necrosis of the laryngeal cartilages as a complication of combined hyperoxygenation and radiotherapy. He has also reported the results obtained from 160 cancer patients treated for their cancers in a high pressure chamber. The one tumor site in which the response was disappointing was the brain. Churchill-Davidson's data are shown in Table 11.4.

**Table 11.4.**   Number of Patients Surviving without Apparent Recurrence in Treated Area[*]

|  | 6 Months | 1 Year | 2 Years | 3 Years | 4 Years | 5 Years | 6 Years | 7 Years |
|---|---|---|---|---|---|---|---|---|
| High-pressure oxygen series | 80/139 (57%) | 40/127 (31%) | 17/106 (16%) | 13/88 (15%) | 9/69 (13%) | 7/58 (12%) | 6/46 (13%) | 3/21 (14%) |
| Air series | 20/62 (32%) | 8/54 (15%) | 4/37 (11%) | 0/21 (0%) | 0/15 (0%) | 0/10 (0%) | – | – |

[*]From Churchill-Davidson.[19]

## 11.12   Reduction of Radiosensitivity of Normal Tissue.

*Regional Hypoxia.*   Regional hypoxia can be produced by arresting the local circulation. Such techniques result in increased resistance to radiation. Clapp and co-workers[20] using the VX2 tumor in the hind leg of rabbits, clamped off the circulation to the tumor and its surrounding normal tissues. They compared the radiosensitivity of those regions to others in which circulation was undisturbed. The same level of tissue toxicity occurred at 2500 R with normal circulation and at 5200 R when circulation had been arrested. Thus, the normal tissue, now hypoxic, had become resistant to the radiation. The tumors also acquired some degree of radioresistance, and it was necessary to give a somewhat higher dose, under circulatory arrest, to begin regression than was necessary when circulation was normal. However, the response of normal tissue to hypoxia was *far* greater than that of tumors, and toxicity of local tissue occurred at rather high dose levels. It was possible to deliver a high tumor dose, and the authors have reported that they were able to produce "cures." None was produced when circulation was undisturbed. These results seem promising, but, at the moment, limited by difficulties in effectively occluding local circulation under all circumstances. Baker and co-workers[21] have begun to adapt this idea to the treatment of human tumors.

*Hypothermia.*   The use of drastically lowered body temperatures to confer radioprotection has a very long history. The method has been shown by Cater and Weiss[22] to induce hypoxia in cooled animals. In mice, cooled between 0° and 1°C, Cater and Weiss have demonstrated that oxygen tension within testes, spleen, bone marrow, and peritoneum fell to the order of 2 mm Hg. This degree of hypoxia would be expected to offer considerable protection against radiation. The animals themselves are protected against hypoxia by profound hypothermia.

The expected protective effect against radiation can be illustrated by an experiment of Hornsey[23] in which colonic temperature in adult rats was reduced to the range of 0° to 0.5°C. The radiation was carried out after breathing and heart contractions had stopped. The $LD_{50/30}$ dose was raised to 1760 R from a normal of 620 R.

The degrees of hypothermia used need not be profound to obtain protection from radiation. Although early reports failed to demonstrate protection by moderate degrees of hypothermia (9° to 29°C), if rats are kept at 25°C for twelve hours before irradiation, some protection was conferred.[24] The difference between this and the earlier experiments is in the time that the animals were hypothermic before irradiation. It is not clear whether this represents an oxygen effect, but it is possible that moderate hypoxia does result after extended periods in moderate hypothermia.

## SUMMARY

1.  Oxygen enhances the magnitude of the radiation effect (an increase of two to three times).
2.  Concentration of oxygen at tumor levels at the time of radiation is a critical factor.
3.  The effect of oxygen is exerted at the time of energy exchange, probably by drawing radiation-produced free radicals into destructive auto-oxidative reactions.
4.  The application of the oxygen effect in radiotherapy is dependent upon presumed hypoxic regions in tumors.

## Text References

1.  Howard-Flanders, P., and Moore, D.: The time interval after pulsed irradiation within which injury to bacteria can be modified by dissolved oxygen. I. A search for an effect of oxygen 0.02 second after pulsed irradiation, Radiation Research 9, 422-437 (1958).
2.  Hollaender, A., Baker, W. K., and Anderson, E. H.: Effect of oxygen tension and certain chemicals on the x-ray sensitivity of mutation production and survival, Cold Spring Harbor Symposia on Quantitative Biology 16, 315-326 (1951).
3.  Wright, E. A., and Howard-Flanders, P.: The influence of oxygen on the radiosensitivity of mammalian tissues, Acta Radiologica 48, 26-32 (1957).
4.  Ebert, M., and Hornsey, S.: Effect on radiosensitivity of inert gases. Effect of inert gases on oxygen-dependent radiosensitivity. Nature 181, 613-616 (1958).

5. Graievskii, E. I. A., and Konstantinova, M. M.: Independence of the antiradiation effect of aminoethylisothiouranium. Br·HBr on the "oxygen effect," Akademiya Nauk SSSR Doklady *140*, 705-708 (1961).

6. Conger, A. D., and Fairchild, L. M.: Breakage of chromosomes by oxygen. Proceedings of the National Academy of Sciences *38*, 289-299 (1952).

7. Gilbert, D. L., Gerschman, R., Ruhm, B. K., and Price, W. E.: The production of hydorgen peroxide by high oxygen pressures, Journal General Physiology *41*, 989-1003 (1958).

8. Parr, W., O'Neill, T., Bush, S., and Krebs, A.: Further investigations into the modification of radiation sensitivity afforded by cobalt, Science *119*, 415-416 (1954).

9. Gerschman, R., Gilbert, D. L., and Caccamise, D.: Effect of various substances on survival times of mice exposed to different high oxygen tensions, American Journal Physiology *192*, 563-571 (1958).

10. Haugaard, N., Hess, M. E., and Itskovitz, H.: Toxic action of oxygen on metabolism, Journal Biological Chemistry *227*, 605-616 (1957).

11. Thomlinson, R. H., and Gray, L. H.: Histological structure of some human lung cancers and the possible implications for radiotherapy, British Journal of Cancer *9*, 539-549 (1955).

12. Warburg, O.: *The Metabolism of Tumors*, Constable, London, 1930, p. 6.

13. Krogh, A.: *The Anatomy and Physiology of Capillaries*, Yale University Press, New Haven, Conn., 1922, p. 196.

14. Mottram, J. C.: Factor of importance in radiosensitivity of tumours, British Journal of Radiology *9*, 606-614 (1936).

15. Scott, O. C. A.: A model system for examining the radiosensitivity of metabolising layers of cells, British Journal of Cancer *11*, 130-136 (1957).

16. Cater, D. B., and Silver, I. A.: Quantitative measurements of oxygen tension in normal tissues and in the tumours of patients before and after radiotherapy, Acta Radiologica *53*, 233-256 (1960).

17. Powers, W. E., and Tolmach, L. J.: Demonstration of an anoxic component in a mouse tumor-cell population by *in vivo* assay of survival following irradiation, Radiology *83*, 328-336 (1964).

18. Hewitt, H. B., and Wilson, C. W.: The effect of tissue oxygen tension on the radiosensitivity of leukaemic mice, British Journal of Cancer *13*, 675-684 (1959).

19. Churchill-Davidson, I.: Hyperbaric oxygenation. The small patient chamber, radiotherapy. Annals of the New York Academy of Sciences *117*, 875-882 (1965).

20. Clapp, P., Charyulu, K. K. N., Tayao, M. S., Tyree, E. B., Nickson, J. L., and Lawrence, W., Jr.: Regional oxygenation and therapeutic response to irradiation, Cancer *18*, 927-936 (1965).

21. Baker, D. J., Lindlop, P. J., Morgan, W. G., Skeggs, D. B. L., Whittle, R. J. M., and Williams, I. G.: Monitored regional hypoxia in radiotherapy, British Journal of Radiology, *39*, 908-914 (1966).

22. Cater, D. B., and Weiss, L.: Measurements of oxygen tension in the tissues of mice cooled to 1°C, Nature *183*, 1521-2 (1959).

23. Hornsey, S.: *Advances in Radiobiology*, Academic Press, New York, 1957, p. 248.

24. Pizzarello, D. J., Isaak, D., Witcofski, R. L., and Lyons, E.A.: Effect of moderate degrees of hypothermia on the sensitivity to whole-body irradiation in adult rats, Radiation Research *20*, 203-206 (1963).

## General References

1.  Churchill-Davidson, I., Sanger, C., and Thomlinson, R. H.: Oxygenation in radio-
    therapy II clinical application, British Journal of Radiology *30*, 406-442 (1957).
2.  Hyperbaric Oxygenation. Annals of the New York Academy of Sciences *117*, 647-
    890 (1965).
3.  Oxygen Toxicity. NASA SP-47. U.S. Government Printing Office, Washington, D. C.
4.  Thomlinson, R. H., and Gray, L. H.: The histological structure of some human
    lung cancers and the possible implications for radiotherapy, British Journal of
    Cancer *9*, 539-549 (1955).

# 12

## Metabolic Expression of Radiation Injury

**12.1  Introduction.**  All the events described in the preceding chapters have occurred at the molecular level—a most basic level of organization in the cell. They are the initiating events leading to damage—the transfer of energy from ionizing radiation to the substance of the cell (ionization) and the subsequent transfer of this energy among the molecules of the substance (free radicals, oxygen effect). But these are not the events that are seen; they are not results of irradiation that are ultimately detected and called "radiation effects." There can be no doubt that events such as those previously described do occur, but, at present, they fall at the very limits of, and often beyond, our ability to detect them.

What *is* detected are the further consequences—developments in cells that *follow* these initiating events, alterations in structure and function at much higher levels of organization, for example, changes in cellular organelles, or in their functions. Curiously, such detectable changes are never seen directly after irradiation of a living system but at some later time. Immediately after irradiation, the irradiated system appears generally unaffected, unchanged by its experience. But the "normalness" of it all is apparent, for later (the time varies; it is related to the magnitude and rate of administration of the dose) changes will appear which can only have been the result of exposure to radiation.

**12.2  Latent Period.**  The time lapse between irradiation and the *appearance* of changes is called the "latent period." It should not, however, be regarded as a time in which nothing related to the radiation exposure is going on. Rather, it is a very important time, the time in which the changes brought about in the instant of radiation exposure are somehow developed into major detectable defects in structure or function. It should, perhaps, better be called a "period of hidden changes," for, in it, the almost infinitesimal amounts of energy put into living things by ionizing radiation, the alterations produced in a few molecules, are multiplied over and over, until structures involving literally hundreds of thousands of molecules and forming major subdivisions of the cell are changed, almost always for the worst.

**12.3 Changes Occurring during the Latent Period.** The nature of the events that take place during the latent period is the subject of the most intensive research, because it is felt that the reversal of such changes, or the stopping of them, offers the best hope for radiation protection. If a protection-giving chemical (Chapter 11) is present at the time of radiation, this will, of course, alter radiosensitivity. But this is really possible only in situations where irradiation is a deliberate and planned event (for example, radiotherapy). In the case of accidental exposure, a hazard which daily becomes more serious owing to the ever-increasing use of radioactive material in industry (it is estimated that one million film badges are in use in the United States each day[1]; this gives an estimate of the number of persons in situations where exposure to radiation occurs as a part of their job), or of exposure incidental to military service, protection at the time of irradiation will probably not be possible. The reversal of changes following the initial events is the best hope for sparing exposed individuals the effects, especially the lethal ones, of a dose of radiation.

**12.4 Nature of Changes Occurring during the Latent Period.** Unfortunately, in spite of the efforts extended to detect and understand what is occurring during the latent period, no clear picture as yet exists. Nevertheless, theories have been proposed, and, even though they may not account fully for what is happening, they probably provide, at least in part, a description of the changes that are actually taking place.

**12.5 Development of Expression of Radiation Injury through Metabolism.** This idea supposes that, when cells are irradiated, many of the interactions of the free radicals and even many of direct hits will occur within one or another of the cell's metabolites. Metabolites, which are relatively small molecular units, are incorporated into one or more of the basic structures of the cell. They are building blocks of protoplasm. Interaction with radiation, either directly or indirectly, *changes* them. If the change is a small one and the structure of the metabolites is not too greatly altered, they are not prevented from incorporation into larger, more complex units. But, once they are incorporated, they, and, consequently, the unit of which they are now a part, cannot perfectly perform the functions for which it was intended. The cell's requirements in this regard are very rigid; all of its parts must conform to very strict specifications of spatial configuration as well as chemical and physical properties for perfect function. An enzyme, which is "wrongly" built, may not be able to function at all with the intended substrate, or may function at a lower or higher rate than is proper for the system. This could result in an accumulation of substrate, if the rate is too slow, or a depletion of substrate, if the rate is too fast, and a deficiency or overabundance of the product of the reaction in which the enzyme takes part. Further, reactions involving these products may be altered. If, for example, the function of an enzyme were to build a particular segment of a protein molecule, and if the enzyme did not function properly, such a segment might be missing entirely or be present in great excess. If, in another example, the enzyme's function were in the synthesis of nucleic acid, defects or superabundances in these very vital molecules are possible. In fact, in this way, key molecules may have been affected by radiation in spite of the fact that the changes made have come about neither by direct nor by indirect action (although the route is certainly indirect enough). It seems highly likely that situations such as this do arise at least some of the time after irradiation, and that processes of this kind are going on in the latent period. Radiation might, for example, interact directly or indirectly with an amino acid; the amino acid will not be exactly what is required by the cell, but it is incorporated into protein. Defective structure results and so does defective function. It is only when the stage of *defective structure* and *defective function* has been reached that the damage or change can be detected. These changes (damages) are called the "radiation effect." In fact, however, they are probably the end-points of a chain of reactions that have gone on unseen — hidden — during the latent period.

## SUMMARY

1. The initial interactions of ionizing radiation and the matter of cells are very difficult to detect.

2. There is a time lapse, called the *latent period,* between radiation exposure and observable, related changes.

3. In the  latent period the energy transferred and the changes brought about in the instant of radiation exposure are developed and magnified through normal cellular metabolism until they become easily detectable structural or functional changes.

## Text Reference

1.  Dobish, A. S.: The film badge, Atomics *17,* 43 (1964).

# 13

# Review of Basic Biology: The Nucleus: DNA

**13.1 Introduction.** Cells, with very few, special exceptions, whether animal or vegetable, whether part of an organism composed of many cells or a single-cell organism, are composed of two major, easily recognizable, subdivisions—nucleus and cytoplasm. The nucleus, bounded by a membrane, is contained within the cytoplasm, and, whenever its membrane is present, is separate from the cytoplasm. Further, in a functional sense these two parts of the cell—the nucleus and the cytoplasm—are separate. The labors of the cell are divided between them; the nucleus coordinates and directs cellular activities whatever they might be (not all cells have identical functions; nerve, muscle, reproductive cells differ from each other), and, in the cytoplasm, these directions are carried out. The cytoplasm is the *site* of metabolism (the building up of protein and other essentials and the tearing down of old and "worn" structures with the production of waste) in the cell, but it is the nucleus that orders, times and directs this metabolism. It should be immediately pointed out that the foregoing is a generalization. There is some overlap; nuclei carry out some limited metabolism, and the cytoplasm of certain cells contains bodies which appear to have functions similar to those of the nucleus.

The separation of nucleus and cytoplasm does not mean that the two are independent. They are, in fact, co-dependent; neither could survive without the other. (An apparent exception to this is the mammalian red blood cell which lives but which is anucleate. This cell, however, is very specialized in function and does not reproduce. It becomes anucleate during specialization or maturation and, subsequently, has a limited life span.) Furthermore, events occurring in either nucleus or cytoplasm will have important effects in the other major component of the cell. Changes brought about in the nucleus can impair its ability to correctly direct metabolism in the cytoplasm. And changes made in the cytoplasm, or even in the membrane that bounds it, can exert an effect within the nucleus; for it is the activity of the cytoplasm (metabolism) that supplies the nucleus with the material it needs for its own existence—that is, its repair and reproduction, and its work.

Because of this intimate co-dependence, changes detected in the nucleus (either of structure or function) may have been the result of events taking place in *either* the nucleus itself or in the cytoplasm. It follows, of course, that changes detected within the cytoplasm may have had their origins in events that have taken place in the nucleus.

The picture can, however, be more complicated than that just described. Cytoplasmic changes that bring about aberrations in nuclear function will almost inevitably have further consequences in the cytoplasm. A changed or injured nucleus, regardless of the source of the change or injury, will not be capable of properly directing cytoplasmic activity. Some observed changes in cytoplasmic function, then, may be the result of impairment of nuclear function, which, itself, came about as a result of an injury in the cytoplasm.

**13.2  Chromosomes.**  The apparatus within the nucleus for directing cellular activity consists of the chromosomes. These bodies (the word means "colored bodies" and is derived from their staining properties) are present in all cells in specific, fixed numbers. The number of chromosomes in a cell is characteristic of a species; all members of a species carry the same number of chromosomes in all comparable cells. Within individuals, however, there will not be the same number of chromosomes in every cell. The germ cells (the male and female gametes) and the somatic cells (the cells of which the body is composed) differ in this regard. The gametes have *half* the number of chromosomes found in the somatic cells; somatic cells have twice the number of chromosomes as the gametes. The germ cells are said to have an "n" number of chromosomes (n is a symbol—it can be any number; it is the *same* number for each individual in a species, but may be different for different species). The chromosomes which constitute the n number are said to be a *set* of chromosomes. That is, the n number is made up of a particular number of chromosomes, each of which is different from the rest. The chromosomes will often differ among themselves in size or shape, but, more important, they differ in content. All of them taken together form a set, a complete set of chromosomes. Such a set, the n set, is very important, for in most organisms it is a minimum requirement for life. Cells that, in one way or another, lose chromosomes (or even parts of chromosomes) so that the basic set is incomplete, cannot live. In fact, even if a cell has more than the n *number* of chromosomes, it will not live if the n *set* is incomplete.

Somatic cells, as stated earlier, have twice the number of chromosomes as are found in germ cells, but it is more than a simple case of a larger number. They actually have two n sets of chromosomes; that is, each chromosome in the n set of the germ cells is present, in somatic cells, in duplicate. The symbol employed, then, is *2n,* and somatic cells are said to have the 2n number of chromosomes, with the understanding that this really represents n + n sets (in man 2n = 46, n = 23; in newts 2n = 22, n = 11; in onion 2n = 16, n = 8, to cite only a few examples).

**13.3 The Importance of Chromosome Sets.** The chromosome sets are of essential, basic importance to cells and to the organism in which they are found. Life is impossible without at least one n set of chromosomes it is true, but sets of chromosomes are vitally important in another way. *The chromosomes are the structures which bear the genes.* They are the bearers of the molecules that direct the metabolism of each cell and, therefore, of the total organism. *In order to have a complete set of genes, in order to have the proper balance between genes, in order for metabolism to be carried out properly, a 2n set of chromosomes is a basic fundamental requirement* (gametes carry out only very limited metabolism; they are a temporary state of affairs). Loss of a chromosome or loss of even part of a chromosome will almost inevitably result in the loss of one or more genes. This in itself can produce metabolic derangement, for, unless another gene is present to take over the function of the lost one, the function itself is likely to disappear. Worse yet, if enough are lost (and even a few genes will constitute enough) life is impossible.

**13.4 The Genes.** It is now possible to state with confidence that genes, the structures which control inheritance and metabolism, are, in most organisms, composed of very large molecules called deoxyribonucleic acid (DNA). The type of molecules of which DNA is a representative is usually referred to as a "macromolecule." Macromolecules are composed of subunits which are, in themselves, stable molecules with characteristics peculiar to themselves. A macromolecule, then, is a large molecule, possessing certain characteristics, which is made up of a number of smaller, discrete molecular units. DNA is just such a molecule; proteins, silk, and rubber are examples of others. Further, in DNA, as in many other macromolecules, the subunits of which the whole is composed are joined together end-to-end, to form a long chain. This process, that of joining end-to-end, is called "polymerization." Such macromolecules are said to have been "polymerized." DNA is spoken of as a "long-chain polymer," a polymer composed of many smaller subunits, connected end-to-end as links in a chain.

**13.5 The Structure of DNA.** Each macromolecule of DNA is composed of two chains, intimately associated, which comprise a single, long, unbranched thread. In the macromolecule the two chains or threads are joined together ladder-fashion (Figure 13.1).

In fact, however, DNA is a twisted or spiral structure, resembling more closely a spiral staircase than a ladder (Figure 13.2). While such a configuration *is* the real one, for the sake of simplicity of visualization the discussion here will center around the molecule as if it were open and untwisted (Figure 13.1).

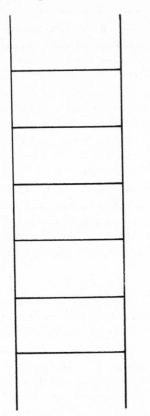

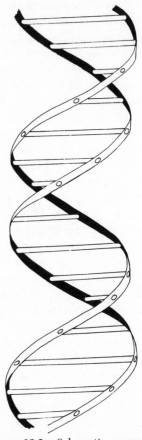

**Figure 13.1.** Schematic representation of part of a DNA macromolecule. Here, the molecule is shown without its characteristic twists and has a resemblance to a ladder.

**Figure 13.2.** Schematic representation of part of a DNA molecule, illustrating its spiral form.

The nature of the linkage of the subunits in the chains and of the chains to each other is extremely important, for in it is the basis of the mechanism by which genetic information is *coded* and stored in the cells as well as the basis upon which this coded information is transmitted to the cytoplasm. It is also important in the proper carrying of genetic information from one cell generation to the next.

**13.6  The Composition of DNA and the Arrangement of Its Components in the Macromolecule.**  The subunits of which DNA is composed are themselves made up of phosphoric acid, the five-carbon sugar, deoxyribose, and an organic, nitrogenous base. These components, taken together, are called *nucleotides,* specifically *deoxyribonucleotides.* It is these nucleotides that are arranged in sequence in each chain making up DNA. In the macromolecule (the double chain) the side pieces or backbones of the ladder are sugar-phosphate, while the rungs are nitrogenous bases (Figure 13.3).

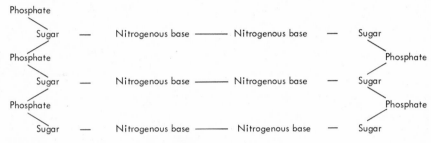

**Figure 13.3.** Schematic representation of the arrangement of subunits (deoxyribonucleotides) in the double-stranded DNA molecule.

**13.7 The Nitrogenous Bases.** Only four nitrogenous bases are commonly associated with DNA. They fall into two categories, purines and pyrimidines, and are called adenine, guanine (purines), thymine, and cytosine (pyrimidines). If the DNA strands are carefully examined, it will be seen that each is made up of nucleotides which differ only in their nitrogenous bases (Figure 13.4).

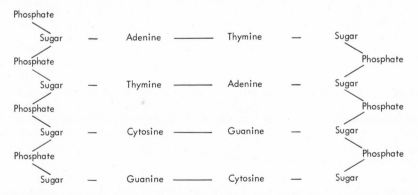

**Figure 13.4.** This represents part of a DNA chain illustrating its make-up. It should be stressed that the example chosen is purely arbitrary; it is intended as a *general* illustration and not to represent any particular real molecule.

The difference is, however, specific and constant. *Wherever adenine occurs in one chain, thymine will be in the chain opposite; wherever cytosine occurs in one chain, guanine will occur in the chain opposite.* The DNA chains, then, have polarity or direction. In the macromolecule each chain is complementary to the other (Figure 13.5).

In nature, it appears that, in most molecules of DNA, there will be equal amounts of adenine and thymine, and equal amounts of

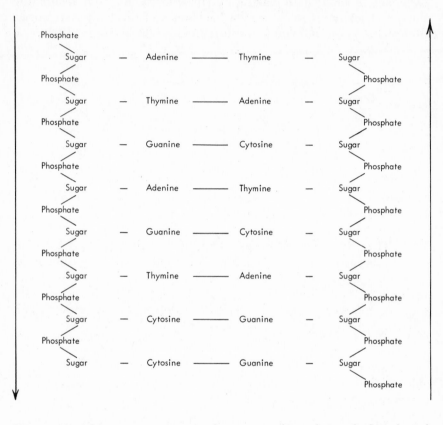

**Figure 13.5.** This is a representation of a segment of two chains of a hypothetical DNA macromolecule. Note the pairing between the bases adenine and thymine and between guanine and cytosine. Each member of the pair is present in amounts equal to the other. Note also that the quantities of guanine and adenine, cytosine and thymine, are unrelated. Finally, it can be seen, by scanning the chains, that they are complementary, but that they are opposite in polarity.

guanine and cytosine, since they occur in pairs. But no necessary relationship exists between amounts of adenine and cytosine or thymine and guanine.

**13.8  Hydrogen-Bonding.** The two chains of the DNA macromolecule are held together by a very weak form of chemical bond called a *hydrogen-bond.* In this form of bonding, two molecules share one hydrogen atom and are held together by the atom they share. In

DNA, each base pair shares two or three hydrogen atoms so that each is bonded at two or three points. Where the chains are joined, the "rungs of the ladder" are complete (Figure 13.6).

**13.9   The Genetic Information or Code.**   It has been stated that cellular metabolism is under control of the genes; that the genes and, consequently, the DNA which makes them up, direct all the activities of any given cell. There is (implicitly, at least) in any such statement the notion that DNA must contain any information necessary about the activities of any given cell to direct those activities. A cell's activi-

Thymine          Adenine                    Cytosine                    Guanine

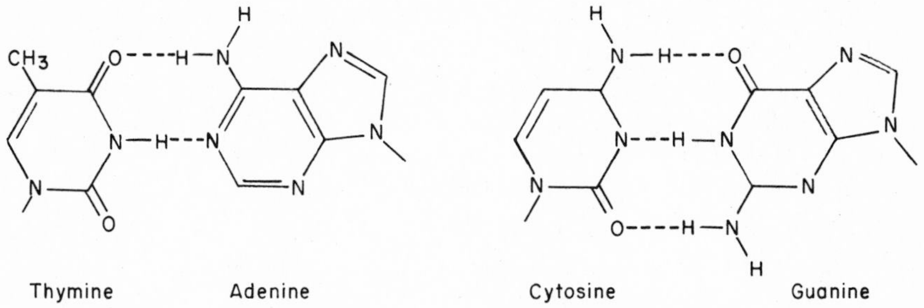

**Figure 13.6.**   Hydrogen-bonding between the bases as it occurs in DNA.

ties include, after all, not only all the chemical reactions going within it, but will, in addition, include whatever intracellular interactions in which the cell might participate (antigen-antibody interactions as an example).

There is such information, and it is stored in the DNA molecule. The sequence of the nitrogenous bases, the purines and pyrimidines, along both chains of the DNA macromolecule *is* the genetic information. *The sequence of purines and pyrimidines, along the strands of the DNA polymer, is,* in a highly distilled or codified manner, *all of the information required by the cell for its metabolic activity.* Consequently the *sequence* of these bases along the chains is very important; it is not the bases themselves that contain the genetic information, but the *linear arrangement* or *sequence* of the bases in the molecule. Any force, then, which changes this sequence will produce a *change* in the information stored on the molecule. Such changes will almost always result in an important change in the metabolism of the cell in which they happen. The changes are called *mutations* and the individuals that bear them, *mutants.*

**13.10   Genetic Mutations.**   Mutation has been known for many years as a naturally occurring phenomenon. Every species of plant or animal studied, including the very simpliest, is known to have members arise in its midst which differ from the rest. These are mutants; they have occurred after a change in the genetic material. Such changes and the mutant individuals they produce appear apparently at random in any population of living things. No *cause* is now known that explains their appearance; as a result they have been termed "spontaneous mutations."

Spontaneous mutations are, then, permanent, heritable changes in individual genes. When genes change (mutate), the change will be, for any given change in any given gene, a rare event, sudden (they occur without prior warning), and discrete; that is, the gene will pass from one state to another, both of which are stable. The stability of both states indicates that genes undergo a *definite* transformation when they mutate, and that, between mutations, they are fixed in composition. The appearance of spontaneous mutations then, in rare, sudden, and discrete fashion, is an indication that the genes have a distinctive chemical structure (configuration) and that a mutation represents a change in that structure which, like any chemical change, is subject to the all-or-nothing rule.

**13.11    The Molecular Basis of Mutation.**    Typically, all somatic cells within any individual contain the 2n number of chromosomes. The genes (or the DNA) are actually part of the chromosomes, and a typical somatic cell may be said to contain the "2n number" of genes and the "2n amount" of DNA. When cells have reached the point where they need to divide (the factors governing the impetus to division are too numerous to be within the scope of this brief review), it will be necessary for the daughter cells of this division to be provided (as are all somatic cells) with the 2n number of chromosomes and with the 2n amount of DNA. If this provision were not made, daughter cells resulting from the division of a mature somatic cell might have different numbers of chromosomes and genes and a different balance between genes. Daughter cells would differ from their parent cell and from other cells in the body of which they are a part. In order to preserve the 2n quantities and balanced relationship between genes, the number of chromosomes and the quantity of DNA in the nucleus double just before cell division. The DNA and the chromosomes *duplicate* themselves. For a time then, before cell division, the cell about to divide will have the 4n number of chromosomes and the 4n quantity of DNA. Half of this 4n quantity (or two complete n sets) will go to each daughter at division. In this way each daughter receives the proper 2n amount of genetic material and has genic balances identical to its parent.

When DNA duplicates itself, it is believed to do so in the following manner. The hydrogen bonds which link the chains of the DNA molecule break, and the chains separate. *Each chain* then directs the synthesis of a complementary chain, *identical to* the one from which it just separated (Figure 13.7).

It is believed that, in the usual situation, the synthesis of new DNA (the new complementary chain) begins at one end of an existing chain and continues to its terminus (in the manner of the closing of a zipper). In the nucleus, all of the four nucleotides (Section 13.6) will be available for the existing DNA to incorporate into the newly synthesizing complementary chain, but, as the new chain is synthesized, only the proper nucleotide, the proper member of the nucleotide pair, will occupy each place in the new chain. This is thought to occur because only *particular* bases, the proper member of each base pair, can form a hydrogen bond with the other member of the base pair while, at the same time, presenting the phosphate group of the nucleotide in the proper position to be bonded in the growing new chain (Figure 13.8).

DNA synthesis, under ordinary circumstances, is really DNA *duplication,* for the *new* DNA is identical to the old; no change comes about. At cell division, each daughter cell (provided that no errors in the *transmission* of DNA occur) will get exactly the same genetic information as had its parent.

In rare instances, however, another sequence of events may take place. The electrons and protons of the molecules of nitrogenous bases can undergo rearrangement. The *distribution* changes within these molecules so that they actually have more than one possible structural configuration. The various forms have the same number of protons and electrons; they are, however, arranged somewhat differently in each molecule. This rearrangement of the parts of the molecule is called a "tautomeric shift," and the various structural configurations in which the molecule may exist are called *tautomeres.* One tautomeric form will be, by far, the most commonly occurring one; most of the molecules of these bases will exist in this form. But on rare occasions, an internal rearrangement (a tautomeric shift) will take place in a molecule which is in the common form, to produce another form—one of the tautomeres—an uncommon, rare one. The tautomeric shifts are not necessarily permanent; these rare forms can undergo further rearrangements either to other rare forms or back to the common one. If a tautomeric shift in one of bases in a nucleotide occurs *during* the synthesis of DNA, it is believed that the resultant *new* DNA will *not* be a duplicate of the old; it will differ from the old in some significant detail. Many consider the phenomenon of tautomerism of the nitrogenous bases as the molecular mechanism of mutation.

If a base in a DNA chain is in its common form during DNA synthesis, it can form a hydrogen bond with only *one* of the other bases (adenine-thymine; guanine-cytosine) and yet present its phosphate

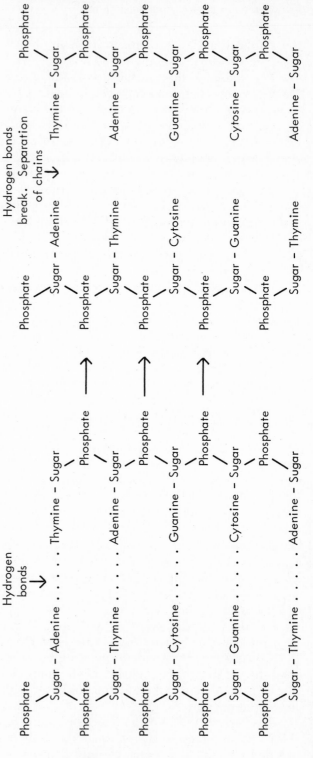

BEFORE REPLICATION (2n quantity of DNA)

SEPARATION OF CHAINS (2n quantity of DNA)

# DUPLICATION OF DNA (4n quantity of DNA)

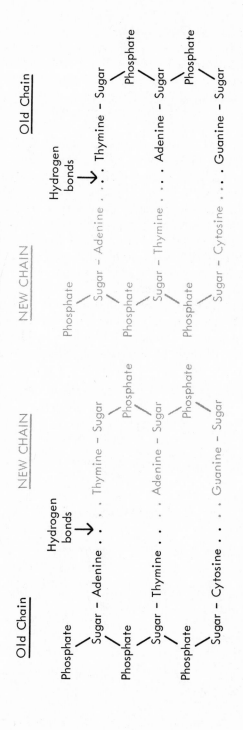

**Figure 13.7.** Schematic representation of the duplication of DNA in a somatic cell. Two DNA macromolecules are formed from the one present before duplication. At cell division (ordinarily this closely follows DNA synthesis), each of the daughter cells will receive one of these macromolecules.

group in the proper position for bonding in the molecule. But, if one of these bases should be in a rare tautomeric state during synthesis, it will *not* be able to form a hydrogen bond (within a *DNA* molecule) with its partner. That is, in the DNA molecule, adenine, in its rare structural configuration, will not be able to pair with thymine. Neither will guanine, in *its* rare state, pair with cytosine. And the same holds true for thymine and cytosine in *their* rare tautomeric states; they will find pairing, in DNA, with adenine and guanine, *impossible.* The rare tautomeres will be able, however, to pair with the base with which pairing is usually forbidden (that is, rare adenine pairs with cytosine and rare thymine with guanine). As a result, if one base is in a rare tautomeric state during DNA synthesis, it will direct the incorporation of the "wrong" partner, the "forbidden" partner, into the new DNA chain *at the level of the rare tautomere.* In a new chain resulting after such an event during synthesis, the sequence of bases (the genetic information) will be *different* from the sequence in the old chain.

At this stage of events, a full-blown mutation does not exist (more must yet come), but, it *is* a transition stage between the old form of the gene and the new; it is the start of a mutation. The rare tautomere in the old chain will probably return to its common state,

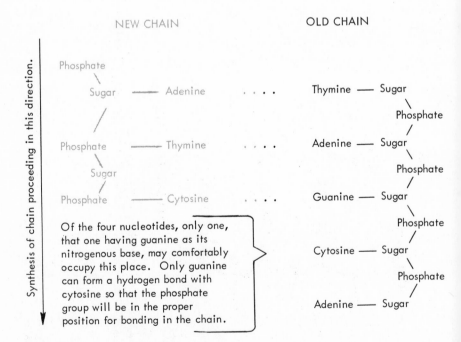

**Figure 13.8.** The synthesis of new DNA in process. This illustrates the specificity of position of each nucleotide in the new chain with relation to the old.

## A SEGMENT OF DNA JUST BEFORE SYNTHESIS

Phosphate
\
  Sugar – Adenine     . . . .          Thymine – Sugar
/                                                    \
Phosphate                                              Phosphate
\                                                    /
  Sugar – Thymine     . . . .          Adenine – Sugar
/                                                    \
Phosphate                                              Phosphate
\                                                    /
  Sugar – Cytosine    . . . .          Guanine – Sugar
/                                                    \
Phosphate                                              Phosphate
\                                                    /
  Sugar – Guanine     . . . .          Cytosine – Sugar
/                                                    \
Phosphate                                              Phosphate
\                                                    /
  Sugar – Thymine     . . . .          Adenine – Sugar

## DNA SYNTHESIS

New DNA chain: it                    Synthesis of new DNA
has a changed base sequence              by this chain
                                           ↓

Phosphate
\
  Sugar – Adenine     . . . .          Thymine – Sugar
/                                                    \
Phosphate                                              Phosphate
\                                                    /
  Sugar – Thymine     . . . .          Adenine – Sugar
/                                                    \
Phosphate                                              Phosphate
\                                                    /
  Sugar – Thymine     . . . .          Guanine*– Sugar
/                                                    \
Phosphate                                              Phosphate
\                                                    /
  Sugar – Guanine     . . . .          Cytosine – Sugar

**\* This Guanine is in a rare tautomeric form at synthesis of DNA.**

**Figure 13.9.** Synthesis of DNA in which the beginning of a mutation has occurred. Guanine in the old DNA chain was in a rare form at synthesis and directed the incorporation of thymine in the new chain in place of the expected cytosine.

and no permanent change will have occurred in that part of the molecule. In the new DNA chain, however, the sequence of bases is permanent; the genetic information it represents is inheritable (Figure 13.9).

Should such a sequence of events have taken place in a cell giving rise to gametes, the mutation would be handed on, through the gametes, to future generations of individuals.

Finally, when the cell that inherits this changed DNA chain prepares to divide, the chain will, of course, direct the synthesis of a chain complementary to itself. It will do so according to the "permitted" pairing of its bases, so that the complementary chain it synthesizes will be different from the one that lay there before (Figure 13.10).

| MUTANT CHAIN | NEW COMPLEMENTARY CHAIN | OLD COMPLEMENTARY CHAIN |
|---|---|---|
| Adenine | Thymine | Thymine |
| Thymine | Adenine | Adenine |
| Thymine | Adenine | Guanine |
| Guanine | Cytosine | Cytosine |

Figure 13.10.   The synthesis of a complementary DNA chain by DNA with a changed sequence of bases. The base sequence in the new complementary chain differs from that in the old chain. The mutation is complete.

This change, too, is inheritable. Both chains of DNA have undergone change, and the mutation is said to be complete.

**13.12   Significance of Genetic Mutations.**   Genetic mutations, irrespective of how they come about, result in deviations, often great in magnitude, from the status quo. The genes — the DNA — are directly responsible for the synthesis of protein. If changes are made in them, it is inevitable that the usual proteins or the usual pattern of protein metabolism will no longer exist. And, as has been stated often before, deviations from the status quo, for the time interval in which they exist, are nearly always deleterious. Because mutations are permanent, the deviations they bring about are also permanent.

The overwhelming majority of genetic mutations are detrimental to the individual in which they occur and even to the species in which mutant members arise. Very few mutations prove to be beneficial. Whether a mutation is detrimental or beneficial to an individual or species depends upon a conspiracy of chance. If a mutation (mutations, themselves, are chance events) *happens* to coincide with a simultaneous environmental change for which it is suited, it will be beneficial. But such coincidental environmental changes and genetic mutations are very rare.

## SUMMARY

1. The center of direction of all cellular function is in the nucleus of the cell, in structures called genes.
2. The genes are composed of macromolecules of DNA and contain all the information required for normal metabolism.
3. This information is codified in the sequence of the nitrogenous bases within the DNA macromolecule.
4. Exact duplication of each DNA macromolecule, before cell division, permits the distribution of precisely the same genetic information from the parent cell to its daughters.
5. Changes in DNA structure brought about during DNA synthesis provide a mechanism which may be the molecular basis of mutation.

## General Reference

1. Watson, J. D.: *Molecular Biology of the Gene*, W. A. Benjamin, Inc., New York, 1965.

# 14

## Review of Basic Biology: The Nucleus:

## The Transmission of the Genetic Material

**14.1  Introduction.**  The genetic information is contained, encoded, as part of the DNA macromolecule. The *sequence* of nitrogenous bases along the chains of that molecule constitutes a sort of "sentence" which has a meaning for the cell in which it finds itself. If this critical sequence is altered, the code (or sentence), and the meaning of the sentence that it makes up, are changed. Such a change is called a *mutation*. Mutations can, of course, arise as a result of improper synthesis of DNA chains due to tautomeric shifts in the structure of bases in a DNA molecule directing synthesis (Chapter 13). But any alteration in the sequence of bases, regardless of how it comes about, will bring about a mutation.

The *expression* of the genes, the way in which they direct cytoplasmic or metabolic activity, is dependent not only upon the genetic sentence on the DNA molecule, but upon the *number* of genes (the 2n number or set) present, and the *balance* between them. Loss of a gene or genes (such a loss will represent the loss of a segment of DNA) may result not only in the loss of the function governed by that gene but also a change in the expression of the remaining genes, because the balance among them is upset. Errors in the *transmission* of DNA from one cell generation to the next, errors which do occur, result in lost genes and a changed expression of those that remain. These errors usually involve changes in *chromosome* structure or inequalities in chromosome distribution at cell division.

**14.2  Chromosome Structure.**  The chromosomes, the bearers of the DNA, are composed both of DNA and protein. While the role of DNA is now well known, the role played by the protein component is not so well understood. The protein component is, in most species of organisms, one of a small molecular weight variety typified by the proteins of the histone group. The manner in which the DNA and the protein are coupled, or whether they are coupled at all times and under all circumstances, is not known.

The chromosome is known, however, to be a long, thread-like structure (some exceptions exist; round chromosomes have been shown in some bacteria) which, like the DNA that is a part of it, have the property of self-replication (duplication). It is further known that the genes are arranged on the chromosomes in a certain, fixed order. The order is a *linear* one; the genes are placed, one next to another, much as beads are sequentially arranged on a string.

**14.3   Transmission of the Genetic Material.**   The genetic material is transmitted *from one cell generation to the next* in a process called *mitosis*. It is transmitted, through sexual reproduction, *from one generation of individuals to the next* by a related, but somewhat more complex process called *meiosis*.

**14.4   Mitosis.**   Mitosis actually encompasses two separate processes—division of the nucleus and division of the cytoplasm. Although, under usual circumstances, the two proceed one right upon the heels of the other, such is not necessarily the case. Both in nature and under experimental conditions the nucleus may divide, often more than once, without a division of the cytoplasm (the eggs of insects, for example, undergo a series of nuclear divisions without division of the cytoplasm), and, under experimental conditions, the cytoplasm of the eggs of amphibia, from which the nuclei have been removed, can be made to cleave (cytoplasmic division without prior nuclear division).

**14.5   Nuclear Division.**   The better part of the life of any somatic cell is spent in what has been called *the resting stage* or, perhaps better, *interphase*. Such cells are not really resting; the term is a misnomer. They usually are engaged in considerable metabolic activity. However, to early investigators who compared their appearance to the more dynamic looking division stages, this phase seemed static and the cell, itself, at rest. Actually, this stage is probably best defined as the phase between cell divisions.

In interphase the nucleus (in stained preparations) appears as a lacework of fine, lightly stained material (because of its staining qualities, called *chromatin*) in a translucent non-colored material (nucleoplasm), surrounded by a membrane. In the interphase nucleus of most cells will be seen one or more bodies (of varied sizes and shapes) called *nucleoli*.

In most cells, with light microscopy, little more than this can be seen, but in a few (the cells of the salivary glands of larval flies, for example) the lacework of chromatin material can be seen to be composed of chromosomes. These chromosomes appear as very long, very slender threads, which lie, often tangled about each other, in the nucleoplasm. While greatly extended, they are not straight, but are slightly coiled about their own long axis (Figure 14.1).

At some point in the interphase the cell will begin to prepare to undergo division. There is little change in the *appearance* of nucleus at this time, but, within it, there is an accumulation of the building blocks of DNA (the nucleotides). This period is called $G_1$, and is the one immediately before DNA is synthesized. When the build-up is

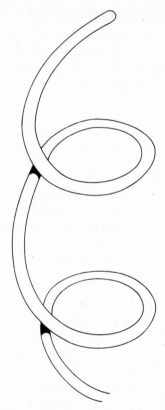

**Figure 14.1.** This is a representation of a portion of a chromosome from an interphase nucleus. While greatly extended, there is some coiling in very loose, open gyres.

complete, DNA synthesis occurs (see Chapter 13 for details of the procedure). This period, the period in which DNA is actually synthesized, is called the S phase. It is likely that the chromosomes reduplicate in this phase as well. Directly after it, there is a period (its lenth is variable and seems to be different for cells of different tissues and for those from different organisms) called $G_2$. In the period of time encompassing the phases $G_1$, S and $G_2$, the microscopic *appearance* of the nucleus of most cells is not changed, but it should be remembered that, by $G_2$, the quantity of DNA in the nucleus has increased from 2n to 4n, and the chromosomes have doubled (2n to 4n).

Each of the chromosomes, during duplication, lays down next to itself, and very close to itself, an exact replica of itself. The precise mechanism is not known, but the fact is that when the chromosomes become cleary visible later in cell division, they are seen to be 4n in number and each member of the 2n set (Section 13.2) will have next to it a chromosome just like it.

The $G_2$ period and, in fact, the interphase, come to an end with the onset of the first of the division phases, *prophase*. The very beginning of the phase is marked by a thickening (in some cases the chromatin takes on a beaded appearance as well) and an increase in the faint stainability of the chromatin. In time and as the phase progresses, the chromatin becomes much thickened, more densely stainable, and its structure at last becomes discernable. It becomes apparent that the observed thickening and increase in stainability are due to a change in the degree of *coiling* of the chromosmes. In prophase the chromosomes begin to condense into more tightly coiled gyres (Figure 14.2).

The process of condensation into ever-tightening gyres continues to the end of prophase. At that time the chromosomes will have

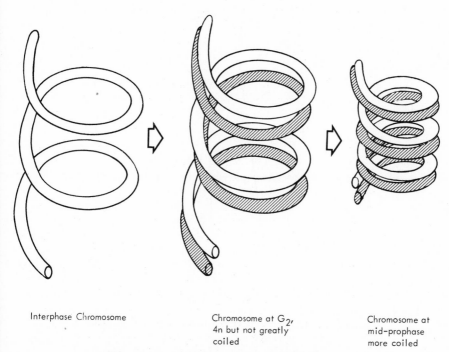

Interphase Chromosome          Chromosome at $G_2$,          Chromosome at
                               4n but not greatly           mid-prophase
                               coiled                       more coiled

**Figure 14.2.**   Coiling of prophase chromosomes.

attained maximum condensation and their morphologic structure is best seen. Each will be endowed with a clear, often spherical-appearing, non-staining area known as a centromere (it is the region of attachment to the spindle, a structure to be described later in this section). Extending from the centromere are what are known as the *arms* of the chromosome. These arms, which may vary in length, undergo the coiling and condensation just described (Figure 14.3).

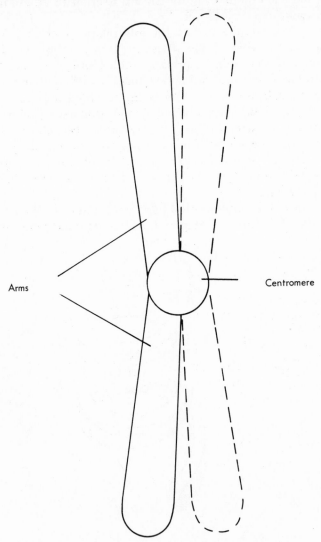

Arms                                                                                     Centromere

**Figure 14.3.** Chromosome structure at the end of prophase. It must be kept in mind that the structure consists of *two* chromosomes (as a result of duplication in interphase) held together by a single centromere.

Prophase is over when the chromosomes reach maximum conden-sation, *and the nuclear membrane as well as any nucleoli disappears.* With the dissolution of the nuclear membrane the nucleoplasm and cytoplasm mix. For all intents and purposes there is no longer a nucleus.

The next phase, *metaphase,* now follows. In it two procedures occur more or less simultaneously. The chromosomes move (the

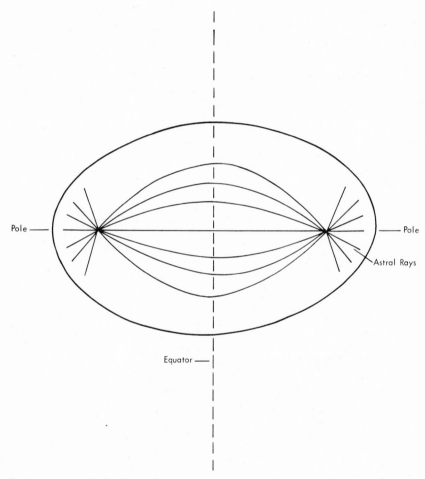

**Figure 14.4.** An idealized cell (no chromosomes are shown) in which there is a large spindle. The spindle crosses the equator at its widest point and draws to a point at the poles. There are fibers extending back from the poles called *"asters"* or *"astral rays."* The function of these fibers is not known.

mechanism underlying the movement is not known) to the center of the cell, to the cell's "equator."

In the meantime the *spindle* forms. It is composed of fibers which cross the cell, linking its poles (Figure 14.4).

When the chromosomes arrive at the equator they take their place (by the centromere or spindle-attachment region) on the spindle. Then the centromere and *only* the centromere divides (Figure 14.5). When this occurs, *metaphase* is complete.

Now begins the *anaphase*. This phase is characterized by *movement* of the chromosomes on the spindle to the poles. Chromosomal movement is always first at the centromere; the arms, in particular the long arms, trail behind. Often at metaphase and even in early anaphase the arms of the duplicated chromosomes are twisted about each other. Frequently, they appear hopelessly entangled. However, in all *normal* divisions they easily unravel and separate cleanly, each following its centromere to the proper pole (Figure 14.6).

When anaphase movement is complete, the chromosomes will have reached the poles and the phase is ended.

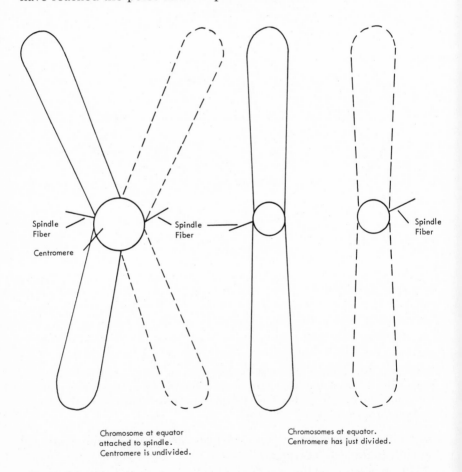

Spindle Fiber

Spindle Fiber

Spindle Fiber

Centromere

Chromosome at equator attached to spindle. Centromere is undivided.

Chromosomes at equator. Centromere has just divided.

**Figure 14.5.** The separation of chromosomes after division of the centromere at metaphase.

Anaphase is followed by the last of the division phases, *telophase*. In it the chromosomes clumped at the poles begin to uncoil. The nuclear membrane is restored and there is a reappearance of nucleoli. As the phase progresses the chromosomal spirals or coils unwind until an interphase nucleus is reconstructed.

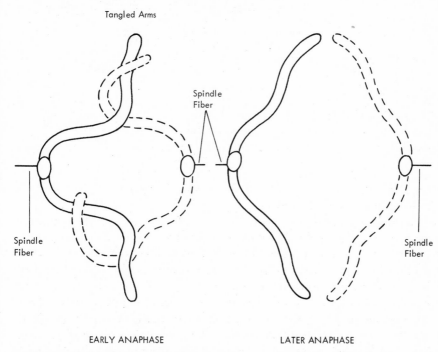

Tangled Arms

Spindle Fiber

Spindle Fiber

Spindle Fiber

EARLY ANAPHASE                    LATER ANAPHASE

**Figure 14.6.**  The anaphase movement of chromosomes. The centromere leads the chromosome to the poles, the arms following. In normal divisions the seemingly tangled arms unravel easily and clean separation of chromosomes occurs.

**14.6  Cytoplasmic Division.**  During the last part of anaphase the spindle undergoes an important change. At the equator of the cell, in the space between the two separating masses of chromosomes, the fibers appear to stretch, the spindle becomes somewhat compressed, and it appears that this portion of the structure is expanding. The action is interpreted as a "pushing" one which is forcing the two groups of chromosomes to the poles (Figure 14.7).

The cytoplasm constricts at the equator, until the cell finally divides (Figure 14.8).

**14.7  Duration of the Mitotic Cycle.**  The time taken for a complete mitotic cycle is different for cells of the different tissues in an organism. It is dependent as well upon the physiologic state of the

Group of Chromosomes                              Group of Chromosomes

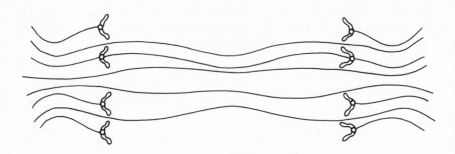

Expanding Spindle

**Figure 14.7.** A representation of the expanding spindle forcing the moving anaphase chromosomes to the poles.

organism. In certain kinds of organisms, external factors, such as temperature, may play a role.

From the point of view of the total organism, the duration of the mitotic cycle of cells in various tissues becomes quite important. Certain tissues (bone marrow, for example) or certain regions of organs (the crypts of Lieberkühn in the small intestine is a good illustration) are centers of high mitotic activity. A great number of cells are produced in these regions, but many of them do not remain where they are formed. Instead, they leave the immediate area and *specialize;* that is, they take on certain, specific functions. Once they specialize, they do not ordinarily reproduce themselves.

The bone marrow is a *germinal* center for the cells of circulating blood. Many circulating cells arise from the division of cells in the bone marrow. They take on specialized functions, begin to circulate in the blood and to perform their special task, but do not reproduce themselves. After a time, they wear out and die. The function they perform, the need for the service they give the organism does not, however, disappear with the death of these cells (the need for oxygen transport, for example, persists in spite of the death of the highly specialized red blood corpuscles). They must be *replaced* by cells from the germinal center.

Since mature, specialized cells die out at a fairly constant time after they are formed, it follows that they must be replaced at a fairly constant rate in order for the function they perform *for the whole organism* to go on at the proper rate and uninterrupted.

The duration of mitosis in the germinal center, then, is quite critical. If, for some reason, mitosis in the germinal center should be inhibited, or the length of a cycle should become greatly extended, mature cells will die out faster than they are replaced. The total organism will suffer; one of its vital functions will have been impaired. On the other hand, if the mitotic time should be shortened, more specialized cells will be produced than is practical. In certain animals (human beings included) this can lead to a disease state. Excessive numbers of red or white blood cells are abnormal conditions and can (although they do not always) arise from a pathologic alteration in the duration of mitosis.

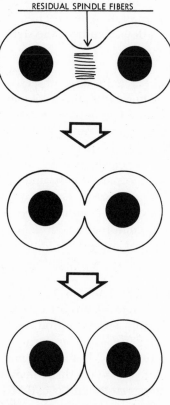

RESIDUAL SPINDLE FIBERS

**Figure 14.8.** Constriction, followed by division, of the cytoplasm. Two daughter cells, lying close to one another, side-by-side, are the result. Cytoplasmic constriction is typical of animal cells; in plants the process is somewhat different, but the result is the same.

**14.8 The Results of Mitosis.** When the process of mitosis is over, the result is two cells, each of which is identical to the parent cell (this is particularly true with respect to the nucleus; unequal distribution between daughter cells of cytoplasmic materials occasionally occurs). In the nucleus of each daughter there is not only the same amount of genetic material (the 2n quantity) as had the parent cell but (barring mutation) the genetic material itself is identical, both in its composition and in its order on the chromosome, to that of the parent. *Mitosis, then, tends to preserve the status quo.* The process confers *stability* upon living things and upon the cells of which they are composed. Agents which tend to disrupt the normal, orderly process of mitosis will tend to bring about errors in the transmission of the genetic material from one cell generation to another. This *can* produce, in some instances at least, a deviation from the status quo equivalent to a mutation.

**14.9  Meiosis.**  Meiosis is a process of cell division that occurs exclusively in cells of the germ line; it is a special kind of cell division, the process through which the genetic material is passed on from one generation of *individuals* to the next. The process is unique (and different from mitosis) in two respects: (1) the resultant cells do *not* have the same number of chromosomes or the same *quantity* of genetic material as does the parent cell, and (2) *the sequence of the genes* on the chromosomes is *not* the same as that of the parent cell. Meiosis, then, is a process which *promotes* genetic variation by the production of changes in combinations of genes on chromosomes. In meiosis the status quo is *not* preserved; genetic variation rather than stability is its aim. The reasons for this are discussed in Section 14.12.

**14.10  Purpose of Meiosis.**  The purpose of meiosis is to provide cells which can carry genetic material from one generation of individuals to another. During sexual reproduction, the germ cells or gametes of two individuals combine to form a new individual. The gametes, of course, are two cells, but at the moment of their fusion a new individual comes into existence that consists of only a one cell (it is the combination of the gametes and is called a zygote). Thereafter, *by mitosis*, first of the zygote and then of the cells that succeed from it, all the cells of the body of this new individual are formed. All of the cells of the new indidivual must have the diploid (2n) number of chromosomes characteristic of the species to which the individual belongs. If the gametes that form that zygote also have the diploid number of chromosomes, the zygote would then contain *twice* this number. In order to prevent the ever-increasing number of chromosomes with each generation, the gametes formed as a result of meiosis have a *reduced* number of chromosomes; in fact, they have a single n set. The zygote resulting from the fusion of two such gametes will be diploid (Figure 14.9).

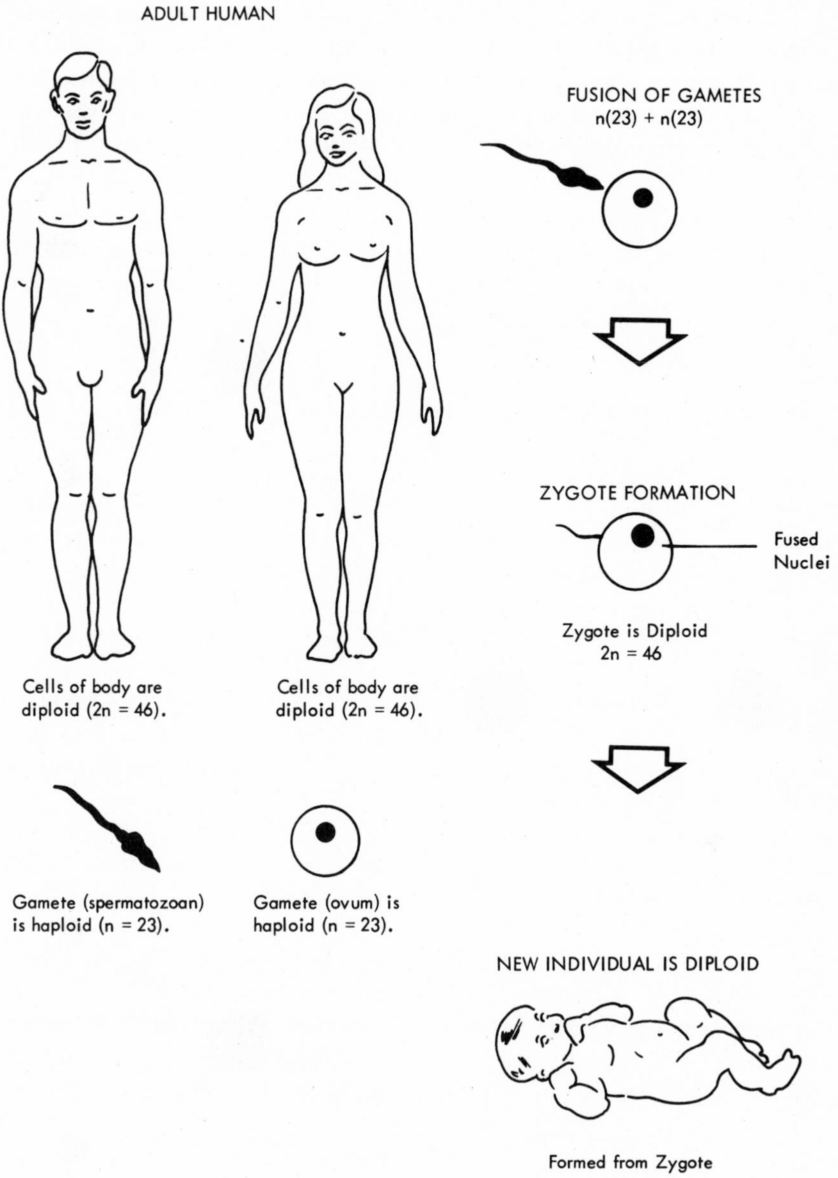

ADULT HUMAN

FUSION OF GAMETES
n(23) + n(23)

ZYGOTE FORMATION

Fused
Nuclei

Zygote is Diploid
2n = 46

Cells of body are
diploid (2n = 46).

Cells of body are
diploid (2n = 46).

Gamete (spermatozoan)
is haploid (n = 23).

Gamete (ovum) is
haploid (n = 23).

NEW INDIVIDUAL IS DIPLOID

Formed from Zygote

**Figure 14.9.** The preservation of the diploid number through the process of transfer of genetic material from one generation of individuals to another. The number of chromosomes (the quantity of genetic material) is reduced in the gamete to the basic n number. Upon fusion of the gametes to form a new individual the number of chromosomes in this new individual is the 2n number. It consists, of course, of two n sets, one provided by the male gamete and the other by the female.

The reduction in chromosome number is accomplished in *two* cell divisions, one following upon the other, in which the chromosomes and the genetic material are duplicated only once. Each parent or germ cell will give rise to four cells after the two divisions, but, because chromosomal reduplication occurs only once, each of the four cells formed will have the n number of chromosomes (Figure 14.10).

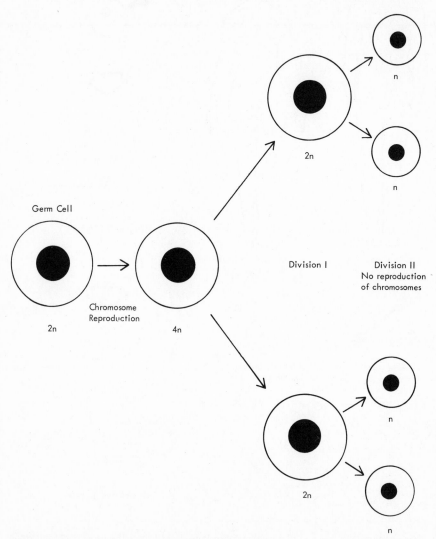

**Figure 14.10.** Schematic representation of the reduction of the number of chromosomes in meiosis. There are two divisions: the chromosomes replicate before the first division so that each daughter retains the 2n complement. No duplication takes place before or during the second division, so that the resultant cells can receive only the *n* number of chromosomes.

**14.11 The Stages of Meiosis.** The first of the meiotic stages is, as it is in mitosis, *prophase*. This phase differs, however, from the prophase of mitosis in that it is very long (there can be distinguished several clearly separate stages within this prophase) and that, in it, the chromosomes undergo a series of important and complicated movements.

The earliest part of it is called *leptonema*. In it the chromosomes become apparent (they attain a certain degree of stainability). Unlike the prophase of mitosis in which the chromosomes are seen to be distributed more or less randomly in the nucleus, the distribution of these chromosomes is ordered. (It will be remembered that in diploid cells there are two sets of chromosomes, one which comes to the zygote from the male parent and one from the female parent—Section 14.10. These two n sets of chromosomes are considered *homologs* of each other. For each chromosme in either n set there will be a homolog—one just like it—in the other. Homologous chromosomes are "like" chromosomes; the genes on each of them govern or regulate the same cellular function. They differ, however, in their origin; one comes from the male parent and the other from the female parent.) In leptonema, homologous chromosomes come to lie *very* close to each other. They are, as are the chromosomes in mitotic prophase, very extended, perhaps even more loosely coiled than those of mitosis.

Homologous chromosomes, so close together in leptonema, now actually pair—effect union. The beginning of pairing (synapsis, as it is called) signals the onset of the next portion of the meiotic prophase—the stage called *zygonema*. All along their length, in a precise, point-for-point fashion, the chromosomes come together in intimate association (Figure 14.11). This act of pairing is of great importance; it is at the very heart of meiosis.

When pairing of the chromosomes is complete, these bodies undergo a longitudinal contraction which results in thicker-looking filaments. When this has happened, zygonema is over and a new stage, *pachynema* (the word means thick thread), has begun. As pachynema progresses, the nucleus appears to contain a group of filaments which are *haploid* (n) in number. An *apparent* reduction has occurred in which the number of chromosomes seems to have been halved. No real reduction, however, has taken place (none does until the *second* meiotic division); homologous chromosomes have paired so closely and so intimately that each pair *appears* as one chromosome.

Now there begins a process, called "crossing-over," which is most important and which is (except in rare circumstances) unique to meiosis.

Transverse breaks develop at the same level in the arms of both homologous chromosomes (Figure 14.12).

The number of such breaks may be different in different chromosomes, but there are some generalizations that can be made about
these breaks. They occur with greatest frequency in chromosomes that
have long arms and more often at positions distant from the centromere than at those near it.

Immediately after the breaks have taken place, *both* segments of
the chromosomal arms interchange (cross-over) and fuse. Thus, a

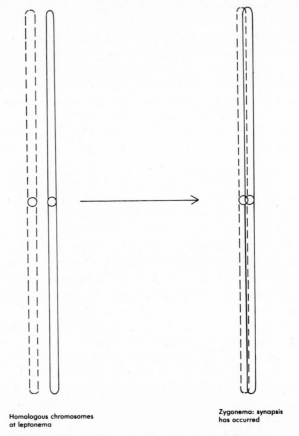

Homologous chromosomes
at leptonema

Zygonema: synapsis
has occurred

**Figure 14.11.** Schematic representation of the pairing
or union of homologous chromosomes in meiosis.

portion of each chromosome (with its genes) is transferred to the
homologous chromosome (Figure 14.13). The genic environment of
*both* chromosomes is changed and the possibility of genetic variation
has come into existence. A gene, whose action is suppressed or
dominated by its homolog on the homologous chromosome, may find
itself — at the end of meiosis — in a cell that lacks this dominant gene. It
is possible, then, that it, and genes like it, can have expression in the
generation that inherits them.

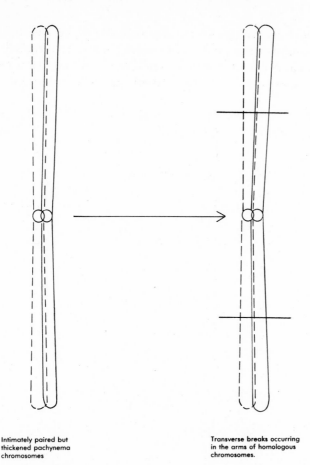

Intimately paired but
thickened pachynema
chromosomes

Transverse breaks occurring
in the arms of homologous
chromosomes.

**Figure 14.12.** Schematic representation of two transverse breaks occurring, one in each arm, of homologous chromosomes.

Crossing-over is the act occurring in meiosis that changes the status quo. As a result of it, different combinations of genes—some new ones—are introduced which permit variation in the expression of those genes. In a sense a "new" chromosome is formed.

When the cross-over, the exchange of parts, is complete, pachynema is over, and a new stage, *diplonema*, starts. The chromosomes begin to separate; the arms repel each other. In prophase separation does not, however, become complete; the chromosomes remain united at the points of cross-over. The points of persistent cross-over in the face of separating or repelling chromosome arms are called *chiasmata* (Figure 14.14).

During diplonema the chromosomes continue condensing; in many such chromosomes the coiled structure is clearly visible. The nucleolus remains visible in this phase but may, late in the phase or early in the next, disappear.

The last stage of this long and important prophase is characterized by great condensation of the chromosomes and by terminalization of the chiasmata. Because the chromosomes continue to shorten, the chiasmata are moved toward (in short chromosomes, to) the ends of

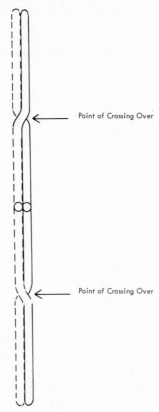

Figure 14.13. Schematic representation of the exchange of parts in two chromosomes at cross-over.

the arms so that the attachment of chromosomes to each other appears terminal or nearly so. This phase is called *diakinesis* (Figure 14.15).

The end of prophase is signalled by the complete disappearance of the nuclear membrane and the formation of the spindle. This is also the beginning of metaphase. As in the metaphase of mitosis the chromosomes move to the equator of the cell and take their place on the spindle. There is an important difference, however, between these and the chromosomes of mitotic metaphase. Whereas in mitosis there is an individual centromere that separates at metaphase (Section 14.5; Figure 14.5), in meiosis there are two separate centromeres (Figure 14.16).

At last the chromosomes, attached by their centromeres to the spindle, begin to move toward the poles. This movement, as in mitosis, signals the end of metaphase and the beginning of anaphase.

It should be stressed that the bodies moving to the poles in anaphase are not quite the same as those which began this division. An exchange of parts has occurred; the arms of the chromosomes now

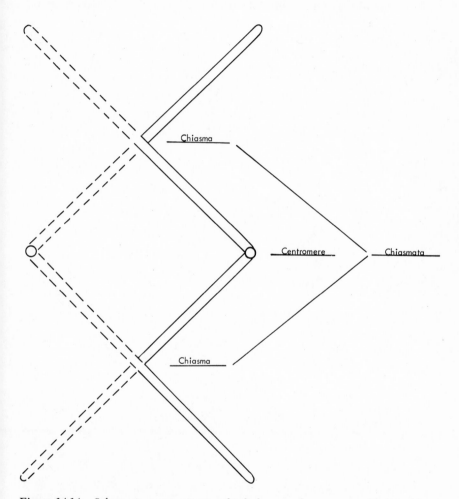

**Figure 14.14.** Schematic representation of a diplonema chromosome with two chiasmata.

possess a different sequence of genes from that possessed by the chromosomes at the beginning of the process.

The arrival of the chromosomes at the poles is both the end of anaphase and the beginning of telophase. In meiosis this stage may be very short or even incomplete. The cytoplasm divides and a very short interphase may ensue. *In this interphase, unlike any other interphase, no synthesis of DNA and no chromosomal duplication take place.*

The prophase of the second meiotic division begins in each of the daughter cells produced in the first division. In this prophase nucleus, unlike any other prophase nucleus, there is the *2n number* of chromosomes and amount of genetic material. It is a short prophase; the spindle forms and *metaphase* of this second meiotic division is said to have begun.

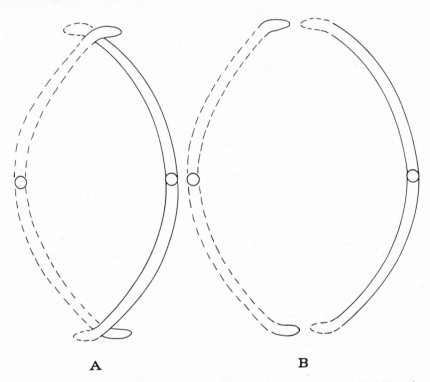

A                                                   B

**Figure 14.15.** Schematic representation of chromosomes in diakinesis. (A) Note that the chiasmata are very nearly at the end of the arms of the chromosomes, and (B) chromosomes are separated.

The chromosomes arrange themselves at the equator of each of the cells, and, as in mitosis, their centromeres separate and their anaphase movement begins.

At telophase, *four* cells will have been formed, each with the n number of chromosomes and *each having a genetic or nuclear content different from the other* (crossing-over). These cells will become the gametes (in higher organisms further specialization is required before the cells become functional gametes).

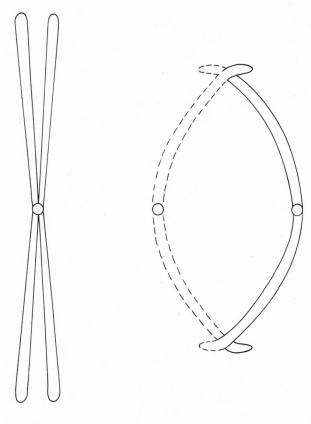

Mitotic chromosome
at metaphase:
one centromere
chromosomes at the metaphase
of the first meiotic division:
two separate centromeres

of the first meiotic division:
two separate centromeres

**Figure 14.16.** Schematic representation of an essential difference between the chromosomes at metaphase of mitosis and
those at the metaphase of the first meiotic division. In mitosis
there is a chromosome held together by an individual centromere. In meiosis there are *two* double chromosomes held
together by their chiasmata. There are, of course, two centromeres.

**14.12   The Essence of Meiosis.**   The very essence of meiosis is
crossing-over. This crossing-over provides a mechanism whereby
genes in different chromosomes can be brought together and combined. If such a mechanism were not available, evolution of species
would be impossible. Without crossing-over, the sequence of genes,
the genic environment itself, would be fixed. The richness, the
diversity of living things as we know them, the ability of species to
conquer new environments would not exist.

While it is of paramount importance that all cells within the same organism retain a good balance both within themselves and with other cells around them (the heart of mitosis is to retain the status quo), it is advantageous for new organisms to vary, both from each other and from their parents. The random, independent combination and recombination of genes accomplished at meiosis raise the possibility of a genic combination better suited to a given environment than any previously existing combination. There is, of course, the possibility of combinations more poorly suited to the environment than the existing ones. This does occur commonly.

But it is through the existence of a mechanism for genic recombination that the testing of genic combinations against the environment comes into being, and the success or failure of various species occurs.

## SUMMARY

1. The transfer of genetic material from cell generation to cell generation is accomplished through a process of cell division called *mitosis.*

2. As a result of mitosis the nuclear content of each new cell is exactly the same (barring mutation) as that of the parent. Both the amount of genetic material and the sequence of genes are preserved intact and passed on to each daughter so that each is, in essence, an exact replica of the parent.

3. The transfer of genetic material from one generation of individuals to the one that succeeds it is accomplished through a process of cell division called meiosis.

4. In meiosis, through a unique double cell division, the number of chromosomes in the four resultant daughter cells is haploid (n) and the sequence of genes in these chromosomes differs both among the daughters and from their parent.

5. Mitosis tends to preserve the status quo; meiosis leads toward genetic variation.

# 15

# Effects of Ionizing Radiation

# in the Nucleus:

# The Genetic Material

**15.1 Frequency of Mutation.** In nature, mutations—those sudden, rare, discrete changes in the genetic material which result in a permanent change in the expression of the genes—take place spontaneously (or perhaps it is more accurate to say that no known cause fully explains their appearance, Chapter 13, Section 13.10). While it is true that there is no way to predict when any given gene will mutate, the rate or *frequency* at which spontaneous mutations occur in many genes is known. It is also known that the frequency of spontaneous mutation is not the same for all genes; in some, mutation occurs more often than in others. It is, however, a rare event even in the genes having the highest rate. It follows, then, that certain genes must be regarded as relatively stable while others are less resistant to forces capable of producing changes within them. To summarize, it may be stated that genes mutate spontaneously at a set rate or with a fixed frequency. The rate is not the same for all genes, but any given gene will mutate with a given frequency.

**15.2 Mutagenesis.** Because mutations occur spontaneously with fixed frequencies, it must not be imagined that the frequency is unalterable. Certain agents, known by the generic term "mutagens," can change the rate. As the name implies (*muta-gen*—to give rise to or generate *change*), these agents *increase* the rate of mutation. Among them (and one of the most effective) is ionizing radiation. In 1927, H. J. Muller[1] noted a higher mutation rate in fruit flies that had been exposed to ionizing radiation (in his experiments, x ray was the source of radiation) than in those not exposed. The *mutations* that appeared were not different from those that occurred spontaneously, but the *frequency* of their appearance increased. It was concluded that ionizing radiation produces changes in the genes identical to those that occur in them spontaneously.

Following the initial observations in fruit flies, the phenomenon has been observed in many organisms and in many, many genes. At present there appears to be no exception in the plant or animal kingdoms; the genes of all are susceptible to the mutagenic action of ionizing radiation.

**15.3 Mutagens.** Many agents increase the mutation rate. Some are fundamentally quite different from others—completely unrelated in structure and mechanism of action. Chemicals (within this large general class alone there is a rich diversity of agents), viruses (certain ones can change the genetic material of the cells they invade), and radiations—both ionizing and those of lesser energy (ultraviolet light, for example)—are mutagens that are quite efficient at producing changes in genetic material. This very diversity indicates that *mutation* is basically a property of the genetic material rather than a property of the mutagens themselves. That is, since mutagens *are* so different from each other both in what they are and how they act, mutation is probably a *response* of the genetic material common to *any* agent that produces ultramicroscopic, point-like, discrete changes in it.

**15.4 The Importance of Ionizing Radiation as a Mutagen.** While ionizing radiation is not the only mutagen it is the most effective one known for producing mutations in quantity. For the geneticist it is almost an indispensable tool because it affords an opportunity to investigate the very nature of the gene. With its use, mutational frequency is increased so that, for all practical purposes, changes are being produced in genes at will. Furthermore the changes that are made give an important clue as to what has been changed. Ionizing radiation is important also, because, by producing mutations in abundance, it facilitates the study of the *consequences* of genetic mutation in individuals (cells or organisms) and in populations in which these mutations arise. Its production of mutations is, in fact, very likely to be its most important biologic effect. None of its other effects is so far-reaching in consequences *both for the individual in which the mutation occurs* (whether the individual is a single cell or a multicellular organism) *and for the population of which a mutant-bearing individual is a member* (whether this is a population of cells or a species of organisms). For physicians utilizing ionizing radiation as a diagnostic or therapeutic tool, the production of mutations may be the radiation's most serious unwanted side-effect.

**15.5.   Radiation Effects on DNA *in vivo:* The Manner of Production of Mutations.**   It has been suggested that in the production of mutations, ionizing radiation acts by ionizing nitrogenous bases in the DNA chains — in particular during DNA synthesis. If ionization of a base occurs during DNA synthesis, "forbidden" base pairs can come into existence in the new macromolecule (Chapter 13, Section 13.11) just as they are formed following tautomeric shifts in the structure of the bases. For example, the "permitted" pairing in DNA is between thymine and adenine; thymine-guanine pairs are forbidden. But if either guanine *or* thymine is ionized (at the proper place in the molecule) *during* DNA synthesis, hydrogen-bonding between guanine and thymine occurs, the phosphate groups of the two "fit" the DNA molecule, and the "forbidden" pair, thymine-guanine, can result. This would of course be a mutation, precisely equivalent to one that occurs spontaneously, namely, as a result of a tautomeric shift in either guanine or thymine (Chapter 13). As a result, the sequence of bases in the newly synthesized chain would be "wrong," and a permanent, heritable, discrete change in the DNA would result. This change, or mutation, would be the *same* as one that occurs spontaneously, so that the frequency of its appearance would have been increased.

Ionization produced in the bases of DNA during *synthesis* is not the only mechanism by which radiation produces mutations. At any phase in the cell's life cycle, *base-change* or *base-deletion* effects[2] which change the critical base sequence of the molecule may occur. Ionization of one or more of the bases, or interaction of one or more bases with free radicals, may so alter their structure that the bases no longer possess the characteristics they had before exposure to radiation. Such an event is a base-change, and it will, of course, alter the base sequence. When a cell in which base-change has occurred prepares to divide, changes are almost certain to be made in the newly synthesized DNA chains which will be the direct result of the base-change in the old chain; the changed base cannot direct the incorporation of the "proper" base in the newly synthesized chain. The daughter cells that receive these DNA chains will receive, as a consequence, base sequences conveying inadequate or even erroneous information. In addition, this information, whatever it is, will be heritable.

*Base-deletion* occurs if sufficient numbers of ionizations take place within one or more bases or if interaction with free radicals so alters one or more of them that they are deleted from the DNA molecule. The effect upon the cell is, of course, quite similar to that of base-change. Some genetic information will be missing. Further, what is left does not necessarily convey the same meaning to the cell as it did before the deletion took place; what is left can actually have no meaning at all. If, for example, very important words are deleted from a sentence (its subject or its verb), what remains will probably be nonsense. On the other hand, if the words deleted are not so important (modifiers), the remainder of the sentence may still have its original meaning; some of the *nuances* or *shades* of meaning will, of course, be lacking.

**15.6  Dependence on LET.** Not all the ionizing radiations are equally efficient in bringing about the changes in DNA that lead to mutation. When the frequency of *base-change* and/or of *base-deletion* mutations in yeast was compared after irradiation with ionizing radiations of increasing LET (Chapter 4), it was found that changes in frequency depended upon the LET of the radiation used. The greater the ion density produced by the radiation (greater LET), the more efficient was the radiation for bringing about this kind of mutation.[2] The relationship does not hold, however, throughout the entire spectrum of LET; a maximum efficiency is reached. Increases in LET beyond a certain point (carbon nuclei were the maximum) did not produce further increases in the frequency of these mutations.

The dependence of base-change or deletion mutations on LET is believed to be due to either the ion density produced within the DNA molecule by the radiation or the quantity of irradiation products (free radicals) produced in cellular material. As the density of ions per unit volume of matter increases—as the LET of radiations increases—there is a progressively greater chance that higher LET radiations will produce several ionizations within the nitrogenous bases of DNA. There will be, therefore, an increasing probability with increasing LET that one or more of the bases will be changed by one or more of these ionizations or that one or more of the bases will be deleted following ionization or free-radical attack.

At the LET having the maximum efficiency for producing these mutations, it is likely that sufficient energy is exchanged per unit of particle track to permit several ionizations to occur even as the ionizing particle traverses a distance as small as a DNA chain. Under these circumstances, when a DNA chain is traversed, the nitrogenous bases are probably ionized several times and, if not deleted outright, are changed.

The relationship of LET to base-change or base-deletion mutation may be explained by an alternate hypothesis. The rise in mutational frequency to a maximum with progressively increasing LET may represent a rise to a maximum in the number or concentration of *mutagenic* agents produced by radiation. Such agents could be the primary decomposition products of ionized water (the free radicals H· and OH·) or even the products of their interaction (Chapter 9) which may react with the nitrogenous bases in DNA and change these bases. The production of the primary products of radiation would be expected to increase—and the concentrations of products of radical-interactions will increase—with radiations of increasing LET. This is true because there is a high probability of interaction between highly diffusible free radicals when they are formed close together, extinguishing some of them and reducing the likelihood of interaction with DNA.

**15.7 The Significance of Genetic Mutations.** Mutations are, as a rule, detrimental to the cell or individual that bears them. They bring about sharp deviations from the status quo; the degree of deviation is, of course, dependent upon the number and importance of the genes that are changed during a mutation.

When mutations do occur, the change is most often in a negative direction, that is, from the presence of something to the absence of the same thing. Any gene, presumably, is the bearer of some bit of information, a particular command which should be carried out by the cell in order to have normal function. A gene may, for example, direct the synthesis of a particular enzyme. If the gene mutates, a *negative* change will probably have taken place. In its changed or mutated form it is unlikely that the gene will be able to direct the synthesis of the enzyme—the gene's "action" will be missing. Part of the deviation from the status quo for this cell, then, will be the permanent loss of an enzyme. In the vast majority of cases this will be detrimental. Usually the cell will need the missing enzyme; the enzyme's function might be irreplaceable. The only circumstances under which a mutation is beneficial is the rare one in which there is a fortituous change in the environment, occurring simultaneously with the mutation, for which the mutation happens to be suited, or if the mutant form is in better harmony with the existing environment. Such events are, however, purely chance occurrences. Mutations are not planned—and they very rarely coincide with environmental changes for which they happen to be suited.

All detrimental changes impair *viability* (for want of a better description—the capability to survive or recover from life-threatening situations). The result of this impairment is a short life for the individual that has sustained the detriment. In gene mutations, the degree of detriment, which will be reflected as the length of time life is shortened, depends on the number or on the importance of the genes changed. Some genes are so important that changes in them bring death essentially immediately. Such changes are called *lethal* mutations. If a lethal mutation occurs in the germ line (the cells giving rise to gametes) the zygote that inherits them will probably be non-viable or, at least, will not survive its embryonic period. Other mutations (like the one that gives rise to *hemophilia,* a condition in which the blood clots very slowly or not at all) are *severely* detrimental yet not immediately lethal. Such mutants may survive into adult life if considerable care is taken to avoid "life-threatening" predicaments. For the hemophiliac, even minor cuts in the skin are life-threatening for he may bleed to death before his blood clots. In many instances, life ends before the mutant attains sexual maturity. Still other mutations (like the one that produces albinism) are less detrimental. An albino, with care, can live a long life, certainly beyond sexual maturity and even into old age. Nevertheless, albinos are at a disadvantage when compared to individuals with normal pigmentation. Human albinos are particularly subject to severe burns from the sun (these can be lethal) and to blindness, for the unpigmented iris of the eye offers the sensitive retina no protection against strong light. Albinos of lower forms of life, owing to the lack of color, stand out against almost any background making them especially obvious to predators.

Finally, there are mutations that cause such small degrees of detriment that they affect viability very slightly; the life span of these mutants may be almost as long as that of non-mutants, although it is shortened.

*All* mutations (barring the few beneficial ones), regardless of how large or small a number of genes are involved or how important or insignificant the changed genes may have been, have, in the long run, the same result. They bring about the loss of life of *at least one* mutant individual. Lethal mutations end the mutant's life essentially immediately. Such a mutation, obviously, ends there; it cannot be passed on to others, and it becomes extinct. But slightly detrimental mutations, because they shorten the life of each mutant by a small amount, have the *same* end result. The mutation is passed from mutant individual to mutant individual through a number of generations. The total life shortening (minutes, days, years) of all of these individuals will eventually equal one normal life-span.

Given enough time, all detrimental mutations become extinct. There is a reproductive pressure against mutants; they are, because of this pressure, "selected" out of a population. Extinction of slightly detrimental mutations may take many, many years; more detrimental ones extinguish themselves sooner. Lethal mutations become extinct almost as soon as they come into existence. The presence of mutations (mutants) in a population imposes a kind of burden upon that population. The mutant-bearing individuals cannot give rise to a line of descendents (except under the rare chance circumstances where the mutation is beneficial) that can become successful. The line is destined for extinction. But before it becomes extinct its members compete with non-mutant members of the species for the essentials of life — food, water, and territory.

If enough mutants in a given species come into existence at roughly the same time the species itself can die out. This is true, because there is competition not only among the members of the same species for food, water, and territory, but also among different species. More than one species will be in competition for the same food and water — sometimes for the same territory. If a large number of mutations arise in a species at about the same time, large numbers of the members of that species will inherit a degree of impaired viability. A pressure will be exerted against that species by those in competition. Since the number of the members that live out a full life is smaller than that of the competing species, some of the food and territory normally accruing to the mutant species will be taken by members of the competing species. The competing species will achieve relatively wider geographic distribution, and localized disasters or calamities (forest fires, earthquakes, floods) will have a lesser probability of exterminating *all* of their members than would those involving a species whose distribution is more restricted.

If few offspring live to reproductive age, another kind of pressure is built against a species. Many of the genetic recombinations achieved at cross-over, which permit individuals and ultimately the species itself to adapt more perfectly to the environment (Chapter 14), may never be expressed (lethal mutation) or passed on (sexual maturity is not reached). The species tends to become static and will not compete with more rapidly adapting forms.

The pressures combine and eventually conspire to hasten the extinction not only of the mutant members of the species, by depriving them of food and space, but also of the species' non-mutant members. A species cannot lose great numbers of its members and still survive. The pressures ultimately become irresistible, and the species dies out.

**15.8 Ionizing Radiation and Large Populations.** When large populations of any kind of organism are exposed to ionizing radiation, mutations will occur in at least some of the cells in some of the organisms exposed. This happens (and has happened from time immemorial) continually to all organisms, including man. The source of the exposure is the natural background (Chapter 3). The amount of radiation to which all matter is exposed, perhaps because it has always been present, perhaps because all things now living have been selected to live in spite of its presence, is not intolerable. The number of mutations that this radiation induces appears compatible with life and the continued success of most species. But exposure to ionizing radiation is increasing. The sources of the added radiation are (for human beings) exposure to medical or dental irradiation, exposure as a result of occupation, and (for all living things) exposure to the radiation from radionuclides "falling out" on earth as a result of the testing of nuclear weapons in the atmosphere.

The use of medical or dental radiation can and will increase the frequency of mutation in the cells irradiated. If these cells are somatic, the experience will be detrimental to them and their descendents. All will be out of balance with the status quo. Depending on the number of descendents of irradiated cells, whole segments of tissues or organs can become composed of abnormal cells. While the production of mutations in *somatic* cells of a few individuals can be seriously detrimental to those in which it happens, it is not ordinarily a serious event from the point of view of the species. And, for that matter, it *need* not necessarily be very serious even to the individual in which it happens. Many kinds of mutant cells are at a disadvantage when compared to those normal areas of the same kind that surround it. They, too, come under population pressures. Like mutant individuals, they will not be able to compete as well as non-mutants for space and nutrient. They, also, die earlier, produce fewer viable descendents, and become extinct. If a few somatic cells mutate, they or their descendents die out, and no *permanent* ill-effect will be experienced by the individual possessing them.

If, however, the radiation passes through and mutates cells of the germ line, this *is* an important and undesirable event from the point of view of the entire species. For the reasons discussed at length in the previous section, the introduction of too many of these mutations can be very detrimental, even life-threatening, to the population as a whole. The hazard to man of exposure to industrial and medical radiation is just that; it can threaten his very existence as a species. As industrial and medical uses widen, the risk of mutation for more and more people comes into existence, and the danger to the population increases.

Fallout radiation from the testing of nuclear weapons in the atmosphere carries larger risks than does industrial and medical radiation. Protective measures that greatly reduce the genetic hazards (these will be discussed in Section 15.10) can be taken when using radiation for diagnostic, therapeutic, or industrial purposes. The exposure to radiation from fallout, however, is different. In the first place, very large numbers of people are exposed, essentially at one time. The numbers are so large that it may be safely said that a major proportion of the human population has already been exposed and is being exposed to an increased radiation dosage as a result of nuclear-weapon tests. In other words, because of these tests, there is now a higher background because this radiation has been *added* to the natural background. At present, there is no feasible way of protecting the population against the results of this increase or against future increases which would result from further atmospheric testing. (It must be remembered that this discussion centers about fallout from *nuclear tests* in the *atmosphere*. It is not concerned with the consequences of nuclear *war*. Fallout shelters may be of some value in protecting human beings from the extremely high amounts of ionizing radiation that would fall back on the earth in the event of such a war. One could likely escape the effects of ionizing radiation by using a shelter until the most intense radiation had decayed. However, people will have to come out of the shelters sometime. When they do, residual [less intense] radiation would remain a considerable genetic risk for many years—possibly for centuries. Fallout shelters would be of no value in protecting against that risk.)

Uniquely, fallout from atmospheric tests does not expose the human population alone, as does medical or industrial exposure. *All* living things are exposed. The plant and animal populations, those populations upon which human beings depend for their existence, for food and air itself, will be weakened by the presence of the mutants that are produced among them. The consequences to these populations is the same as those for human beings—reduced viability, smaller number of offspring, and a tendency toward genetic stasis. The effects brought about in the lower populations will have inevitable echoes for the human beings who have produced them.

### 15.9 Mutation Frequency, Dose, and Dose-Rate.

The magnitude of increase in mutation frequency is dependent upon dose. The relationship is a linear one; each increment of dose produces as many mutations or as great an increase in mutation frequency as the one preceding it.

Such a relationship suggests (although incontrovertible direct evidence has not yet been provided) that there is no dose of radiation too small to produce no increase at all in mutation frequency. That is to say, any dose of radiation, regardless of how small, probably increases the frequency of mutation. At exceedingly low doses of course, the increase in frequency will be very small—almost small enough to be at the limits of detection. It is this fact that leads to difficulty in experimentally demonstrating increases in mutations after exposure to very small amounts of radiation.

It is not, however, unreasonable to expect any dose of radiation to have an effect on the genes. [3,4] So long as enough energy is available to ionize the bases of the DNA chains (and, of course, any ionizing particle can ionize any atom) or to produce chemical mutagens, there will be a probability of producing gene mutations. Doses as low as 5 R given in a single exposure to the gametes of members of both sexes of fruit flies produce mutations at a rate linearly proportional to the effects of 1000 R and 2000 R.[3] The linear relationship over such a wide range of doses makes tenable the assumption that the same linear relationship will also hold in the small range between 5 R and zero. Nevertheless, however reasonable, this does remain an assumption.

The production of mutations by irradiation *appears* independent of the rate at which the radiation is given[4-8] or of whether a dose of radiation is given all at once — without interruptions — or interrupted, in fractions.[9,10] Such a relationship is in good agreement with the nature of gene mutations, which are *permanent* changes in the DNA. Any dose of radiation, irrespective of how given, will produce the same total number of changes in DNA. But there is evidence for repair of changes in DNA at low dose-rates. A dose-rate influence is therefore possible (Section 25.4). *Permanent* changes produced in any fraction of dose accumulate with those produced in any other fraction. This is not to say that mutations are irreversible. Some mutations can be and are reversed and the gene is restored to its original form. But the back-mutation is itself a mutation, a bona-fide change in the DNA.

**15.10   Protection for the Human Population.**   Ionizing radiation is so valuable a tool in so many efforts that its continued and increasing use is foreordained. In medicine and dentistry it is indispensable; in industry its value increases daily; in research the contributions that can be made with its use are difficult to overestimate. It is inevitable, therefore, that greater and greater segments of the human population will, in time to come, be placed under risk of radiation exposure. Since it is known that exposure to radiation can, through its potent mutagenic properties, seriously weaken the population, its increasing use carries with it an obligation to protect the population — in particular, future populations — against this happening. Because every mutation (except those rare beneficial ones) brought into a population eventually results on the average in the death of one individual (Section 15.7), this fact should be carefully weighed whenever any mutagen is used.

At present nothing is known which can selectively reverse radiation-induced mutations. Neither is anything known which can completely prevent radiation from changing DNA. These areas, of course, are and should be ones for intense research, because, in the last analysis, protection against radiation and damaging mutations will reside in the ability to bring about the repair DNA or to prevent the occurrence of the mutational change in the first place.

There are, however, some things which can be done at present to assure that the minimum of mutations will be introduced into populations of living things. Medically, radiation should be used only when it is *necessary*. It is not enough to limit its employment to those cases in which it is useful or helpful but, more strictly, only to those in which its employment is a necessity. If another, non-mutagenic procedure will give the desired information (in the case of a diagnostic test) or results (in the case in which it is used therapeutically), that is the procedure that should be employed. When radiation is used, strenuous effort should be made to limit the exposure only to that part of the body in which it is needed. Always, under every possible circumstance, it is imperative to spare the genitals any radiation exposure. This is often very simple to do, and can take only a few seconds. It will be time well invested. Lead screening devices placed between the gonads and the beam of radiation will protect them. During many procedures they can be unirradiated. In this way there is no possibility of adding mutant individuals to the *population* during those procedures.

The medical user of radiation should always be conscious of how much of the body is exposed during any given procedure. Radiation cannot be seen and, without care, larger segments of the body than is necessary or intended can be irradiated. This can be avoided simply. A beam of visible light originating from the same source as the radiation can be directed at the patient before the radiation is used. The parts of the body illuminated will be those irradiated. Corrections or accommodations can then be made to limit radiation exposure only to the necessary areas.

There is, of course, some genetic risk to the patient during radiation procedures, but there can be a far greater risk to the operators of the radiation equipment—those who give the radiation dose. Usually, a patient is exposed once or, at most, a few times. But an x-ray technician or a radiologist may be exposed every day of his working life. Of course, *any* avoidable exposure should be shunned. Radiation should be given by remote control from behind a protective shield. The instrument delivering radiation should be operated by competent personnel. It should be adequately shielded so as to deliver its beam, with as little scattering as possible, in the direction of or at the object desired. It should be checked frequently to evalutate its continued proper operation.

Finally, personnel should wear detection devices (film badges, for example) at all times to record how much, if any, radiation is being absorbed by their bodies. The knowledge of how much radiation is absorbed in any given time period can give an incentive to improving the physical setup until none or nearly none is given to personnel.

Industrially, the same rules apply. Only the absolute minimum of exposure to radiation should be the acceptable standard. Effort should be continuously expended to reduce the minimum even further.

Exposure of the world's population due to testing of nuclear weapons in the atmosphere, however, cannot be stopped without discontinuing these tests. Since the signing of a treaty in 1963, testing in the atmosphere by many nations has stopped and there has been an important decline in the background. But not every nation attempting to develop nuclear weapons has agreed to discontinue atmospheric testing and, in fact, such tests continue. If they are not stopped the atmospheric burden of radiation will again rise, the mutational frequency will increase, and the unfortunate effects of this increase will encumber all men, now and for many years to come. Against this kind of thing, there is no protection.

## SUMMARY

1. Ionizing radiation increases the frequency of mutations. The same mutations are produced as occur spontaneously; their appearance is more frequent.
2. Mutations are produced by bringing about changes in base sequences in DNA chains. This may be accomplished by base ionization, permitting "forbidden pair" production, by base-change, or base-deletion, brought about either by ionization or free-radical interactions.
3. Mutational frequency increases with increasing LET. It reaches a peak and diminshes thereafter.
4. Except for very rare cases all mutations have a detrimental effect.
5. Exposure of populations to ionizing radiation is detrimental to the population.
6. Mutational frequency increases linearly with dose of radiation and is independent of dose-rate.

### Text References

1. Muller, H. J.: Artificial transmutation of the gene, Science 66, 84-87 (1948).
2. Mortimer, R., Brustad, T., and Cormack, D. V.: Influence of linear energy transfer and oxygen tension on the effectiveness of ionizing radiation for the induction of mutations and lethality in Saccharomyces cerevisiae, Radiation Research 26 (4), 465-481 (1965).
3. Glass, H. Bentley, and Ritterhoff, R. K.: Mutagenic effect of a 5-R dose of x-rays in Drosophila melanogaster, Science 133, 1366 (1961).
4. Uphoff, D. E., and Stern, C.: The genetic effects of low-intensity irradiation, Science 109, 609-610 (1949).
5. Muller, H. J.: The mechanism of structural change in the chromosomes of Drosophila, Journal of Genetics Suppl., pp. 221-222 (1941).
6. Muller, H. J.: An analysis of the process of structural change in chromosomes of Drosophila, Journal of Genetics 40, 1-66 (1940).
7. Ray-Chandhuri, S. P.: The validity of the Bunsen-Roscoe law in the production of mutations by radiation of extremely low intensity, Journal of Genetics Suppl., p. 246 (1941).

8.  Spencer, W. P., and Stern, C.: Experiments to test the validity of the linear R-dose/mutation frequency relation in *Drosophila* at low dosage, Genetics *33*, 43-74 (1948).
9.  Patterson, J. T.: Continuous versus interrupted irradiation and the rate of mutation in *Drosophila*, Biological Bulletin *61*, 133-138 (1931).
10. Tirnofeeff-Ressovsky, N. W., and Zimmer, K. G.: Strahlengenetische Zeitfaktorversuche au *Drosophila melanogaster*. Strahlentherapie *53*, 134-138 (1935).

# 16

## The Effect on

## Transmission of the Genetic Material:

## Chromosome Structure

**16.1 Effects of Ionizing Radiation upon the Structure of the Chromosome.** Alteration of the structure of chromosomes brings about effects on the expression of the genetic material of a greater order than those caused by point chemical changes within the genes themselves (structural changes in DNA). An alteration in the structure of a chromosome will bring about permanent changes in the linear order of the genes on that chromosome, and, in cases where more than one chromosome is involved, can even influence the distribution of the genes among the chromosomes in a given nucleus. Such structural changes are reproduced at mitosis and meiosis so that they are heritable, both by succeeding generations of cells (mitosis) and individuals (meiosis).

**16.2 Chromosome Breakage.** The important first step in the production of structural alterations in chromosomes by ionizing radiation is breakage of the chromosome. Chromosome threads are broken either by the passage through them of an ionizing particle or by an attack upon them by the products of irradiated cellular material—usually of irradiated water. But a severed or broken end has the important property or capability of joining with and *adhering* to any other fractured or broken end that it happens to meet—usually with the *first* one it chances to encounter. When the broken ends do meet, the adhesion of the fragments causes continuous chromosomal threads again to be formed—threads capable of reproducing themselves in exactly the same way as does any intact chromosome. When a chromosome arm has been broken, it most frequently rejoins the piece from which it has been broken. This is true because the segments usually lie very close together after a break, and each is, predictably, the first broken end either is likely to encounter. They can—and do—heal, so that the recombination of the broken ends results in a thread that is exactly the same as the original, unbroken one (Figure 16.1). This process—that of reconstituting the original chromosome after a break—is called "restitution."

Whether restitution of the two broken ends of the same chromosome takes place may be dependent—at least in part—upon the stage of the cell's division cycle in which a break takes place. The longer a break remains open or unhealed, the greater is the chance that the broken ends of the same chromosome will not heal with each other.[1] A broken end can join, after a relatively short time, with the broken end of another chromosome (provided that more than one chromosome in the same nucleus is broken), but it is also possible for fragments to remain uncoupled for long periods of time[2,3] or even to remain open indefinitely. Dewey and Humphrey report that chromosome breaks

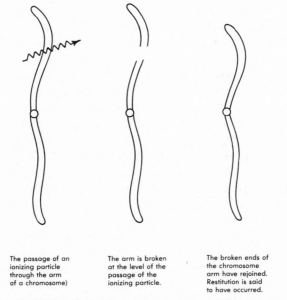

| The passage of an ionizing particle through the arm of a chromosome) | The arm is broken at the level of the passage of the ionizing particle. | The broken ends of the chromosome arm have rejoined. Restitution is said to have occurred. |

**Figure 16.1.** Diagrammatic representation of the reconstitution of a chromosome, following a break in that chromosome, which precisely restores the chromosome to its original unbroken state. The process is called "restitution."

brought about by irradiation in the cells of hamsters remain open for less than five minutes, if irradiation is given in the $G_1$ phase, that is, the phase just before DNA synthesis in the cell's life cycle. However, the same kinds of breaks remain open for *more* than sixty minutes if irradiation is carried out when the cells are in the S phase, in DNA synthesis itself.[4,5]

It has also been suggested, although not yet proved, that there is a site or location within the nucleus, one that is *not* part of the chromosomes, which is in some way involved in the restitution of breaks in chromosomes.[5] If this site is damaged by irradiation, fewer chromosome breaks heal and restitution will go on at a lower rate than might occur if the site were spared.

**16.3  The Results of Chromosome Breakage.**  The consequences to the cell of chromosome breakage, except when restitution occurs, are usually very serious. Exactly what happens and how serious the consequences will be depends upon (1) how many chromosomes in any given cell are broken, (2) how many breaks occur in any given chromosome in that cell, and (3) how many breaks occur within any given arm of a chromosome. These factors are, in turn, dependent upon the dose of radiation given and upon the LET of the radiation that is used.

**16.4  Single Breaks in One Chromosome.**  The most serious consequence of a single break occurring in an arm of a chromosome is the possibility of permanent loss, on the part of the broken end, of its attachment to the rest of the chromosome and, consequently, its loss of attachment to the spindle. *The loss of the attachment to the spindle of either a chromosome, or any part of a chromosome, will ultimately result in an error in the transmission of the genetic material at cell division.* The most serious consequences of a single break in a chromosome, then, do not usually occur in the cell in which the break is experienced; the loss of the attachment to the spindle does not seriously impair the function of the genes in a non-dividing, "resting" cell. The consequences will be reserved for the daughters of this cell, those daughters which will be formed after division.

If, after a break, restitution fails to occur *before* the synthesis of DNA and chromosome replication take place, at the proper time for replication both broken fragments of the strand will reproduce themselves (Figure 16.2).

The newly synthesized chromosomal strand will have a broken or detached end just as the mother strand had. In many cases, *both* the broken ends will have the property of adhesion. Since they are so very close together, contact between them is very likely to occur. When (and if) it does, they fuse. The results are called *isochromosomes,* that is, threads consisting of two identical parts which are joined so that each forms a mirror-image of the other (Figure 16.3).

If the fragments have no centromere, they are called *acentric.* Those provided with a centromere are called *centric.* Often *isochromosomes* will have more than one centromere. Two are not uncommon (these are called *dicentrics*) and more are possible.

It is clear that, during mitosis (or even meiosis, should this have happened then), the acentric fragment will not be able to get on the spindle. At anaphase it will not move and at telophase it will be excluded from the re-forming nucleus. Usually, it will be in the cytoplasm of one of the two daughter cells; its location depends exclusively upon the side of the division plane on which it happens to lie during division of cytoplasm. The consequence of these events is an error in the transmission of the genetic material at mitosis: one daughter cell receives *more* than the 2n number of chromosomes and genes (it will be the daughter that receives the acentric fragment, which has, of course, doubled but not divided), and the other will

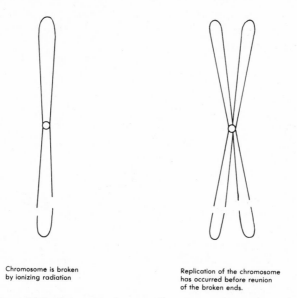

Chromosome is broken
by ionizing radiation

Replication of the chromosome
has occurred before reunion
of the broken ends.

**Figure 16.2.** Schematic drawing showing a single break in the arm of a chromosome that has failed to undergo reunion and restitution before chromosomal replication. The broken fragment, like the continuous remnant, has reproduced itself.

receive *less* than the 2n number. The *number* of genes lost to the one daughter and possessed in duplicate by the other depends merely upon the level at which the original break in the chromosome occurred.

But the fate of the acentric fragment will not be the only error in transmission of genes that occurs here. At metaphase of mitosis the two centromeres of the dicentric fragment will be oriented to opposite poles, and, at anaphase, these centromeres will move toward their respective poles. The joined ends of the isochromosome, however, remain fused. The isochromosome is stretched, under tension, between the two separating masses of chromosomes. Such a configuration is called an *anaphase bridge* (Figure 16.4).

The dicentric isochromosome may fail to enter one or the other or even both daughter nuclei. If that happens, the nucleus (or nuclei) that lacks this isochromosome will be deficient for the genes that it carries. Should it happen that one nucleus fails to get both the dicentric and the acentric pieces, it will, of course, be deficient for the genes on the entire chromosome. It is also possible for the dicentric, under tension at anaphase, to break again (although not necessarily at the level of the original break). The fragments will be drawn into their respective daughter nuclei where, after duplication for the next division, the ends may heal and they may again form a dicentric isochromosome. At the next anaphase a bridge may again form and the process will start once more. Ultimately the entire chromosome or a major part of it will be lost.

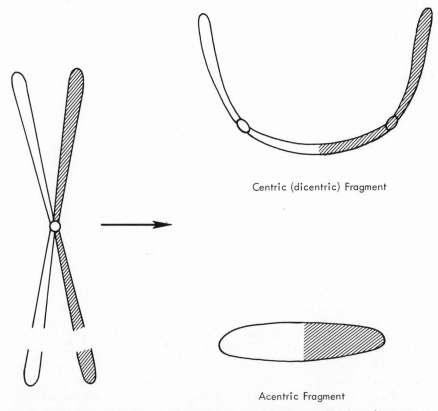

Centric (dicentric) Fragment

Acentric Fragment

**Figure 16.3.** Drawing showing a representation of the fusion of broken chromosome arms to form *isochromosomes*. Such fusion must take place *after* DNA synthesis and chromosome replication occur. The result, in this case, is two isochromosomes, a centric and an acentric fragment, each of which is composed of two identical parts. After division of the centromere at metaphase the centric fragment will, of course, be *dicentric*.

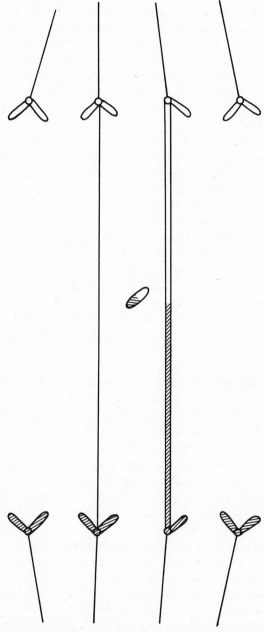

**Figure 16.4.**   "Bridging" by a dicentric isochromosome at anaphase. Note that the acentric piece is not on the spindle and has not moved.

The consequence of a single break in a chromosome, one that does not restitue, is a very large, permanent, deviation from the status quo. There will be genetic deficiency in the cell which fails to inherit the acentric isochromosome; the degree of the deficiency depends on the number of genes in the fragment. And, when the daughter that does inherit the acentric fragment undergoes division, the fragment again cannot attach to the spindle. Once again only one daughter of *this* division inherits the acentric isochromosome. In time this isochromosome will be extruded and lost altogether; its genes will be permanently lost.

If enough genes, or the right genes, are lost, the deviation from the status quo can be so great that cells in which this happens cannot live. But even if they should survive and be able to reproduce, they will be abnormal. They can give rise to many abnormal daughters, sometimes leading to whole segments of organs or tissues composed of their descendants, of genetically abnormal cells.

If isochromosome formation occurs in the germ line, if it takes place during meiosis in the formation of either sperm or egg, the individual formed from such a gamete is certain to be abnormal. All the cells of its body (for all the cells of any organism are derived ultimately from the gametes) will inherit a deficiency of genes. The metabolic functions directed by those genes will be missing. If enough genes are deleted, the individual may not survive embryonic life.

**16.5  Single Breaks in Separate Chromosomes.**  If two chromosomes within a single nucleus sustain a break, both may behave exactly as already described. That is, restitution of one or both breaks may take place, or isochromosome formation giving one centric and one acentric piece may result in either one or both of the broken chromosomes. But when two separate chromosomes within a single nucleus sustain a break, another possibility arises, namely, *rearrangement* of the broken parts. The broken end of one chromosome may unite with the broken end of the other broken chromosome. Such an event is called a *translocation* (Figure 16.5).

If the parts are translocated in such a way as to yield a dicentric and an acentric piece (Figure 16.5, b), the eventual loss of all parts of both chromosomes is inevitable, provided, of course, that the cell in which this has happened subsequently undergoes division. If this cell never divides, none of the parts will be lost (it is the loss of spindle attachment that ultimately causes loss of the genetic material), and the cell is likely to function normally. The mechanics whereby the chromosome is lost are the same as those already described in the previous section for the behavior at cell division of dicentric and acentric isochromosomes.

However, if the centric and acentric fragments of both chromosomes have joined (Figure 16.5, a), there is a different result. Both
isochromosomes have a centromere and can be regularly transmitted
at mitosis *without* loss of the genetic material. The cells that receive

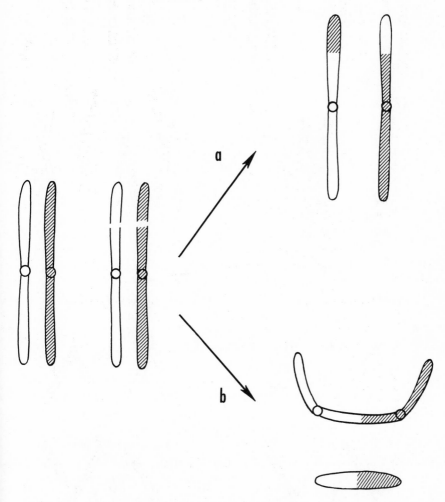

**Figure 16.5.** Schematic drawing illustrating *translocation,* one of the consequences of
the production of a single break in two separate chromosomes. After the two chromosomes are broken, two alternate translocations may take place. In the first (a) the centric
and acentric fragments of each have joined. In the second (b) the two centric fragments
join to form a dicentric union, and the two acentric parts have united to give still another
acentric piece.

them will be viable; they will have been affected by the radiation only
in that the *order of the genes* upon two of their chromosomes will have
been changed. In somatic cells the consequences will be negligible
since the nuclei of these cells will contain the full complement of

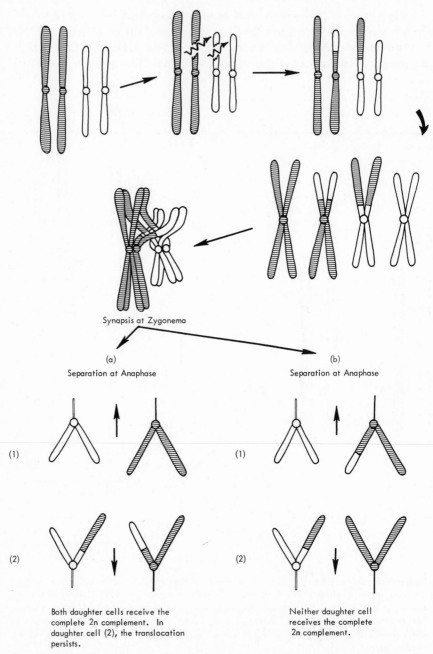

Synapsis at Zygonema

(a)                                                    (b)

Separation at Anaphase                              Separation at Anaphase

(1)                                                    (1)

(2)                                                    (2)

Both daughter cells receive the                    Neither daughter cell
complete 2n complement. In                         receives the complete
daughter cell (2), the translocation               2n complement.
persists.

**Figure 16.6.** Schematic drawing illustrating the possible distribution of chromosomes and genes at the first meiotic anaphase when a translocation of part of the chromosome arms has taken place. If separation takes place as in (a), both daughter cells receive a complete gene complement. If it occurs as in (b), neither receives a complete gene complement; there will be a deficiency as well as a duplication of genes in both daughters.

genes and the balance between them will be as it was before the breakage (the status quo, practically speaking, is unaltered).

However, should such a break and reunion have occurred during maturation of the germ cells (meiosis), the results can be quite damaging. In the prophase of the first meiotic division (at leptonema), *homologous* chromosomes lie side by side in the nucleoplasm. Then, at zygonema, they affect synaptic union (Chapter 14). If there has been a translocation resulting in the formation of two isochromosomes both of which have a centromere (Figure 16.5, a), portions of homologous chromosomes will have to make a kind of accommodation when they pair (Figure 16.6).

Depending entirely upon the separation at anaphase of the first meiotic division, the daughter cells may receive the full chromosome complement (although, as in the parent cell, the translocation will still exist) or daughter cells may be formed, each of which will lack the genes on a portion of one chromosome and possess, in duplicate, those on a portion of another (Figure 16.6).

The movement of particular chromosomes to either pole at anaphase appears dependent on chance. Since this is so, the probability of daughter cells, formed at this division, of receiving either the full genetic complement or the deficiency and duplication (Figure 16.6) is equal; that is, the deficiency and duplication is passed on to one half of the daughters.

If the deficiency is large enough, the individuals that inherit it will not be viable; they probably will die during or just after embryonic development. If the deficiency is small, they may survive into adulthood, but viability will be impaired; their life will be shortened.

Offspring that inherit the full genetic complement, also inherit the translocation. When *their* germ cells begin to undergo meiosis, separation of *their* chromosomes in the first division will be exactly as it is in their parent (Figure 16.6), and, as in the case of the parent, about half the gametes will inherit a gene deficiency. Half of the offspring will be genetically deficient—if the deficiency is grave enough, that half may not be viable at all. The remaining half passes on the translocation so that half of the offspring of each succeeding generation will sustain some detriment, possibly severe enough to be lethal.

This kind of chromosome aberration is responsible for the death of or detriment to very large numbers of individuals. Even after many generations, its effect may be felt, because it may require many generations for the aberration to die out.

It is, of course, possible for the breaks to have taken place in the arms of *homologous* chromosomes and for the broken portions to have either become acentric or, as above, to have formed a mutual translocation. If acentrics are formed, they will not be transmitted at mitosis or meiosis, and the cells resulting from them probably will not be viable. If a mutual translocation occurs, there will be no effect in somatic cells. Should, however, the breaks have occurred at two *different* levels in the arms of the homologous chromosomes (and this, owing to the random nature of radiation interaction, is the most probable event), there will be an effect on cells in meiosis. Gametes will be formed which will either have a deficiency or a duplication of part of a chromosome arm (Figure 16.7).

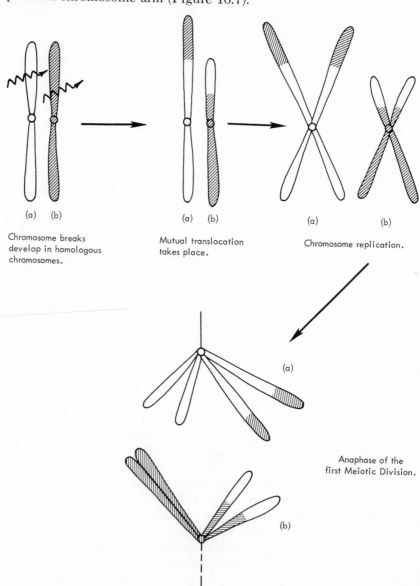

(a)  (b)

Chromosome breaks develop in homologous chromosomes.

(a)  (b)

Mutual translocation takes place.

(a)  (b)

Chromosome replication.

(a)

Anaphase of the first Meiotic Division.

(b)

Anaphase of the Second
Meiotic Division

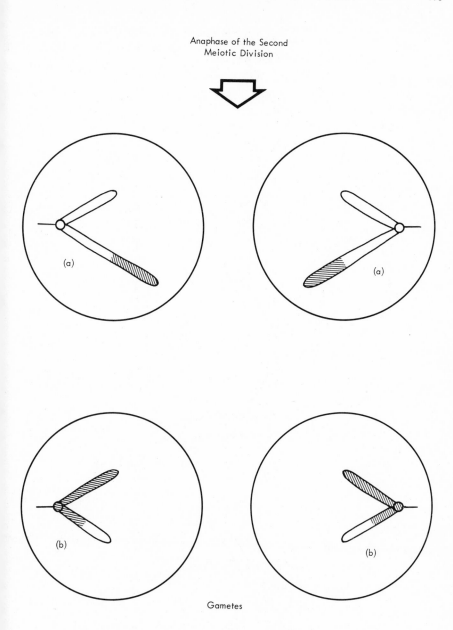

Gametes

**Figure 16.7.** Schematic drawing illustrating the consequences of breaks occurring *at different levels* in the arms of homologous chromosomes in cells of the germ line. Of the gametes formed, half will have a sequence of genes repeated (present in duplicate), while the remaining half is deficient for the same sequence. In the mutual translocation, chromosome (a) has acquired a segment of chromosome (b) which has a duplication of a gene sequence already present in the arm of (a). Chromosome (b) is deficient for the same sequence.

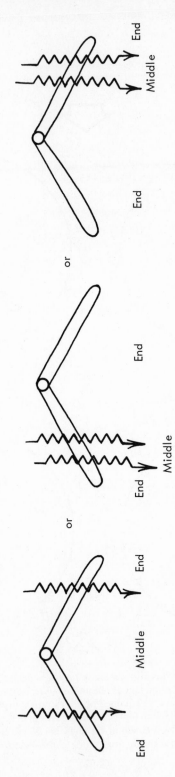

**Figure 16.8.** Schematic representation of the direct consequences of two breaks occurring within the same chromosome. Three fragments are formed.

In any zygote which will result from fertilization by male gametes (if the above are male gametes) or fertilization of female gametes (if they are female gametes) there will be an *imbalance* among its genes: some zygotes will have genes present in an excess; others will lack the same genes. While gene deficiencies almost always result in death (particularly if they are large), duplications do so less often. But any gene imbalance is a departure from the status quo. Duplications will result in improper *dosages* of genes, and an improper balance, within cells, of gene products. Such imbalances are abnormal and can bring about loss of viability and life-shortening. For example, in human beings certain "syndromes" (constellations of signs or symptoms, apparently unrelated but occurring together, which characterize a disease), such as Klinefelter's syndrome and mongolism, are the result of having an *extra* chromosome and the genic imbalance which this brings about.

**16.6   Two Breaks in the Same Chromosome.**   If two breaks occur in the same chromosome the diversity of final effects is greatly enriched. But the immediate result is the formation of three fragments, two end pieces and one piece in the middle (Figure 16.8).

The location of the centromere depends, obviously, on the location of the breaks, but the way the chromosomes reconstitute after this kind of breakage will determine the ultimate effect in the cell (Figure 16.9).

The degree of deviation from the status quo brought about by *deletion* of part of a chromosome will depend, as in the previously described cases, upon the number and importance of the genes lost in the deleted piece. If there are enough of them or if they are important enough, their loss could be lethal to the daughter cell or cells that fail to inherit the deleted piece at mitosis. Even very small deletions, which may not be lethal, result in the loss of genes and can be expected to result in cells or individuals that are grossly abnormal.

If (as in Figure 16.9, b) the centric fragment chances to heal to itself, a circular chromosome will be formed. The remaining fragments may either fuse to form a single acentric piece (Figure 16.9, b), or they remain unfused to yield two acentrics. The consequences, of course, will not be expressed until the cell divides, but at mitosis, the acentric piece or pieces will be lost. As in previously described cases, this alone might be lethal. But, if it were not lethal, the further consequences would depend upon whether or not the "ring" chromosome chanced to twist before healing into a ring. If it did not twist, it would replicate itself and divide normally at mitosis. Should a twist have occurred in the chromosome *before* replication, the resulting circular chromosome would form two interlocking rings and would not, without breaking, be able to separate at anaphase (Figure 16.10).

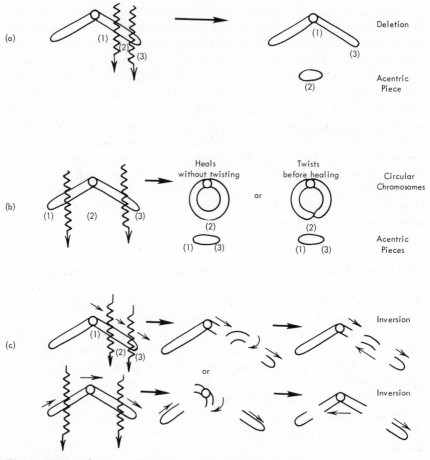

**Figure 16.9.** Schematic illustration of the possible chromosomal recombinations and/or rearrangements following two breaks in the same chromosome.

Non-interlocking circular chromosomes are passed on normally from generation to generation. The cells inheriting them do, of course, lack the genes lost from tips of the chromosome in the acentric pieces, but, if these are dispensable, an abnormal but viable cell or individual will be the result.

Those that interlock cannot be transported to either daughter at division so that those cells, deficient for the whole chromosome (the acentric fragments and the ring), do not survive. These rings may break open and the chromsomes may be transported to daughter cells. Of course, these chromsomes will be genetically deficient.

In time, all individuals bearing ring chromosomes, whether interlocking or not, become extinct. In meiosis, if a ring undergoes crossing-over with its homolog (it does not matter whether the homolog is a ring or not) a dicentric which is incapable of being properly carried to daughter nuclei is inevitably formed. Fewer germ cells capable of producing normal viable offspring are formed by individuals bearing ring chromosomes than by those in whom the chromsomes are normal. There is a reproductive disadvantage which inevitably leads to extinction.

During reunion and healing following two breaks in the same chromosome it is possible for all parts to be successfully incorporated

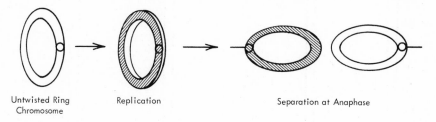

Untwisted Ring        Replication                    Separation at Anaphase
Chromosome

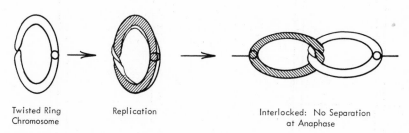

Twisted Ring        Replication            Interlocked: No Separation
Chromosome                                        at Anaphase

**Figure 16.10.**   Schematic drawing illustrating replication and anaphase movement of twisted and untwisted circular chromosomes. Twisted ring structures cannot separate at anaphase, for, during replication, two interlocking rings will have formed.

into the reconstituted chromosome. In the process, however, the linear sequence of the genes on the chromosome may have been changed. Such a phenomenon is called *inversion* (Figure 16.9,c). Because all elements of the chromosome are present in the cell following an inversion, and because all these elements are provided with a centromere so that attachment to the spindle is possible, inversions do not produce change or damage in somatic cells that inherit them. At meiosis, however, if crossing-over occurs *within* the inverted region of the chromosome, two chromosomal arms will be formed, one with a segment missing and one possessing the same segment in duplicate (Figure 16.11).

As in all the previously discussed cases, the result of deletion and duplication arising from inversion is genetically imbalanced offspring. These will be abnormal and will have their viability impaired. The number of individuals passing on the imbalance will become smaller and smaller until, in time, these individuals become extinct.

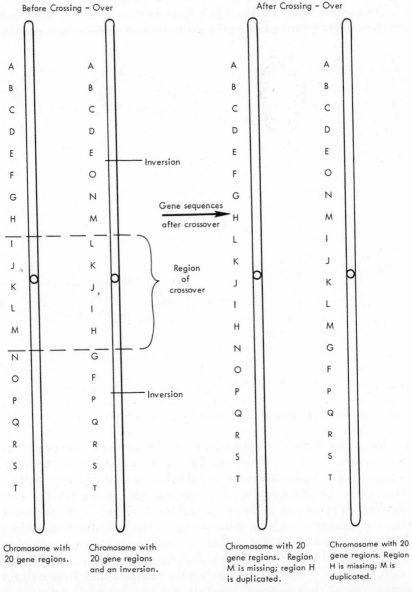

**Figure 16.11.** Schematic representation of the inequality in the distribution of genes to homologous chromosomes when crossing-over takes place within an inverted area. Sequences of genes are lost; others are present in duplicate.

**16.7  Breaks Resulting in Rearrangements of Greater Diversity.**  As the number of breaks in the chromosomes in a single nucleus increases, so will the diversity and complexity of the structural rearrangements. These rearrangements will, however, be combinations of those already described. For example, if three or more breaks occur in two chromosomes it is possible for mutual translocations *and* inversion to occur; insertions also may occur (a fragment is *inserted* between two fragments of a chromosome) as well as many other rearrangements. The greater number of breaks, the greater is the probability of genetic imbalance, and the greater the damage from radiation.

**16.8  The Relationship to LET.**  The production of chromosome aberrations by ionizing radiation is dependent, in addition to the physiologic state of the cells involved,[6-10] upon the wavelength or energy of the incident radiations.[11,12] Generally speaking, high-energy radiations (radiations of low LET) are less efficient for breaking chromosomes than are low-energy radiations.[12] The differences in efficiency do not reflect any real differences among the radiations themselves but only in the amount of energy that the radiations transfer in any given volume of matter. When different radiations with similar and dissimilar linear energy transfer properties were compared with respect to the production of chromosome aberrations, it was shown that the yield of aberrations is dependent upon LET; radiations of similar LET gave similar yields while those of different LET gave different yields.[13]

It is dangerous (with the present state of knowledge), however, to make too much of the relationship between the relative effectiveness of radiations of differing LET for producing chromosome breaks and aberrations. The picture is not clear—there are several complicating factors. LET values themselves for a particular type of radiation are not always a single function; they may cover a wide spectrum. Since this is the case, it may be expected that radiations of high *average* LET will have a component of lower LET. And, of course, the reverse of this statement will also be true. Comparisons of the number of chromosome aberrations produced by radiations of high and low *average* LET respectively cannot be straightforward since neither radiation will be "pure" with respect to LET.

Beyond this complication, however, is the fact that some of the energy of even the fastest, most energetic electrons (those with the lowest LET) is dissipated in the form of slow secondary electrons. These secondary electrons (delta rays) could have LET values in a high range, a range capable of producing chromosome aberrations in numbers not anticipated when predicted from the LET of the primary ionizing particle.

Finally, in comparisons of radiations of high and low LET for the production of any biologic end-point, the presence of oxygen and the amount in which this element is present will be of critical importance. This is, of course, as true in the production of chromosome aberrations by ionizing radiation as it is for any other end-point. The biologic effects of radiations of high LET (alpha particles, for example) are nearly independent of any enhancement by oxygen. But the efficiency of sparsely ionizing radiation for producing chromosome aberrations will be altered even by very small changes in cellular oxygen tension.[14-20]

Generally speaking, however, when all factors are accounted for, it may be properly anticipated that the relative effectiveness of radiations for producing chromosomal aberrations will increase with increasing LET. A maximum effectiveness should be reached, and at very high LET the efficiency may be expected to diminish. This is so because, as LET increases, more energy (ionizations) is deposited in any given area. There is a high probability of a particle with high LET passing through a chromosome, breaking that chromosome. At the same time, however, as LET values increase, the energy of particles is quickly expended (the particles interact so frequently that they come to rest after moving very short distances) so that the probability of moving any great distance through tissues and in cells and of passing through a chromosome thread begins to *decrease.* When very high LET values are reached, particles come to rest so quickly that there is only a small chance that they will traverse a chromosome. If one does, however, it will almost certainly break the chromosome.

**16.9  Dose, Dose-Rate, Dose-Fractionation.** The production of chromosome aberrations by ionizing radiation is related to both the dose of radiation given and the time taken to administer the dose. It was shown early[21-24] that, using x ray as the source of radiation, simple aberrations (one break in one chromosome) increase linearly with increasing dose (that is, each increment of dose produces about the same number of such aberrations as any previous increment) and that the number of these aberrations is unaffected by changing the dose-rate or by splitting the total dose into fractions. Such aberrations have been called "one-hit" aberrations to contrast them with aberrations of greater complexity which can occur only after more than one break has been produced in a chromosome (see Section 16.5). The linear relationship to dose and independence of the aberrations from dose-rate or fractionation have led to the conclusion that chromosome breaks occur independently of one another (the existence of one break neither increases nor decreases the probability of another occurring).

But a linear relationship with dosage of x ray does not occur with "two-hit" aberrations—those resulting in chromosome dicentrics and rings. In these cases, if two doses of x radiation are given over the same period of time, and if this period of time is relatively short, the appearance of these types of aberrations increases in proportion to the *square* of the dose. This is to be expected on the basis of the random nature of energy exchange from x radiation. A beam of x ray will enter the nucleus, setting off secondary electrons which will move through the nucleus in many different directions (the angles at which electrons are ejected from atoms relative to the direction of propagation of an x ray may be very wide) so that there will be a fairly homogeneous distribution of electrons in the nucleus. Under circumstances such as these there is a greater probability of many chromosomes sustaining a single break (the number of these increases linearly with dose) than of a few chromosomes sustaining several breaks.

More densely ionizing particles, such as fast neutrons (in soft tissue fast neutrons produce *protons*, a densely ionizing particle) and alpha particles, produce any kind of aberration, simple or complex, independent of intensity and in a more nearly linear relationship with dose. Such behavior indicates (1) that not *all* such breaks are independently produced and (2) that the exchange of energy from these particles is not as randomly distributed in matter (in this case, cell nuclei) as is that of x ray. The latter is true; the trajectory of alpha particles and protons is quite straight, and the exchange of their energy will occur within a rather discrete volume, rather more discrete than that of x ray.

The rate at which any given dose of radiation is delivered to the nucleus of a cell will be of fundamental importance to the number of *complex* aberrations eventually produced. In order for *any* kind of complex chromosome aberration to occur, it is first necessary for two breaks (whether in one or more chromosomes) to be open at the same time. Broken ends do, of course, restitute, and, if radiation is delivered at a very slow rate, there will be time for some of the breaks to undergo restitution before another break can occur. The net effect on the chromosomes when radiation is delivered very slowly is relatively few aberrations of any kind; in particular, fewer of the complex ones. The same total dose, however, given more rapidly will have the effect of breaking several chromosomes at once or at nearly the same time, increasing the probability of interchange among the fragments.

**16.10 The Significance of the Stage in the Cell Cycle.** Both the number of chromosome aberrations and the kind of abberations produced by exposure to radiation are dependent, in part at least, upon the stage in the cell cycle in which cells are irradiated.[25,26] In terms of chromosome damage, the DNA *post-synthetic stage* ($G_2$) is more radiosensitive than either the DNA synthesis stage itself (S) or ($G_1$) the pre-synthetic stage.[25] Smaller amounts of ionizing radiation bring about chromosome damage in $G_2$ than either in S or $G_1$. Further, the *kind* of aberrations produced is dependent upon the stage in the cell cycle in which radiation is given.[26] If cells are irradiated in $G_1$, many complex aberrations (dicentric and ring chromosomes) are seen as well as some of the simple aberrations. If cells are irradiated in either S or $G_2$, only simple aberrations are detected.

Observations like these may give a clue to the structure of the chromosome. While chromosomes appear (in the stages of the cell cycle where they may be stained and visualized) as single units, they may actually be made up of two subunits. These may be jointed in $G_1$ but might separate at the very end of the phase or as S begins. If this is so, then breaks produced in chromosomes in $G_1$ would be expected to produce aberrations of entire chromosomes (dicentrics, rings) while breaks produced in S or $G_2$, when the subunits are separate, may occur in only *one* of these subunits, resulting in simpler defects in only a part of a chromosome.

While there is a difference, then, in the "radiosensitivity" of chromosomes which is dependent on the time in the cell cycle at which the chromosomes are irradiated, it must also be said that the chromosomes are sensitive to the induction of breaks and their resultant aberrations at any stage in the cycle. The chromosomes are never immune to radiation damage.

**16.11 The Production of Chromosome Aberrations in Man.** The chromosomes of the cells of man, like those of all living things, are broken by ionizing radiation. They can restitute or form unions which are aberrant. The doses of radiation necessary to elicit this result need not be high. Aberrations can and have been detected in human beings following exposure to diagnostic or therapeutic radiation.[27-34] All have been seen in cells of blood drawn at varying times after an exposure to radiation and cultured *in vitro*. But, it should not be concluded from this that cells of tissues other than blood are not affected in this way. Blood is the only tissue that has yielded relatively easily to methods of analysis needed to determine whether or not aberrations have been produced.

It seems certain now that the chromosome abnormalities detected in blood following radiation therapy (for cancer as well as other disease states) are, in fact, the result of irradiation of formed elements of the blood (bone marrow). The picture, however, is not yet as clear with respect to diagnostic radiation. Aberrations have been detected in blood cells after diagnostic radiation,[29] but not enough data are available to make certain whether these are, in fact, the result of the irradiation. While that is the indication, more work must be done before the picture will be clear.

**16.12  The Significance of Chromosome Aberrations.**  The production of chromosome aberrations by ionizing radiation is of enormous importance both to the individual in which it occurs and to the population in which an aberration-bearing individual lives. The loss of a portion of a chromosome is often lethal to the cell in which it happens. If aberrations arise among only a few of the *somatic* cells within an individual, the consequences to that individual can be insignificant. But, if aberrations arise among large numbers of cells, many may, at or after division, die. For the tissues in which this is happening, the sudden loss of a large number of cells is a serious situation.

However, if the aberration involves only a small portion of a chromosome (for example, a very small segment is deleted), the cell in which this occurs may not die, but it will behave as if it sustained a genetic mutation. The situation is very similar to one in which the deleted genes, instead of having been deleted, had undergone a mutation in which their function had been lost. The change or loss of function is heritable and will be passed on to all the affected cell's descendants. Furthermore, as in the case of mutation, environmental and population pressures will eventually cause the small deletion to become extinct.

Chromosome aberrations occurring in cells of the germ line result in genic imbalances that will either be immediately lethal for individuals inheriting them or will produce offspring ill-equipped for life. For these offspring, minor illnesses and accidents of life become serious hazards, even threatening their very existence. Like those bearing genetic mutations they are at a disadvantage and cannot successfully compete with the "normal" members of their species. Unlike genetic mutants, however, the aberration-bearing individual *usually* has a more marked deviation from the genetic status quo and is even less able to compete for its necessities. Such individuals will tend to become extinct even more quickly than mutants. But, for the period of time that they are members of the population they are a burden upon it. The addition of individuals to the population ill-equipped to survive in the environment will, if such individuals are introduced in sufficient numbers, undermine the population as a whole and cause it to shrink, possibly even to undergo extinction, from the pressures upon it generated by other species and populations.

The warnings against the unnecessary exposure of the human population to ionizing radiation expressed with regard to genetic mutations obtains no less emphatically in the case of chromosome aberrations. The precautions taken to avoid *unnecessary* exposure are just as important. Medically and industrially, as few people as possible should be exposed. In those who *must* be exposed, *whenever possible* exposure of the gonads should be avoided.

## SUMMARY

1.  Ionizing radiation can, either by direct or indirect action, break chromosomes. Such a break may restitute, causing no change, but, on the other hand, structural rearrangements of chromosomes and even loss from cells of parts of as well as whole chromosomes may ensue following a break.
2.  Loss of chromosomes or of chromosome fragments produces sharp deviations from the cellular status quo. Even the loss of very small pieces of chromosomes is damaging to the cells in which it happens, and the loss of larger ones is serious enough to bring about cell death within a few cell generations.
3.  The production of chromosome breaks varies with dose of radiation, LET, and stage in the cell life cycle.
4.  Chromosome aberrations are produced in many cells during radiation therapy and may occur following radiation exposure as part of diagnostic tests.

## Text References

1.  Evans, H. J.: Chromosome aberrations induced by ionizing radiation, International Review of Cytology *13*, 221-321 (1962).
2.  Bishop, C. J.: Differential x-ray sensitivity of *Tradescantia* chromosomes during the mitotic cycle, Genetics *35*, 175-187 (1950).
3.  Wolff, S.: in *Radiation Protection and Recovery*, vol. 7. p. 157. A. Hollaender (ed). Pergamon Press, New York, 1960.
4.  Dewey, W. C., and Humphrey, R. M.: Restitution of radiation-induced chromosomal damage in Chinese hamster cells related to the cell's life cycle, Experimental Cell Research *35*, 262-276 (1964).
5.  Dewey, W. C., Humphrey, R. M., and Jones, B. A.: Comparisons of tritiated thymidine, tritiated water and cobalt 60 gamma rays in inducing chromosomal aberrations, Radiation Research *24*, 214-237 (1965).
6.  Alexander, M. L., and Stone, W. S.: Radiation damage in the developing germ cells of *Drosophila virilis*. Proceedings of the National Academy of Sciences *41*, 1046-1057 (1955).
7.  Alexander, M. L.: Dominant lethal damage in meiotic and spermatogonial cells of *Drosophila virilis* with 22 Mv x-ray and 200 kv x-ray. Radiation Research *9:*85 (1958).
8.  Alexander, M. L.: Dominant lethal and translocation damage in the immature germ cells of *Drosophila virilis* from fast neutrons, Genetics *41*, 631-632 (1956).

9. Alexander, M.L.: Radiation damage in the developing germ cells of *Drosophila virilis* from fast neutron treatment, Genetics 43, 458-469 (1958).

10. Alexander, M. L.: Biological damage in developing germ cells of *Drosophila virilis* in oxygen and nitrogen with 14 Mev neutrons, Proceedings of the National Academy of Sciences 44, 1217-1228 (1958).

11. Kirby-Smith, J. S., and Daniels, D. S.: The relative effect of x-rays, gamma rays and beta rays on chromosomal breakage in *Tradescantia,* Genetics 38, 375-388 (1953).

12. Arnason, T. J., and Morrison, M.: A comparison of the effectiveness of radiations of different energies in producing chromsome breaks, Radiation Research 2, 91-95 (1955).

13. Giles, N. H., and Tobias, C. A.: Effect of linear energy transfer on radiation-induced chromsome aberrations in *Tradescantia* Microspores, Science 120, 993-994 (1954).

14. Thoday, J. M., and Read, J.: Effect of oxygen on the frequency of chromosome aberrations produced by alpha rays, Nature 163, 133-134 (1949).

15. Giles, N. H., Jr., and Riley, N. P.: The effect of oxygen on the frequency of x-ray induced chromosomal rearrangements in *Tradescantia* microspores, Proceedings of the National Academy of Sciences 35, 640-646 (1949).

16. Giles, N. H., Jr., and Riley, N. P.: Studies on the mechanism of the oxygen effect on the radiosensitivity of *Tradescantia* chromosomes, Proceedings of the National Academy of Sciences, 36, 337-344 (1950).

17. Giles, N. H., Jr., and Beatty, A. V.: The effect of x-irradiation in oxygen and in hydrogen at normal and positive pressures on chromosome aberration frequency in *Tradescantia* microspores, Science 112, 643-645 (1950).

18. Conger, A. D.: The effect of oxygen on the radiosensitivity of mammalian cells, Radiology 66, 63-69 (1956).

19. Evans, H. J.: The relative biological efficiency of single doses of fast neutrons and gamma rays on *Vicia faba* roots and the effect of oxygen. Pt. II. Chromosome damage and the production of micronuclei, International Journal of Radiation Biology 1, 216-229 (1959).

20. Hornsey, S.: The effect of oxygen on the sensitivity of mammalian tumour cells to neutrons and x-rays, International Journal of Radiation Biology 2, 37-44 (1960).

21. Sax, K.: Chromosome aberrations induced by x-rays, Genetics 23, 494-516 (1938).

22. Sax, K.: The time factor in x-ray production of chromosome aberrations, Proceedings of the National Academy of Sciences 25, 225-233 (1939).

23. Sax, K.: An analysis of x-ray induced chromosomal aberrations in *Tradescantia,* Genetics 25, 41-68 (1940).

24. Sax, K.: Types and frequencies of chromosomal aberrations induced by x-rays, Cold Spring Harbor Symposium on Quantitative Biology 9, 93-103 (1941).

25. Hsu, T. C., Dewey, W. C., and Humphrey, R. M.: Radiosensitivity of cells of Chinese hamster *in vitro* in relation to the cell cycle, Experimental Cell Research 27, 441-452 (1962).

26. Dewey, W. C., Humphrey, R. M., and Sedita, B. A.: Cell cycle kinetics and radiation-induced chromosomal aberrations studied in oxygen. Pt. II. Chromosome damage and the production of micronuclei, (1966).

27. Tough, I. M., Buckton, K. E., Baikie, A. G., and Court-Brown, W. M.: X-ray-induced chromosome damage in man, Lancet 2, 849-851 (1960).

28. Boyd, E., Buckanan, W. W., and Lenox, B.: Damage to chromosomes by therapeutic radioiodine, Lancet 1, 977-978 (1961).

29. Stewart, J. S. S., and Sanderson, A. R.: Chromosomal aberrations after diagnostic x-irradiation, Lancet 1, 978-979 (1961).

30. Warren, S., Meisner, L, and Amarose, A. P.: Chromosomal abnormalities induced by therapeutic radiation, American Journal of Pathology 43, 25a-26a (1963).

31.  Bender, M. A.: Induced aberrations in human chromosomes, American Journal of Pathology *43*, 26a (1963).
32.  Amarose, A. P.: Chromosomal patterns in cancer patients during treatment, New York Journal of Medicine *64*, 2407-2413 (1964).
33.  Amarose, A. P., and Baxter, D. H.: Chromosomal changes following surgery and radiotherapy in patients with pelvic cancer. Obstetrics and Gynecology *25*, 828-843 (1965).
34.  Nasjleti, C. E., Walden, J. M., and Spencer, H. H.: Polyploidization and aberrations of human chromosomes induced *in vitro* and *in vivo* with ionizing radiations, Journal of Nuclear Medicine *7*, 159-176 (1966).

# 17

## The Effect on the Transmission of

## the Genetic Material:

## The Mitotic Apparatus

**17.1   Introduction.**   Ionizing radiation interferes with the normal, orderly process of cell division. In fact, interference with cell division is the most immediate, conspicuous effect of ionizing radiation on the *transmission* of the genetic material. The effect appears to be on part of the mitotic apparatus, that is, upon the centromeres, the regions of attachment of the chromosomes to the spindle.

**17.2   Inhibition of Mitosis.**   All ionizing radiations have the effect of inhibiting mitosis. It is a property they share in common with ultraviolet radiation as well as with many chemical mutagens. And it is an effect which requires very small doses of radiation to be produced. All mitoses are not stopped; cells *in* mitosis (as far along as mid or late prophase) when radiation is given may complete their division. But those in interphase, those about to enter prophase, will be prevented from doing so, and their division will be inhibited. Those in the early stages of prophase may not complete division but instead regress, returning to the interphase condition.

The duration of inhibition is variable; it depends upon both the dose and the kind of cells irradiated. When inhibition is over, the cells affected enter prophase along with unaffected cells, those that normally would begin to enter their mitotic cycle; then all will divide. The net effect in tissue is a profusion of mitoses following the period of inhibition. This profusion is itself followed by a period of time in which few mitoses are seen. In this period the inhibited cells, those which have just completed division, would normally have been dividing. There is, in short, a synchronization of mitoses in irradiated groups of cells or tissues which is the result of the initial inhibitory response. Waves of mitoses alternating with troughs or depressions in mitotic frequency continue, thereafter, to occur in a kind of regular pulse or beat. Each succeeding wave and trough, however, becomes less and less marked until the synchrony imposed after irradiation is lost (Figure 17.1).

The *duration* of inhibition is, as has been stated, related to dose; it is, in fact, proportional to dose. The *actual* dose that is required to produce inhibition, however, is dependent on the *number* of chromosomes in the nucleus. It is inversely proportional to that number (that

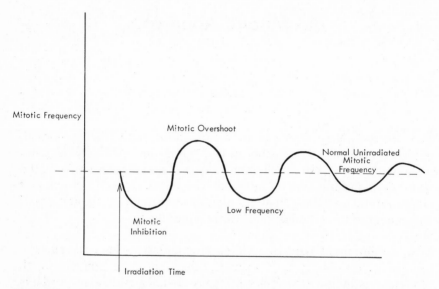

**Figure 17.1** Schematic representation of the consequences of irradiation upon mitotic frequency in a tissue. Initially, mitosis is inhibited in some cells, and the frequency drops sharply. Then, however, when inhibition is over, those cells join others going into division and divide with them. That is expressed as a burst of mitoses resulting in an overshoot of the normally observed frequency in the unirradiated tissue. All of these cells return at the same time to interphase, so that a valley in mitotic frequency is encountered next. Cells which should have been dividing during this period, owing to their previous inhibition, have just re-entered interphase; they cannot now divide. Mitotic synchrony has been produced. Synchrony is temporary, however; the peaks and valleys of mitotic frequency become progressively lower and shallower until the unirradiated frequency is restored.

is, the more chromosomes present, the *smaller* the dosage of radiation required to bring about mitotic inhibition), but it is *independent* of the length of the chromosomes. These two facts suggest that mitotic inhibition is brought about by an effect of radiation upon the *centromeres*. If the quantity of *chromatin* present were the governing factor, two cells having equal amounts of chromatin but unequal numbers of chromosomes (this is possible when one cell has a few long chromosomes while another has a large number of small chromosomes; the total *quantity* of chromatin in each is the same) should require the same dosage of radiation to bring about mitotic inhibition. But that is not the case; the *number* of chromosomes and, therefore, presumably, the number of centromeres (since the quantity of chromatin is not the same) will determine that dosage.

**17.3   Effects on the Distribution of Chromosomes at Cell Division.** A commonly observed effect following exposure of cells to ionizing radiation is an erroneous distribution of chromosomes from an irradiated cell to its daughters. This may occur as a result of either *nondisjunction* or *lagging,* two processes that can occur in irradiated cells when they divide. At metaphase of mitosis, it will be recalled that the doubled chromosome is "joined" by a single or yet-undivided spindle-attachment region or centromere. The centromere then separates or divides, giving rise to separate bodies. These, the chromosomes, move at anaphase to their respective poles (Chapter 14). When the centromere separates, the chromosomes are said to "disjoin." If the centromere fails to separate, the chromosomes, of course, will fail to disjoin. This failure is spoken of as "nondisjunction." The result is that the entire nondisjoined chromosome will travel to *one* of the two poles. One of the daughters, then, will fail to receive any of the genetic material borne on the chromosome, while the other will have the same genetic material present in duplicate. Neither will have the proper amount of genetic material. In one there will be a great deficit; in the other, the proper balance among the genes and dosages of genes will have been destroyed.

Nondisjunction may occur in meiosis as well as in mitosis. It may occur at the metaphase of the first or of the second meiotic division, but in either of these cases the same result ensues. Gametes will be formed half of which have an extra chromosome and half of which are missing a chromosome. The effect is, of course, the same as for any sharp deviation from normal genic balances; individuals with reduced viability—fewer numbers of viable individuals—and the eventual extinction of the deviant genetic material are the result.

Genetically unbalanced cells are also formed as a result of *lagging,* a frequently observed phenomenon at division of irradiated cells. In it a chromsome "lags" on the spindle, either failing to move at all or trailing after the separating masses of chromosomes at anaphase. As a consequence, the chromosome fails to be included in the nucleus of either daughter, although, depending on which side of the cytoplasmic division plane it chances to be on, it will be in the cytoplasm of one. One daughter, then, lacks the chromosome and the other has its genes in duplicate (neither, of course, has the chromosome in its nucleus). This extra-nuclear chromatin eventually degenerates so that lagging, unlike nondisjunction, although it *initially* results in cells having one extra or one missing chromosome, ultimately produces cells all of which lack a chromosome.

Nondisjunction and lagging both occur without radiation; as with genetic mutations there is a "spontaneous" frequency. Radiation, however, greatly increases that frequency so that, in irradiated material, nondisjunction and lagging may be said to be commonly observed.

**17.4   Effects on Crossing-Over.**   Ionizing radiation exerts a powerful influence on crossing-over (Chapter 14). Crossing-over is, for the most part, confined to cells of the germ line and restricted to regions of chromosomes *distant* from the centromere. Near the centromere, crossing-over rarely occurs. While it is true that, on a purely mechanical basis, crossing-over is less likely to occur very near the centromere (a relatively long length of chromosome thread is requisite before the chromosomes may conveniently cross over), it seems that the centromere actually inhibits crossing-over in the chromsomal region near it. Following irradiation, crossing-over will occur in that region. So powerful is this influence on crossing-over that sometimes regions of *somatic* chromosomes near their centromere may, following irradiation, undergo crossing-over. Consequently, the promotion of crossing-over near the centromere is interpreted as an effect of radiation *on the centromere,* not as an effect on the chromosomes themselves.

Regions of meiotic chromosomes distant from the centromere — those regions which normally undergo crossing-over — may after irradiation show some *decrease* in cross-over frequency. But this decrease is probably a result indirectly brought about by the promotion of crossing-over elsewhere. Because the chromosome has crossed-over near the centromere, it has been "shortened" (the twists will reduce its remaining effective length) and crossing-over further along the thread will have suffered some mechanical interference.

It is possible that the injury to the centromere which results in the effect on crossing-over is related to the effects on the centromere that cause it to fail to disjoin (nondisjunction) and to fail to move properly on the spindle (lagging).

The result of induced crossing-over is, like any cross-over, the production of changes in the linear order or sequence of genes on chromosomes. After *meiotic* divisions, this will result in a changed order of genes in the gametes so that different gene recombinations occur. Since it may occur in somatic cells, it will change the gene sequences there as well. It will be recalled that somatic cells have as their chromosome constitution two n sets of chromosomes — one contributed from the male parent (the paternal set) and one from the female gamete (the maternal set). For each chromosome in each set there will be a similar one, a homolog, in the other set.

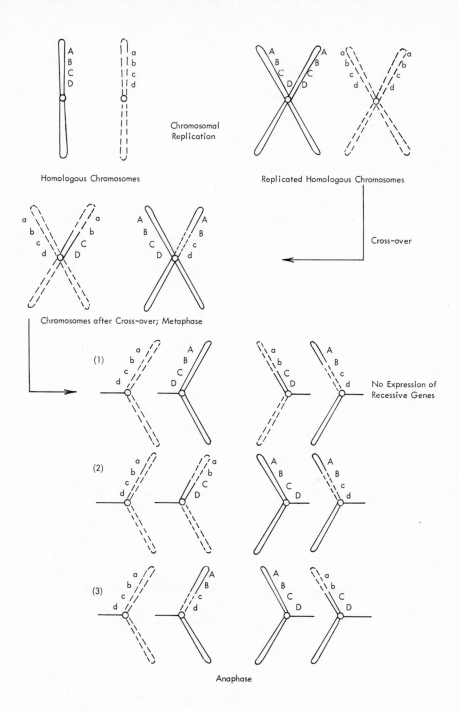

Homologous Chromosomes

Chromosomal Replication

Replicated Homologous Chromosomes

Cross-over

Chromosomes after Cross-over; Metaphase

(1) No Expression of Recessive Genes

(2)

(3)

Anaphase

**Figure 17.2.** Schematic representation of the distribution of somatic chromosomes at anaphase after cross-over. In (1), the expression of genes will not differ from that in the parent cell; for the recessive set, abcd, there will be simultaneously present in the same cell ABCD which will dominate that cell. In (2) and (3) the recessive ab and cd respectively will produce their effects, because in the daughters formed at these divisions, either AB is missing (2) or CD is missing (3). Note that the cross-over has involved genetic material *near* the centromere of each chromosome.

Along the length of *each* chromosome in the homologous pair and at the same location on each chromosome, there will be genetic material that is responsible for the control of a particular cellular function or body characteristic. In many instances, however, the materials on each chromosome in the homolog pair are *not* of equal strength; the genetic material on one is said to *dominate* that on the other. Conversely, the material on one may be said to be *recessive* to the other. Every function or characteristic — in diploid or 2n organisms — is under *dual* genetic influence; the genetic material on each homologous chromsome has a part in its control. In the case where the genetic material of one chromosome dominates the other, only the *dominant* genetic material will have expression (the function or characteristic will operate or appear as if the *dominant* genetic material were the only material present). Cross-over makes possible chromosome recombinations which allow previously unexpressed recessive genetic material to have expression. For example, if the sequence of genetic material on the parental homologous chromosomes is ABCD on one and abcd on the other where ABCD is dominant over abcd, only ABCD will be expressed. The organism will *appear* as if abcd is not present at all. After cross-over, depending on the separation at anaphase, this situation may change (Figure 17.2).

If somatic crossing-over occurs in a cell that is subject to proliferation, a part of the body to which it is ancestral (should this occur in an embryonic cell that part of the body may be large) may exhibit *recessive* characteristics.

It is not known how widespread the promotion of somatic crossing-over might be. It has been detected very often in the *Diptera* (flies), but probably occurs with a much reduced frequency in other species. The induction of somatic crossing-over will, of course, depend upon whether or not homologous chromosomes occur together in pairs in mitotic prophase. In the flies there is an extraordinary tendency for the homologous chromasomes to occur together in pairs in mitotic prophase, but this is not the case in most other organisms. The promotion of cross-over in *meiotic* cells by ionizing radiation is, however, an important factor in many kinds of organisms.

## SUMMARY

1. Exposure of cells going into prophase to ionizing radiation inhibits cell division. The length of inhibition is dependent on dose, but inhibition is transitory.
2. The dose required to inhibit mitosis depends on the number of

chromosomes (the number of centromeres), but is independent of the quantity of chromatin.

3. Ionizing radiation brings about *nondisjunction* of centromeres at metaphase and the unequal distribution of chromosomes to daughter cells at anaphase.

4. Ionizing radiation causes *lagging* of chromosomes on the spindle at anaphase, an effect ascribed to changes brought about in the centromere.

5. Ionizing radiation promotes cross-over in the region of the centromere. This has been attributed to an effect of radiation on the centromere, not on the chromosome.

# 18

## Relative Radiosensitivity of the

## Nucleus and the Cytoplasm

**18.1  Introduction.** Any discussion of radiation lethality in cells must compare the roles of the nucleus and the cytoplasm as they contribute to that end-point. Since the metabolic activities of the cell occur primarily in the cytoplasm, extensive damage there might be expected to cause cellular death. But permanent lethal changes (serious damage to genetic function and consequently to metabolism) must occur in the nucleus. It must, therefore, be questioned: When the cell as a whole is irradiated, with enough radiation to kill it, where has the immediately *lethal* damage actually been produced—in the nucleus or in the cytoplasm, or, in both? (Refer to Section 13.1.) A variety of experiments have been undertaken in an attempt to determine the relative radiosensitivity of the nucleus and the cytoplasm and which of these regions sustains the damage that kills the cell.

**18.2  The Role of the Nucleus in Cellular Radiosensitivity.** The overwhelming mass of experimental data tends to show that the nucleus is the radiosensitive region of the cell; damage done to it is likely to be lethal for the cell as a whole. A classical series of experiments demonstrating nuclear radiosensitivity has been done by Rogers and von Borstel[1,2] who used the eggs of the wasp *Habrobracon* to study the phenomenon. The newly laid wasp egg is more or less crescent-shaped; its nucleus lies against the chorion at one tip of the crescent. Because of its location the nucleus can be easily reached and irradiated by short-range, weakly penetrating alpha particles of polonium 210 (the range of these particles in tissue is $39\,\mu$). Since the egg *is* elongate ($160 \times 600\,\mu$) and the nucleus is found at one end, shielding of one or the other end permits irradiation of either nucleus or cytoplasm alone. Calculations made from such irradiations showed that the passage of only *one* alpha particle through the egg nucleus inactivated the entire cell; on the other hand, a total of $1.6 \times 10^7$ alpha particles was required for inactivation of only 50 per cent of the eggs if the cytoplasm alone was irradiated. In addition, inactivation of the whole cell after irradiation of the nucleus alone increased as an exponential function ("single" hit, Chapter 10) while inactivation after cytoplasmic irradiation was a sigmoidal function ("multi-hit," Chapter 10), results that indicate the production of lethality by two different mechanisms.

Another experiment performed by Whitney,[3] using *Habrobracon* eggs, also illustrates the greater radiosensitivity of the nucleus as compared with that of the cytoplasm. When virgin wasps are irradiated with doses greater than 2400 R, the egg *nuclei* are killed. If these eggs are then fertilized by *normal* (unirradiated) male sperm, males will develop. (In *Habrobracon* as in some other organisms, sex is determined by the number of chromosome sets. Females have the diploid chromosome number [2n] while males are haploid [n]. These males (called androgenic because their chromosomes have come from the male parent) continue to hatch even as the dose of radiation is increased. At doses greater than 15,000 R their numbers begin to decline; none hatches at doses greater than 54,000 R. The irradiated cytoplasm, then, appears to remain essentially normal up to doses of 15,000 R; it can be fertilized by normal sperm and normal male embryos develop. At 15,000 R, cytoplasmic irradiation begins to have an effect on *hatchability* (though not, apparently, on fertilization), and none hatches after doses greater than 54,000 R. Thus much higher levels of radiation are required for an equivalent effect after cytoplasmic injury than after nuclear injury.

Another, more recent experiment, compares the radiosensitivity of the cytoplasm and the nucleus in tissue culture cells of the Chinese hamster. Marin and Bender[4] compared the effect of the weakly penetrating $\beta$-rays from tritium-labeled thymidine incorporated into cells (these $\beta$-rays will irradiate only the nucleus; thymidine is taken up exclusively by DNA and will produce nuclear irradiation alone) and tritium-labeled uridine (uridine is taken up in both nucleus and cytoplasm and irradiates both). Based on the results of the cell-killing action of the tritium-labeled thymidine, the cell killing by tritium-labeled uridine could be accounted for exclusively on the basis of irradiation of the nucleus. There was no observable contribution from the cytoplasmic exposure.

The work of Brown and Nelson-Rees[5] also illustrates the role of nuclear damage, more particularly the role of chromosomal damage. In the mealybug (*Planoccus citri*), both males and females are diploid, but, in the male, one chromosome set is inactive; in females, both are active. Doses of radiation up to 30,000 R given to males do *not* cause any *dominant* lethality in *their* male offspring (these offspring receive an *inactive* chromosome set from the male parent). On the other hand, only 10 per cent of the female progeny of irradiated males survive (they receive an irradiated, damaged set of active chromosomes from their male parent). After irradiation of the female parent, the survival of both male and female progeny is reduced about the same amount (both irradiated maternal chromosome sets are active). Thus, in terms of the induction of lethality, irradiation of the inactive set of chromosomes has no adverse effects, while the production of aberrations in the active set of chromosomes results in marked dominant lethality. Although this does not prove a cause-and-effect relationship between aberrations and lethality, it clearly indicates that the genetic material — in the nucleus — is the primary site of the lesion that caused death.

Further evidence for the role of the chromosome and the DNA as the most radiosensitive portion of the cell is seen in the *range* of radiosensitivity between living organisms. Early work showed a relationship between virus size and radiosensitivity; but later work showed a better correlation with nucleic acid volume (for small viruses). A relationship has also been shown between sensitivity to ionizing radiation and DNA content in mammalian, avian, and yeast cells.

Sparrow and co-workers,[6] using higher plants, have shown that the radiosensitivity (measured either as the acute lethal dose or the chronic dose required to produce growth inhibition) is correlated with the mean interphase chromosome volume. This was defined as the *ratio* of nuclear volume to chromosome number. The larger the mean chromosome volume the greater the radiosensitivity. These observations have been extended[7] by determination of the mean DNA content of the chromosomes, and the values have a similar correlation. These studies also indicate that the radiosensitive site is in the nucleus.

**18.3  Radiosensitivity of the Cytoplasm.**  From the experiments detailed in the previous section, it seems apparent that the nucleus is the target or the location of the targets whose injury leads to cell death. However, the cytoplasm as a target and as a factor in the development of injury to the nucleus should not be overlooked.

The transfer studies of Duryee,[8] using amphibian eggs, indicate a prominent cytoplasmic component in radiation lethality. Isolated frog-egg nuclei (removed by microdissection) were more resistant to radiation pyknosis (clumping of chromatin) than were the nuclei irradiated in intact cells. Irradiation of the isolated nuclei in the presence of cytoplasmic extracts conferred radiosensitivity in about the same degree as that conferred to the nuclei irradiated in intact eggs. Further, the transfer of small amounts of irradiated *cytoplasm* into unirradiated eggs produced pyknosis of their nuclei. It would appear that irradiated *cytoplasm,* in this system, played an important role in the production of *nuclear* damage.

In the previous section the irradiation killing of the *Habrobracon* egg nucleus followed by apparent normal fertilization was described.[3] A different result was obtained by Nakao[8] when a similar experiment was attempted with silkworm eggs. A definite effect was seen on the paternal chromosomes in the irradiated egg cytoplasm. Even with doses of 2580 R, there was a definite effect on the sperm chromosomes.

**18.4   The Role of the Cytoplasm in the Development of Radiation Injury.**   It is possible for cytoplasm to play a role in repair of irradiated cells. Evidence from the irradiation of arbacia sperm and eggs has shown considerable repair of the radiation lesion upon storage of irradiated eggs, but little if irradiated sperm are stored. Further, it has been shown that repair of irradiated sperm does take place if the sperm are inside the egg cytoplasm (where presumably they can use the cytoplasmic components for repair processes).

Further evidence for repair by the cytoplasm is supplied by experiments on multinucleate amebae. Supralethally irradiated amebae are able to recover after transplantation of a portion of the cytoplasm of non-irradiated amebae. By stratification of the unirradiated cytoplasm it was shown that the essential factor for recovery is likely to be mitochondria.

**18.5   The Role of Membranes in Cellular Radiosensitivity.**   It has been suggested that radiation brings about its effects by damaging cell membranes. In this view, effects on the genes are seen as the results of alterations of membranes in the cytoplasm which permit the release of destructive products (enzymes) and their diffusion through the nuclear membrane to the chromosomes. Electron micrographs of irradiated cells (generally large doses have been used) have demonstrated swollen mitochondria and swollen endoplasmic reticulum. These effects have been interpreted as the result of changes in membrane permeability. Lysosomes are structures in the cytoplasm containing autolytic (self-destructive) enzymes which could be released if their membranes were broken or become more permeable.

While this idea is attractive, the effects on membranes that have been shown occur at very high doses (3000 to 10,000 R) and it cannot now be said that similar changes are responsible for effects in cells which result from *moderate* doses of radiation.

**18.6   Conclusions.**   From the evidence of a variety of experiments it is clear that the nucleus is more radiosensitive than the cytoplasm and its role as the target for the lethal radiation lesion appears well established. The experiments of Brown and Nelson-Rees (in which the radiosensitivity of active and inert genetic material was compared) and the correlation of radiosensitivity with mean interphase volume (Sparrow and co-workers) give convincing evidence that the specific target within the nucleus is the genetic material. Cellular death, however, may also occur after high radiation doses to the cytoplasm. Further, the less radiosensitive cytoplasm may play a role in the repair of nuclear damage.

## SUMMARY

1. The nucleus (the genetic material) probably is the target for the lethal radiation lesion.
2. Irradiation of the cytoplasm to high levels can also cause cellular death.

## Text References

1. Rogers, R. W., and von Borstel, R. C.: Alpha-particle bombardment of the Habrobracon egg. I. Sensitivity of the nucleus, Radiation Research 7, 484-490 (1957).
2. von Borstel, R. C., and Rogers, R. W.: Alpha-particle bombardment of the Habrobracon egg. II. Response of the cytoplasm, Radiation Research 8; 248-253, (1958).
3. Whitney, A. R.: Androgenesis as evidence for the nature of x-ray induced injury, Radiation Research 2; 71-78, (1955).
4. Marin, G., and Bender, M. A.: A comparison of mammalian cell-killing by incorporated ³H thymidine and ³H uridine, International Journal of Radiation Biology 7; 235-244 (1963).
5. Brown, S. W., and Nelson-Rees, W. A.: Radiation analysis of a lecanoid genetic system, Genetics 46; 983-1007 (1961).
6. Sparrow, A. H., Schairer, L. A., Sparrow, R. C.: Relationship between nuclear volumes, chromosome numbers, and relative radiosensitivities, Science 141; 163-166 (1963).
7. Duryee, W. R.: The nature of radiation injury to amphibian cell nuclei, Journal of the National Cancer Institute 10; 735-795 (1949).
8. Nakao, Y.: Action of irradiated cytoplasm on untreated chromosomes of the silkworm, Nature 172, 625-626 (1953).

## General References

1. Bacq, Z. M., and Alexander, P.: Fundamentals of Radiobiology, Pergamon Press, New York, 1961, pp. 263-279.
2. Davies, D. R., and Evans, H. J.: The role of genetic damage in radiation-induced cell lethality. In Advances in Radiation Biology, L. G. Augenstein, R. Mason, and M. Zelle (eds), Academic Press, New York, 1966, pp. 245-258.

# 19

## Effects in the Total Organism:

## The Immediately Lethal Effects

**19.1 Introduction.** To this point, all information given has centered about the effects of ionizing radiation at the cellular level, that is, the consequences *for cells* of irradiation damage to one or more of their parts. Cells have been considered alone as more or less self-sufficient entities, not in relation to each other or to the organism of which they might be a part. From this point, the effect of ionizing radiation on whole organisms and the organs and tissues that compose them must be considered.

**19.2 Immediately Lethal Effects.** The principal effect of exposure of the *whole body* to *penetrating* ionizing radiation is the shortening of the life of the exposed organism. The length of time life is shortened is dependent on the dose-level to which the organism is exposed. (It will also depend upon various other factors such as species differences, age of the organism at the time of irradiation, sex of the irradiated organism, time in a circadian cycle at which radiation is given — to name only a few of them). It is possible that there are *very* low doses of total-body radiation which do not elicit the earlier death of the irradiated animal. But that is not proved, and most evidence tends to indicate that if such a threshold does in fact exist, it will be very low indeed.

Total-body irradiation of mammals with rather large doses of ionizing radiation (approximately 300 R or more) causes death of the organism — usually more or less immediately after radiation is given. Doses of radiation that bring death within *approximately* thirty days are referred to as "immediately lethal" and the action of the radiation is said to have been "acute." Immediately lethal, of course, is a relative term; animals may not die immediately after a total-body dose of radiation, but they have not escaped its effects. The effects will be manifest later in their lives; in contrast to acute effects, they are termed "late effects."

**19.3   Effects of Dose.**   The *observed* response to *single exposures* of ionizing radiation given uniformly over the total body is primarily dependent on dose. For any *similar* group of *mammals,* exposure to increasing doses results in the appearance of a growing number of signs (those commonly observed are nausea, sometimes with vomiting; hair loss; loss of appetite; malaise—a general but undefined feeling of being unwell; soreness in the throat; petechia—tiny, local hemorrhages into tissue; diarrhea; and weight loss, in some to the point of moderate emaciation) indicating that response to the radiation is occurring. But ultimately, a dose-level is attained at which, in addition to the above signs, some of the animals begin to die. The dose-levels at which any *particular* sign appears or at which the first deaths occur will not be the same for all animals. There will be significant species variations (some animals, like pigeons, are very resistant to total-body radiation), and, even within species, significant variation may occur. Nevertheless, for nearly all *mammals,* and for most other vertebrates, the observed constellation and pattern of signs with increasing dose will be very similar.

As dose is increased beyond that which begins to kill some of the irradiated animals, more animals will die, and survival time of the animals that die grows shorter. But deaths at *any* dose-level (high or low) will occur *randomly distributed* about a mode (there can, at certain dose-levels, be two modes). That is, at any dose-level, death of any particular irradiated animal *may* occur at *any* time (long or short) after radiation. In practice, however, it has been observed that the greatest number of deaths will occur, for any given dose, at a particular time (a certain number of days or hours) after irradiation. The time when the greatest number of deaths occur will be the *mode.* It will, of course, vary with species and with other variation-producing factors, but for groups of *similar* (if not identical) animals, the modes for given dosages will occur at nearly the same time after irradiation.

When *mean* survival times (means are distinct from modes; a mean is a point *midway* between two extremes) are computed for each dose of radiation *greater* than that which begins to cause death, a pattern, consistent for nearly all species of mammals studied, emerges (Figure 19.1).

The pattern of response has three clearly distinguishable components. Initially, over a dose-range of 200 or 300 to about 1000 R, the response is dose-dependent; mean survival time, as dose is *increased,* *decreases* from weeks to days. The second phase, extending over the very wide range of approximately 1000 to 10,000 R, is a plateau. The response is *independent* of dose; mean survival at any dose in that range is about 3.5 days. Finally, the last component of the pattern is again dose-dependent. As dose *increases,* mean survival time *decreases* from a period of days to hours and, finally, even to minutes. In the dose-ranges where response is dependent on dose, variation in the length of time that *individual* organisms survive can be quite wide. In the dose-*in*dependent range, on the other hand, there is

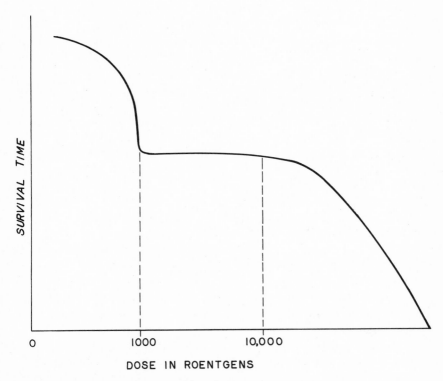

**DOSE IN ROENTGENS**

**Figure 19.1.** Diagram depicting the *mean* survival time for mammals following a single dose of radiation to the total body.

usually little variation. Because of the variance in survival of individual animals at any given dose of radiation, it is not possible to predict with absolute accuracy how much time after radiation will elapse before *all* the animals in an irradiated group die (if, indeed, all do die). Because some animals in any irradiated group may live for a long time, they are not representative of the group as a whole. As a result the immediately lethal response from a single dose of total-body radiation is often described as the dose required to kill a certain fraction of a given group of irradiated animals within a given period of time. Thus, a dose of radiation may be expressed as the $LD_{50/30}$ (the lethal dose for 50 per cent of the animals within thirty days of radiation), or $LD_{50/18}$ (the lethal dose for 50 per cent of the animals within eighteen days of radiation), or, of course, any similar expression. This method of evaluation is used in order to minimize the influence (in dose-response studies) of animals that may live for extended periods after irradiation. It will also be a reflection of variation-producing factors.

**19.4 The Radiation Syndromes.** The three regions of the dose-response pattern (Figure 19.1) are widely believed to reflect radiation damage to and the failure of three different organ systems after radiation. In the first region, death may occur within weeks to days; it is believed to be due to the result of radiation damage to and failure of the *hemopoietic system* (the organ system responsible for manufacture of the corpuscular elements of the blood). This is not to say that other organ systems are unaffected by their exposure to radiation; many cells in many organs and organ systems will be damaged by the total-body exposure. Also, in that range of dose-levels, many cells in organ systems other than the hemopoietic system will have sustained enough damage so that the organ or organ system will also fail to function (for example, the gonads and the lymph nodes are badly damaged in that range of doses), but *death* is due to the failure of the hemopoietic system—the organ system whose proper function is vital to the organism as a whole. Animals can survive without gonads and lymph nodes. The *syndrome* (the complex of signs and, in the case of human beings, symptoms) preceding death is the result of radiation damage to many, if not all, of the organs in the body, but the hemopoietic system is the *radiosensitive* system whose failure brings about death.

Therefore, at the lowest *immediately* lethal doses (those at which some, although not all, animals die, usually within thirty to forty-five days after total-body radiation), death may be ascribed principally to the failure of the hemopoietic system. As the dose is increased, more animals die and the *mean* survival time grows shorter and shorter. However, as dose is increased, all organ systems (and, in fact, all cells) are more greatly affected. A dose range is finally reached in which large numbers of cells of the *gastrointestinal tract* are badly damaged by the radiation. When enough are damaged, death of the irradiated animals will occur principally as the result of damage to and the failure of *that* system to function properly. This occurs in the region of dose independence. *Mean* survival time for most mammals will be about three to four days following radiation (for man, the period is estimated at approximately six days), and there will be little variation about this mean.

Finally, in the dose-range over 10,000 R, *mean* survival again varies with dose. In this region, death is due principally to the failure of the *central nervous system,* and the syndrome is referred to as the *central nervous system syndrome.* While death is due to the failure of the central nervous system, all other organ systems will also be seriously damaged. The gastrointestinal and hemopoietic systems will both be severely damaged and they will fail, just as they do at the lower doses. But the failure of the central nervous system brings death very quickly (in less than three days) so that the consequences of failure of the other systems do not have time to express themselves.

The shift from one mode of lethality to the next is not a sharp, well-circumscribed thing. Rather, as dose is increased, more and more cells of the next most radiosensitive *vital* system (hemopoietic → gastrointestinal → central nervous system) will be damaged. Totally irradiated animals in the dose-region *near* the shift from one syndrome to the next may die from the failure of *either* of the systems, depending on the animal itself. Some animals will die from the failure of one of the systems while others die from the failure of the other (Figure 19.2).

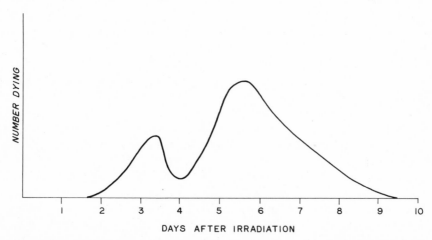

**Figure 19.2.** The pattern of survival (or death) following a single dose of total-body radiation at a dose-level near the transition between two syndromes. There are *two* modes.

There will be two modes of death, then, following irradiation, one occurring sooner after irradiation than the other. And (if other signs are present to confirm it) this is usually interpreted as the animals in each mode dying as a result of the failure of different organ systems. The responsible system is not too difficult to identify in the transitional region between bone marrow and gastrointestinal syndromes. The signs accompanying each of them are rather different and the survival times from each of the two are relatively distinct. In the transitional area of dose between *gastrointestinal* death and *central nervous system* death, on the other hand, it is often impossible to state with certainty whether the failure of one or the other organ systems has been responsible for death of the animals. All of the signs of the gastrointestinal syndrome are usually present as, of course, will be those characterizing central nervous system failure. The *time* of death (or the survival time) is often the only practical parameter that can be used to separate the two. Animals surviving *two days* or less are more or less arbitrarily said to have died from central nervous system failure while those that live longer than two days are said to have died from failure of the gastrointestinal tract.

**19.5   Tissue or Organ Radiosensitivity.**   The sensitivity of the various tissues and organs to radiation appears dependent upon the rapidity with which their mature functional cells die out and are replaced by new cells. These new cells are a result of *cell division* among *undifferentiated* (immature, unspecialized) cells in the tissue. This relationship, noted very early in the history of radiation biology, was codified and put in the form of a law by Bergonié and Tribondeau. The burden of the law says that radiosensitivity of tissues depends upon the *number of undifferentiated* cells which the tissue contains, the *degree of mitotic activity* in the tissue, and the *length of time* that cells of the tissue stay in *active proliferation* (that is, the *number* of cell divisions between the earliest, immature state of a cell and its final mature, functional state).

It is known that, in all tissues of the body, mature functional cells wear out, become defective or inefficient, and are replaced. They are replaced by cells which *differentiate* (or specialize; take on special functions), but which are themselves immature and unspecialized. An undifferentiated cell in the tissue or organ will divide. One of the daughters will differentiate (either then or after it divides one or more times) and replace a worn-out cell while the other daughter remains undifferentiated and "replaces" the undifferentiated cell from which both daughters arose. In this way, tissues remain in a steady state with respect to numbers of cells; the *total* does not change; sufficient mature, functional cells are always present to carry out the functions of the tissue or organ, because the rate of reproduction and replacement is always equal to that of cell loss.

Some tissues have a high rate of cell renewal (bone marrow and gastrointestinal tissue are good examples) so that, at any time, relatively large numbers of their cells are dividing and differentiating. Also, as is known, the division cycle is a singularly radiosensitive phase of cell life. Radiation interferes with division proper through its effects on the centromeres; division is inhibited and loss of chromosome parts (through breaks and recombinations) and bridging of chromosomes occur during division. In the $G_1$, S, and $G_2$ phases there is a high probability of genetic effects, a high frequency of chromosomal breaks, and a lower frequency of restitution. If a tissue has a high rate of mitotic activity it is reasonable to expect it to be radiosensitive, for many cells in it will be especially vulnerable to radiation damage.

## SUMMARY

1. Irradiation over the total body significantly shortens the life of the irradiated organism.
2. The degree of shortening depends on dose, but, at high enough doses, death occurs "immediately" — from a period of weeks to hours after radiation is given.
3. The immediately lethal action of total body radiation, dependent on dose, can be ascribed to the failure of a vital organ.
4. The order of *sensitivity* of the vital organ systems to radiation, progressing from the most sensitive to the most resistant, is the hemopoietic system, the gastrointestinal system, and the central nervous system.
5. The radiosensitivity of organs seems dependent on renewal of cells in the organs; the *law of Bergonié and Tribondeau* states (in substance) that radiosensitivity of a tissue will be dependent upon the number of undifferentiated cells it contains, the degree of mitotic activity in the tissue, and the length of time that the cells remain in active proliferation.

# 20

## The Bone-Marrow Syndrome

**20.1  The Bone-Marrow Syndrome.**  The bone-marrow syndrome occurs following a *single* exposure of radiation (requiring a few minutes to, at most, a period of a few hours to give), distributed *uniformly* over the whole body. Death occurs in at least some (though not necessarily all) of the irradiated animals within a few weeks after irradiation. The source of radiation must be an external source of either x or gamma rays (or other *penetrating* radiation, such as might be obtained from a particle accelerator), for, while the bone marrow itself might be affected, even *selectively* affected by an internal source of radiation, a *uniform* exposure of the total body is not likely to result (Chapter 8). Nearly any isotope taken into the body by nearly any route — given orally, by inhalation, or by injection — will have *differential* distribution and retention in various organs. Some organs will take up more than others and be heavily irradiated; some may escape irradiation altogether. This will not be *uniform* radiation in the strictest sense and a full *syndrome* of total-body effects does not necessarily occur.

**20.2  Manifestations.**  In all species studied, disturbance in the function of the gastrointestinal tract occurs within a few hours after irradiation. This disturbance, which may persist for a short (few hours) to a long (few days) time consists of feelings of nausea, sometimes accompanied by vomiting, and a modification in gastric emptying time. The period of gastrointestinal distress is called the *prodromal* period. It is followed by a period of variable length, in which the irradiated organisms are free of signs (in human beings, free of symptoms as well), called the *latent period*. It must be stressed that this latent period is not a period of inactivity. Actually, during this time, the most important consequences of radiation exposure leading to its lethal effects are in progress (the beginnings of the destruction of the bone marrow). This period is "latent" only in the sense that the irradiated organism apparently feels well and is, on the surface, relatively sign- and symptom-free.

The latent period is itself followed by a period of severe illness. In it, signs of gastrointestinal disturbance reappear. Diarrhea, often bloody, sometimes quite severe, begins. Hemorrhage into the tissues occurs, fluid imbalance accompanies it, and, ultimately, serious infection. These are the signs, then, which precede death and which lead to it. At death it can be seen that nearly every organ in the body has been affected. Death comes, of course, as a result of damage to all the organs, but principally as a result of the failure of one, the *bone marrow*.

Concomitant with the above signs, several processes will be in progress; these are also the result of irradiation, but they do not lead directly to death. Among them will be weight loss (the loss of weight is actually a good sign that radiation has been received), the loss of hair (this, too, is a common reponse to irradiation), and depression of spermatogenesis or oogenesis. These, however, are not part of the *syndrome* that leads to death. They occur at the same time but are unrelated to the syndrome.

**20.3 Histologic Changes.** Most species show the *same* histologic changes in the bone marrow following total body irradiation in the low dose-range. The degree (or severity) of the response (the number of cells responding and the intensity to which they respond) depends on dose. And, of course, the dose that elicits the response in the first place will vary with species.

Almost *immediately* after irradiation (depending on dose — the first few hours to days) the structure and architecture of the bone marrow are disrupted. The marrow normally consists of *nucleated* cells, a small amount of fatty material, and some circulating blood in vessel-like channels (it is the blood supply of the marrow itself). After irradiation it becomes *rapidly* and *markedly* reduced in the amount of cellular material. The decrease in the number of cells is compensated by dilation of the blood sinusoids (the vessel-like channels), by *hemorrhage* of blood (extravascular red cells) into the cell-depleted regions, and by an increase in the amount of the fatty substance. Ultimately, if the dose is high enough, cell depletion becomes very severe; the bone marrow can become entirely acellular, and the marrow space filled with pooled blood. Circulation of blood does not entirely cease (hemorrhage has not so disrupted the channels that they carry no blood at all), but it does become very sluggish and reabsorption of extravascular blood goes on only to a limited extent.

Of course, every cell in the marrow will not be killed; it is doubtful that even at extremely high doses all are killed. Some start to undergo mitosis and an attempt at regeneration (re-population of the bone-marrow space) will begin. At higher dose-levels (and, as always, the actual dose-level depends on species) these first attempts at regeneration may fail or *abort*. The cluster of dividing cells regresses and disappears. Later in time regeneration will again begin. Precursors to red and white cells will appear after a general *hyperplasia* that seems to characterize the beginning of this more "real" regeneration.

The start of regeneration, even of true regeneration, does not indicate that an irradiated animal will escape the immediately lethal effects of its experience. Regeneration of bone marrow may begin, even after fairly high doses of radiation, even in animals that will soon die from that exposure to radiation.

Lymphoid tissue (in mammals, the lymph nodes and the thymus gland) is severely affected in the dose-range that produces the bone-marrow syndrome. In a very short time after a dose of total-body radiation, the nodes become very severely depleted of cells and node architecture is completely disrupted. Regeneration of the nodes occurs, usually soon after radiation and, depending on dose, can be rapid. As opposed to effects in the bone marrow, cellular depletion of lymph nodes and thymus is much less dependent on species (less dependent on $LD_{50}$). A given dose of radiation affects lymphoid tissues in many species of mammals to about the same degree.

**20.4  Cytologic Changes.**  The *number* of cells in mitosis in the bone marrow falls precipitously after irradiation. This is followed by a rise which may occur at varying times after irradiation (the steepness or rapidity of that rise depends on dose), that results in an "overshoot" of the normal frequency. There is another fall, returning to a level below that of the normal frequency, followed, in turn, by a second rise (Chapter 17).

Although the mitotic frequency is eventually restored to the normal unirradiated frequency, it does not mean that the cells that divide will be normal. Rather, to the contrary, many will have been injured and they can be very abnormal. Large numbers of abnormal-looking mitoses are not, however, often observed in *regenerating* bone marrow of irradiated mammals. It is, of course, possible that the damage to chromosomes is quickly repaired in these cells, but the more likely event is that the injured cells are rather quickly eliminated (see the previous chapters on the fate of cells in which mitotic or chromosome abnormalities have been produced by radiation). Some few cells with damage to the chromosomes, do, predictably, survive (the genes affected were not important enough to have caused their immediate death) and continue to multiply. These, in animals that survive the bone-marrow syndrome, can be detected many years later.

Within a *few hours* after irradiation and well *before* bone-marrow regeneration (of course, the exact time depends on dose and on species), a range of *nuclear* abnormalities of cells in the bone marrow can be seen. The nuclei of some of these cells (for the most part those cells which will give rise to red cells) will be shrunken, their chromatin will be clumped and will stain heavily (pyknosis). The nuclei of others (also red blood cell precursors) will appear very faint, as if their chromatin were dilute or dissolving. These cells are dying (if they are not already dead); the injury from radiation has killed them even before they were able to divide. Still others will have abnormal or aberrant chromosomes in bizarre-looking nuclei. Nuclei may be swollen; there will be chromosome bridges, broken chromosomes, and cells in division in which the spindles have more than two poles (obviously, daughter cells of such divisions—there will be three or more—will have unequal numbers of chromosomes) as well as other grossly abnormal-appearing cells.

Most of the directly damaged cells (the pyknotic ones or those in which the nuclei are undergoing dissolution) are quickly eliminated and will be in the marrow for only a short time after irradiation. But those with slightly injured chromosomes may persist for some time in irradiated organisms. They, too, will eventually be eliminated.

The *elimination* of cells directly following radiation is probably responsible for the loss of total cellularity in marrow of irradiated organisms. Of course, not every cell is destroyed, and, in some, no obvious damage can be seen. But this does not mean that no damage has occurred. It is reasonable to expect some of these survivors to have sustained mutations. It is also to be expected that some change in the time and even the length of the mitotic cycle will have occurred (mitosis will almost certainly have been inhibited in some).

**20.5 The Latent Period.** These changes, these degenerative changes in the bone marrow, as well as the attempts at early (though abortive) regeneration go on during the prodromal and the *latent* periods. The latent period has been described as a period of relative well-being, but, as can be seen, the *important* changes, those degenerative processes in the bone marrow which will lead to death of the organism, are in progress during this period. For death, as a result of the *bone-marrow syndrome*, is believed to be due to the loss or failure of the bone marrow to carry out its function—that is, supplying the organism with the functional cells that it needs in its circulating blood. The direct loss of some red and white cell precursors due to injury from radiation, the later loss of some of the remaining from injury to their nuclei (mutation and chromosome aberrations), and the inhibition for varying periods of time of the mitoses of some of those cells that escape immediate death from radiation will leave, in a short time, a critically short supply of circulating cells (the degree of that shortness of supply depends on dose). This is true for several reasons. For one, circulating cells have limited life-spans. Most are highly specialized, carefully adapted for a particular function, or, at most, for a few functions, which they carry out until they are worn out or become useless. They do not divide and perpetuate themselves, but depend instead upon cells in the marrow to supply the organism with their successors. The cells of the bone marrow, then, are regarded as "stem cells," cells which are themselves undifferentiated but which divide frequently, giving rise to cells that are differentiated, specialized, and which function. These stem cells are the cells that radiation directly eliminates. The cells circulating in the blood wear out or end their lives as do those same cells in unirradiated animals, but none, or very few (the actual number depends on dose), are produced in the marrow to replace them and preserve the function which they perform for the organism. The loss of that function by the organism (if such a loss persists too long) can result in the organism's death.

**20.6   The Blood Counts.**   The loss of precursor cells in the bone marrow is reflected by the number and kind of cells in the circulating blood. Changes from the usual numbers of cells found in circulating blood and from the numbers of individual cell types usually present will indicate when the supply of these cells is running short. After radiation, there is a drop in blood count; its severity depends on dose. If the animal will be a survivor, regeneration of the blood-forming elements of the marrow will go on, so that survivors from the immediately lethal effects of radiation will show an eventual increase in the numbers of circulating cells.

The *anemia* (loss in the level of circulating blood cells) following total-body radiation in the bone-marrow syndrome dose-range is *not* due entirely to the lack of production of red cells by the marrow. A drop in production of red cells, of course, does occur, but this is not initially very great and the length of life of circulating red cells is rather long. Red cells are lost from circulation, however, by several other mechanisms related to radiation exposure. There is breakdown of the wall of capillaries in many species causing large numbers of very small hemorrhages into the surrounding tissue (petechia). Some, though not all, of these cells return to circulation so that a loss of red cells (the degree of severity of this kind of loss appears highly species dependent) from the circulation can occur this way.

Another, more important, mechanism is a deficiency in the number of *platelets* (a blood cell type involved in clotting) which results in a significant increase in *clotting time* after irradiation. No change in the actual clotting mechanisms or of the efficiency of the clot itself has been shown, but the time required before a clot *is* formed is longer in irradiated than in non-irradiated animals. This time factor is believed due to the loss of platelets and, indeed, the injection of *fresh*, intact platelets into irradiated animals corrects the defect.

**20.7  Infection.**   In both human beings and lower animals, infections are associated with the terminal phases of the radiation syndrome. In human beings (evidence was gathered from the survivors of the atomic explosions at Hiroshima and Nagasaki), fever is common and, at death, evidence of general infection is found. This is also true of large animals; they experience a temperature rise (even to levels above 105°F) and overwhelming infection can be seen in many organs. In small animals (mice), bacteremia is present (in this condition bacteria are present in the blood stream). It is distinguishable from the situation in man and large animals in which infection, though very severe, is not as widespread. However, the methods used to detect bacteremia have differed between mouse and man. That used in mice is more sensitive. It is possible, then, that bacteremia may occur in man and large animals, but that it goes undetected.

The bacteria isolated from infected animals are all from the normal intestinal flora of the animals. This is as true of large animals and man as it is of mice.

Infection by these bacteria *greatly* influences the time course of survival of irradiated mammals. Pretreatment with antibiotics (so as to "sterilize" the intestine) will bring about a longer mean survival time if pretreated animals are later irradiated. Moreover, if lethally irradiated animals are treated with antibiotics soon after irradiation, their mean survival time is longer than that of animals not so treated. Finally, germ-free animals survive radiation doses that would kill like animals that are not in the germ-free state.

It appears then that there is an increased susceptibility to infection in totally irradiated animals compared to those not irradiated. This susceptibility increases *both* with respect to organisms *not* normally pathogenic and those that normally are pathogenic.

Infection, then, has an important part to play in mortality. The length of survival as well as the dose which may be immediately lethal is determined by infection. The precise cause of infection after total body radiation is not known, but it is *correlated* (though not *proved* to be causally related) with the loss of circulating blood cells, namely, granulocytes. With the initial severe drop in these cell types directly after irradiation, there is some mortality. Mortality decreases during the *abortive* regenerative period.

## SUMMARY

1.  Total-body radiation, if given in sufficiently low single exposures, brings death within a few weeks.
2.  While many organs and tissues are damaged, and death is due to

the damage in all of them, it will come about *principally* as a result of damage to the bone marrow.

3. The time course of survival and the signs and symptoms that accompany it are called the "bone-marrow syndrome." In its initial phase the obvious manifestation is nausea, sometimes accompanied by vomiting, but it is at this time that the lethal effects are beginning and undifferentiated stem cells in bone marrow start to die. New cells for the circulating blood are no longer produced. The next major manifestation is a period of apparent well-being, the latent period. But, during this period, more precursor cells in the bone marrow die and the marrow spaces become nearly cell free. As time goes on, because circulating cells are not renewed, a drop in blood count is observed. At the same time a period of severe gastrointestinal disturbance begins (diarrhea, later becoming bloody); it is the result of radiation damage to the gastrointestinal tract. Hemorrhage into tissue, fluid imbalance, serious infection, and, ultimately, death follow.

4. Death is the result of the failure of the bone marrow and the body systems which combat infection. However, if infection is artificially controlled, these organisms will still die as a result of failure of the bone marrow.

## General References

1. Patt, H. M., and Brues, A. M.: in *Radiation Biology* Vol. I, part 2, Chapter 15, A. Hollaender (ed.), McGraw-Hill, New York, 1954.
2. Bond, V. P., Fliedner, T. M., and Archambeau, J. O.: *Mammalian Radiation Lethality*, Academic Press, New York, 1965.

# 21

# The Gastrointestinal Syndrome

**21.1 Introduction.** When mammals are exposed to single doses of penetrating ionizing radiation in amounts greater than 1000 R, mean survival time of the irradiated animals reaches a constant number of hours or days over a very wide range of doses (up to approximately 10,000 R). Survival time is about 3.5 days for *most* mammals tested (there are, of course, species variations), but, regardless of precisely how long the survival time is, the important fact is that it will be *independent* of dose. Since survival time due to failure of the bone marrow is clearly dose *dependent*, it is reasonable to assume that, where survival time is *not* dose-dependent, death is not due to the failure of the bone marrow alone and that another system or systems are primarily involved.

**21.2 The Syndrome.** The signs and symptoms that characterize the syndrome are the result of radiation damage to and failure of *two* organ systems: (1) the cells lining the intestinal tract (the *mucosa*) and (2) the cell renewal system of the bone marrow. The true or complete *gastrointestinal* syndrome can be obtained only after *total* body radiation; irradiation of the gastrointestinal tract alone can be fatal, but the full syndrome must involve the cell renewal system of the bone marrow as well.

After irradiation, in all species of mammals tested, there occurs a lack of appetite, sluggishness and inertia that increase with time, diarrhea, and signs of infection and dehydration. Animals irradiated will lose weight, voluntarily take in little food or water, retain the food and water in the stomach for long periods, and, with time, less and less of the food eaten will be absorbed. At the same time the numbers of circulating white blood cells will drop to nearly zero.

The last or terminal phase of the syndrome is over very rapidly (often it lasts for less than a day). It is characterized by diarrhea which becomes very severe with time, vomiting, and complete exhaustion. The increasingly severe diarrhea brings severe dehydration, marked weight loss, and distinct emaciation. Irradiated animals become inert, lying or sitting at rest, moving scarcely at all. Finally at death, which will occur in most species with regularity between three and four days after irradiation, blood volumes will have changed, electrolyte levels in the serum will be altered, and there may be evidence of bacteremia (bacteria in the blood). There are, of course, species variations in the mean length of survival following irradiation; man and monkey present interesting variants, for mean survival in these species is closer to six days than to three or four.

Autopsy of animals of any species shows severe wasting and dehydration. The stomachs of some show retention of food and water. The small bowel itself may be swollen, and may contain a bile-colored, liquid material, generally bad-smelling and often tainted with blood. The large bowel may contain liquid stools which often are bloody. There will be large quantities of mucus in the gut as well. The mucosal layer of the small intestine will be badly damaged; villi will be shrunken, there will be areas which lack the cellular lining altogether, and many of the crypts will be empty (Figure 21.1).

In the stomach and rectum, areas will exist which have been denuded of cells and which are ulcerated. The bone marrow is formless, completely without structure.

**21.3   Degenerative Changes in the Lining of the Small Intestine.**   At the dose-levels producing the gastrointestinal syndrome, changes, severe in nature, appear soon after irradiation in the epithelial lining (the mucosa) of the small intestine. Changes also appear in these cells following much lower doses of total body radiation (they can be seen after doses of 100 R), but few cells are involved and the changes produced in the gut itself seem to be minimal. As dose is increased, more cells are, of course, involved, but intact or unaffected cells in the gut divide rapidly to replace them so that *regeneration* more than adequately compensates for cell loss. At much higher doses the *degeneration* of the intestinal mucosa is clearly seen and can be described.

**21.4   Histologic Changes.**   Soon after irradiation, usually during the first day, there can be seen in the *crypts* progressive destruction of the cells that line them. The nuclei of these cells become pyknotic (the chromatin agglomerates, its amorphic structure indicates that it has condensed into a formless mass, and it becomes densely staining), both nuclei and cytoplasm swell, and, in some, there is dissolution or liquefaction of the damaged cells. These cells are dead (or dying) so that a measurable decrease in the number of cells in the crypt lining follows. Those cells that remain have abnormal-appearing nuclei and are often swollen or enlarged. Few cells in mitosis are seen (and the crypts of the small intestine are usually *very* active mitotic centers), and those that are seen will be abnormal (the aberrancies of mitosis discussed in earlier chapters are present). The debris of the dead cells, which becomes detached from the crypts, begins to build up in the crypt lumina. In time, however, this is passed down the intestine and disappears. With time, more and more crypt cells die

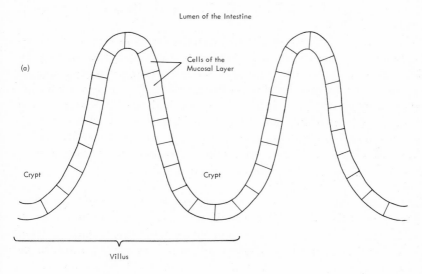

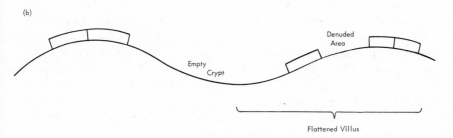

**Figure 21.1.** The appearance of a segment of small intestine before and after irradiation in the amounts leading to the gastrointestinal syndrome. The normal shape (columnar epithelium) of the absorptive cells in the mucosal layer is distorted; these cells become thin and stretched. Patches of mucosa are gone so that areas of the gut are denuded of cells; the crypts, usually an active center of cell proliferation, are empty; and the villi are flattened and shrunken.

and are sloughed; few mitoses occur so that these cells are not replaced, and soon regions of the crypts appear that are substantially stripped of cells. Those few cells that remain usually appear grossly abnormal.

The villi themselves lose cells, progressively more and more of them with time, and begin to shorten or shrink. The rate of cell loss and shrinkage is dependent on dose; it occurs faster at higher doses of radiation. At death, these villi are very nearly flat and almost completely free of cells.

The precise time schedule of these events and the time required before the intestine is entirely denuded of cells varies with species. In mice, rats, dogs, and goats this condition is reached between three and four days after irradiation, but in the monkey or in man it probably does not occur until the fifth post-irradiation day. The *sequence* of events, however, is the same for most mammals tested (there is some question whether the hamster or the guinea pig, which have a somewhat different pattern, die from a gastrointestinal syndrome of the same sort as that which affects other mammals).

**21.5   Regeneration.**   As in the case of bone marrow, not every cell in every crypt of the small intestine will be killed by irradiation, even at high dose levels. Of those that remain, some will be very damaged and are unable to reproduce, but others will have escaped enough damage so that they will be able to reproduce themselves. This is not to say, of course, that they have been unaffected by their exposure to radiation. It merely means that the capability of reproduction has not been destroyed in them. They will form the nucleus or a focus of regeneration of the gut. Simply stated, an attempt to *regenerate* a new gut lining *can* be made. At doses of radiation well into the range that produces a gastrointestinal syndrome, death usually comes to the irradiated animal before any significant regeneration is possible. But, at lower dose levels near the transition range between the bone marrow and gastrointestinal syndromes, uninterrupted regeneration does occur. There is an increase in the mitotic rate, the epithelial lining of the crypts begins to be repopulated from cells within them capable of division, and these cells begin to move into the villus to replace those which have been sloughed. New nests of cells can appear which are thought to represent new crypts.

At still lower doses (those in the range producing the bone marrow syndrome), regeneration of the intestinal lining is more rapid, and an intact lining may again be produced. Unfortunately, of course, repair of the intestinal lining is no insurance against eventual death brought about by loss of function of the bone marrow.

**21.6   The Large Intestine.**   The remainder of the gastrointestinal tract undergoes a pattern of changes very similar to those observed in the small bowel. The main difference is that the changes occur more slowly so that, at the time that death comes following a gastrointestinal syndrome, the large intestine is rarely completely denuded of its epithelium. This is to be expected; it is in accordance with the renewal requirements and turnover of mature cells in the large and small bowels.

**21.7  The Effects on Cell Renewal.** The mature, differentiated, functional cells of the gut epithelium are those lining its villi, in particular those at the tips of the villi. The crypts, much like the bone marrow, are a generative center. The cells in them are undifferentiated and unspecialized. The specialized, functional cells of the villi (in particular, those of the small intestine) have a short life. In the normal course of events and under normal circumstances they wear out and are sloughed into the lumen of the intestine only a few days after they have become functional. The gut lining, then, undergoes very rapid renewal. The cells in the crypts undergo cell division often and are the source of replacement of the rapidly renewing epithelial lining (Figure 21.2).

As in the case of the bone-marrow syndrome, radiation strikes at the cells that are the source of the differentiated functional cells (those responsible for the proper function of the organ). Much as in the case of the bone-marrow syndrome, this is to be expected, because it will be these cells that will be most frequently active in mitosis and

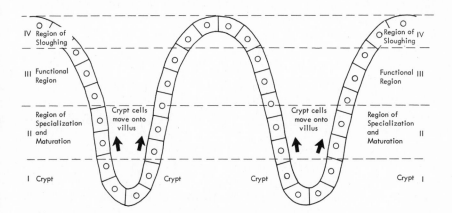

**Figure 21.2.**   Schematic diagram of the regions of a normal intestinal villus. In region I, the crypt, there will be a high mitotic rate in the unspecialized, undifferentiated cells that compose it. Cells produced in the crypts move up the villus to region II where they begin their maturation and specialization. They move up into region III after having specialized in region II and begin to function. They continue to move up the villus through the functional region and at the tip (region IV) are extruded or sloughed. There is, then, an orderly procession of cells from the crypts up the villi through a region in which they mature, through another in which they function, to the villus tip where they are extruded and sloughed.

synthesizing DNA, so that many of them will be vulnerable to radiation damage.

**21.8  Effects on Mitosis.**  Mitotic index, usually high in the small intestine, may be expected to drop after irradiation as those cells going into mitosis are inhibited. In the species tested this was indeed the case. Over a wide range of doses (75 to 900 R in the rat; 35 to 325 R in the mouse), cells in mitosis all but vanished in the small intestine within thirty minutes after exposure. The length of time mitosis was inhibited depended on dose. After inhibition had passed, a rise in the number of mitoses occurred followed by a second drop or depression in the mitotic count. The initial rise in mitoses as well as the length of the second depression in mitosis is also dose-dependent (Figure 17.1).

Many of the cells that do survive to divide have nuclear abnormalities which kill them. There will be chromosome lagging, stickiness, and broken chromosomes. These cells, often immediately, sometimes after one or two divisions, die.

**21.9  Precursor Cells.**  The crypts of the epithelial linings of the bowel are generally regarded as the generative region for the mature cells of that lining. The relationship, however, unlike that of the bone marrow to circulating cells of the blood, has been difficult to establish. Morphologically, these precursor cells, unlike precursors of circulating cells, are not different from cells in the region of maturation (the cells in region I, Figure 21.2 cannot be *morphologically* distinguished from those in region II). Nor, as can be done for bone marrow, is there any way at present to determine whether the generative cells (precursor cells, "stem cells") have in fact lost the ability to proliferate (the bone marrow of irradiated animals may be transplanted to other animals where the proliferative capacity can be evaluated in the absence of the complicating factors of the bone-marrow syndrome). It is not possible, then, to obtain *directly* an estimate or measurement of the sensitivity of these cells to radiation and to compare them — for that characteristic — to bone marrow cells. But, an indirect mechanism has been devised. It is based on the *assumption* that death *is* due to a reduction in precursor or stem cells below a critical number. Death, then, results if radiation kills or inactivates enough stem cells so that their number is either exactly equal to or less than this critical number. Thus, animals are irradiated using two dose schedules: (1) a single lethal dose, or (2) two doses (split-dose) sufficient to kill the organism. Dose-survival curves are then plotted, and the information obtained permits some observations about the epithelial precursor cells. The dose required to reduce the number of such cells to any particular fraction of the normal is much higher than the dose required to reduce the number of bone-marrow cells by the *same* fraction. One would predict (on the basis of the above assumption) that bowel cells

are less sensitive than bone-marrow cells and that, if lethality following from the failure of these two organ systems results from the
reduction of the number of stem cells to the same critical value, then
the dose required to kill 50 per cent of irradiated mammals in the
gastrointestinal syndrome range will be expected to far exceed that for
bone marrow. Experimental observations are in agreement with this
prediction.

**21.10  The Bone Marrow.** Cells in the bone marrow, at the
dose-levels required to produce a gastrointestinal syndrome, will, of
course, be very badly damaged by their irradiation. And damage to
bone marrow is an integral part of the *full* gastrointestinal syndrome.
The bone-marrow renewal systems are completely depleted within a
few days after irradiation at the gastrointestinal syndrome level. In
particular, the granulocyte count in nearly all species tested reaches
*very* low levels within three days of irradiation following doses over
1000 R. There will be a severe lack of those cells during the very
period in which the signs and symptoms of the gastrointestinal
syndrome are reaching their apex. A depletion of other types of cells
originating in the bone marrow does not occur (in spite of the fact that
the bone marrow itself is completely depleted) simply because death
comes long before these circulating cells have had time to become
exhausted. In these high dose-ranges, there is little change in red cell
count. The bleeding that does occur is related to ulcerated and
denuded sections of gut. Unlike the bone-marrow syndrome, frank
hemorrhage does not have time to occur.

**21.11  Fluid and Electrolytes.** Animals in the last throes of the
gastrointestinal syndrome become very obviously dehydrated. Near
death, dehydration is so severe that the blood becomes exceedingly
thick, so thick in fact that it is difficult even to withdraw a sample.
There is a profound reduction in body fluids and of electrolytes (salts)
so that the normal fluid and electrolyte balance is completely destroyed. The loss of these things *can* be accounted for by the reduction
of intake of food and water resulting from the loss of appetite
associated with this syndrome. However, the severe diarrhea, loss in
the efficiency of intestinal absorption, and leakage of fluid into the
lumen through the damaged intestine are the factors principally
responsible for fluid and electrolyte loss.

    While the fluid and electrolyte losses are not great in the early
phases of the gastrointestinal syndrome, they become very important
in the phase of most serious illness. With the onset of severe diarrhea,
serious fluid and electrolyte loss begins. During this terminal period,
the fluid stool increases both in quantity and in frequency, in time
even becoming hemorrhagic. This diarrhea, the cause of the fluid loss,
is probably brought about by the failure (or the inability) of the distal

end of the small intestine to resorb bile salts and the resulting irritation of the colon by these salts. Bile, excreted into the small intestine, normally is resorbed by the distal ileum. But, this segment of gut, stripped of functional absorbing cells due to sloughing and the failure of the renewal system in its crypts, does not resorb the bile. The salts go through, into the colon, irritating and causing stool to be defecated.

If the bile duct is tied off in irradiated animals, or if the bile flow is diverted so that it does not go into the intestine, this will prevent the diarrhea. But liquid bile or bile salts introduced into the intestine of irradiated animals in which the bile duct has been tied off or diverted will produce diarrhea. Equal volumes of ordinary saline solution will *not* give the same effect.

**21.12  Infections.**  Animals irradiated to dose-levels resulting in the gastrointestinal syndrome may be expected to become infection prone. Indeed, infection does appear to play a major role in causing death at these dose-levels. Irradiated animals are in a poor nutritional state; lymphoid tissue including that of the intestine is destroyed (in many species, within three days of irradiation). The intestine is denuded. This allows bacteria in the intestine to gain access to underlying tissue. Antibiotics are of some value in extending the life of the lethally irradiated animals. Germ-free animals survive doses and live longer than do conventional animals irradiated to the same dose. Fever has been shown in dog and in man irradiated to these levels. All these things point to the role played by infection and it appears to be a significant one.

## SUMMARY

1. The full gastrointestinal syndrome is brought on only by *total body* exposure.
2. Death is the result of damage to many tissues but the most important of these is the gastrointestinal epithelium and the renewal systems of the bone marrow.
3. Death itself is due to fluid and electrolyte loss, infection, and nutritional impairment. The irradiated animal dies in shock.

## General Reference

1.  Bond., V. P., Fliedner, I. M., and Archambeau, J. O.: *Mammalian Radiation Lethality*, Academic Press, New York, 1965.

# 22

# The Central Nervous System Syndrome

**22.1 Introduction.** Mean survival time following radiation doses that bring on a gastrointestinal system syndrome is rather constant and, with increasing dose, is dose-independent. But, dose cannot be increased indefinitely without bringing about a change in the length of the mean survival time. At some dose-level (the threshold for this effect is not particularly well defined) and at doses above this level, mean survival time will again become dose-dependent. The "threshold" for this effect is, in most species tested, in excess of 5000 R and, from this dose (whatever it might be for any given species) to doses so high that death occurs even while the radiation is being given, the signs and symptoms elicited are characteristic of damage to the central nervous system. Accordingly, the syndrome of effects has been labeled the "central nervous system (CNS) syndrome."

**22.2 The Syndrome.** The course that the syndrome follows includes periods of agitation alternating with remarkably apathetic behavior; these manifestations give way to disorientation (in species where this can be evaluated), upsets of equilibrium, loss of coordination of muscular movement (ataxia), diarrhea, vomiting, tetanic spasms of the muscles of the back (the head and lower limbs bent backward and the trunk arched forward), convulsive seizures, prostration, coma, and death.

In some species (among them, monkey) one or more of these signs may occur during irradiation. The time of the onset of the others and their progression depend to a certain extent on dose. During the irradiation itself, animals can become exceedingly active and irritable. Also during irradiation, these manifestations can be followed by apathy; in some cases the degree of apathy can be very profound. Occasionally, there also will be vomiting (in animals that can do so), salivation, diarrhea, and nystagmus (oscillatory movements of the eyeballs).

The foregoing can, in a sense, be regarded as a prodromal period, for after irradiation there is a period (variable in length) in which the irradiated animals may appear to be normal. Even during that period, however, there is a sign characteristic of irradiated animals: minimal *voluntary* movement or activity is observed.

Following this phase (which can, dependent to an extent on dose, last only a few moments) other signs make their appearance — uncoordinated movement, random, undirected movements, and tremor. Irradiated animals may go into convulsions even in response to stimuli that usually do not provoke such reactions. Tremors, convulsive seizures, rolling of the eyes, vomiting, repeated evacuation of the bowel, diarrhea (usually quite watery), and a hysterical state, resembling meningitis, are often observed, sometimes alone, sometimes in combination. Prostration and coma follow; breathing is labored; there is gasping, and blood pressure reaches the low levels observed in shock. This is the terminal period of the CNS syndrome; it is the most prominent stage in the syndrome. The most characteristic or remarkable attributes are the tremors and convulsions, circling of the animal when attempting to walk, and, even when the animal is lying down, walking movements in the extremities.

**22.3   Histologic and Inflammatory Changes.**   Blood cells, in particular granulocytes, mononuclear types, and macrophages, filter into the meninges (the membranous coverings of the brain) following the very large doses of radiation that produce the CNS syndrome. Vasculitis (inflammation of blood or lympth vessels) is a common finding only a few hours after a high radiation dose. Veins and arteries of all sizes undergo changes which involve infiltration of granulocytes in foci about the vessel. In the cerebrum this is a striking alteration; the cerebellum, brain stem, and spinal cord seem less involved. While these alterations appear first in gray matter, ultimately white matter becomes most seriously involved.

The inflammation of the meninges, beginning as granulocytic infiltration, commences very early, increases to a maximum, and falls off very little during the remainder of the course of the syndrome.

The choroid plexuses are quickly affected by the radiation; liquid infiltration (edema) and infiltration of leukocytes occur soon after irradiation. They reach a peak and then diminish, but they are still detectable late in the course of the syndrome. The reason for these reactions is unknown, but it has been supposed that they occur in response to the production by radiation of minute, non-septic areas of tissue damage. Such areas do exist (microhemorrhages and necrosis have been found in the nearby tissue), and have been taken as evidence supporting such a view. The infiltration occurs so very quickly that bacteria, as causative agents, may be ruled out. Radiation damage to the tissue itself and/or damage to capillaries resulting in leakage from them and foci of pressure which injures and kills tissue are the probable causative agents.

**22.4  Cytologic Changes.**  Pyknosis of the *granule neuronal cells* of the cerebellum is a characteristic finding following total body (and head) irradiation. The nuclei of these cells take on a more intense stain and shrink in volume. These changes, while dose-dependent, occur very soon after irradiation (at higher doses more cells will be affected and more irradiated animals will show this kind of damage), and increase with time. They do reach a maximum, however, and, in some if not all species, appear reversible.

The mechanism underlying shrinkage and pyknosis in these cells has been represented as the shifting or migration of fluid out of the nucleus. There *are* changes in specific gravity and water content of the brain after irradiation which may tend to substantiate this view. But, if this is the case, the reason underlying such fluid movement can be ascribed *either* to a direct action of radiation upon the cell nucleus or to a response of the cell membranes (a change in permeability), or that of the capillaries (again, a permeability change), to irradiation (Section 18.5). The observations made in the brain support either view and cannot separate them.

In the remainder of the central nervous system, few morphologic changes have been observed following *total-body* exposure. Those that have been seen can as well be attributed to post-mortem changes or to changes resulting from edema as to radiation itself. It is possible that all changes at the histologic level may not become morphologically apparent during the short survival time.

**22.5  Consequences of Vascular Damage.**  The damage to blood vessels (both large and small) already cited (vasculitis) and changes in capillary permeability permit leakage, into the brain itself, of the substances usually confined to the blood vessels in the brain. There is, however, disagreement as to whether the vascular changes observed are the primary consequences of radiation in this dose-range that lead to death. While some feel that these are the critical events, others believe them to be quite incidental. Nevertheless, by permitting extravasation of fluids and dissolved components into brain tissue itself, damage to the astrocytes (the cells some believe to be responsible for maintaining the blood-brain barrier) can result and the *blood-brain barrier* may have broken down. Aside from this, however, edema which results from vessel damage *is* responsible for some local cellular damage.

In some species, after irradiation of the head only and following irradiation of the total body, there is evidence of some gross edema of the brain. There is an *increased* water content of the brain in those whose head only has been irradiated. Such an increase has not yet been shown in totally irradiated animals. If such changes in fluid balance do indeed occur after total body irradiation, they may have resulted from damage to the vascular system.

**22.6   The Immediate Causes of Death.**   While the cause or causes of death are not known, it is known that the CNS syndrome is truly a *total-body* syndrome. Death is *presumed* to result from events taking place within the skull (the brain itself, the meninges, blood vessels; everything contained *within* the skull), but irradiation of the head alone does not produce death when it is given in the same dose-range as that which elicits death from the CNS syndrome; much higher doses directed to the head alone are required to induce death.

Lack of evidence of large necrotic areas in the brain suggests that, while the neurons *may* have been lethally irradiated, they do not appear to have died or to have stoppped functioning at the time death comes to the total organism. Death, then, is not likely to have come about from a loss of the neurons' function.

The increase of fluid content of the brain may cause the organ to swell, even if only slightly. The bony confines of the skull will not permit much expansion without resulting in a buildup of pressure in the brain. Swelling in irradiated tissues is not unusual; it has been noted to occur transiently after irradiation in both tumors and normal tissues.

All these observations suggest the possibility that damage to the cells of the brain due to an increase in intracranial pressure, damage to the blood vessels of that organ, and edema are the mechanisms of death resulting from the CNS syndrome. But this has not as yet been proved.

### SUMMARY

1.   Mean *survival time* for the central nervous system syndrome is dose-dependent, but there appears to be a "threshold" dose-level, species-dependent, at and above which the syndrome comes into existence.
2.   Clinical signs include agitation, apathy, disorientation, loss of equilibrium, loss of coordination of muscular movements, diarrhea, vomiting, tetanic spasms, convulsive seizures, coma, and death.
3.   The principal changes noted are infiltration into the meninges, vasculitis of the brain, and edema. Neuronal cells of the cerebellum undergo pyknosis and nuclear shrinking indicating a disturbance in fluid balance in these cells.

4.  Death is attributed to (although not proved to be caused by) neuronal damage due to vasculitis, edema, and increased intracranial pressure.

## General Reference

1.  Bond, V. P., Fliedner, T. M., and Archambeau, J. O.: *Mammalian Radiation Lethality,* Academic Press. New York, 1965.

# 23

# The Late Effects

**23.1 Introduction.** The effects of radiation, as already noted, fall rather naturally into two general categories—immediate or acute and late. While *all* the biologic effects occur as a result of energy transfer to cells in the instant of irradiation, some effects are not expressed for a long interval of time after irradiation—in some cases for months or years. Those that fall into this latter category comprise the genetic effects and the late somatic effects. Genetic damage is not always *expressed* until mutant genes find themselves in a genetic environment that *permits* expression; this *can* require several generations of recombinations. In this chapter only the late somatic effects will be considered.

**23.2 Modifying Factors.** The nature of the late effects, indeed whether they will occur at all, is dependent on a number of factors. These will be considered separately in a forthcoming section, but, to briefly list a few, there will be the inevitable *species variations, dose-dependent responses (the radiation dose absorbed* will determine the frequency of occurrence of some of the late expressions of radiation damage), *dose-rate* dependency and others.

**23.3 Sterility.** Most data obtained on the induction of sterility following irradiation are taken from work done on experimental animals (many experimental studies on the effects of radiation on the sexual capacity and/or on the genetic material of man are immoral and, of course, unethical) so that the situation in man remains somewhat in doubt. Inferences may be made, based on animal studies, but data obtained in animals is not *always* extrapolatable to man so that a degree of uncertainty must remain.

It can, however, be stated that exposure to radiation in *males* does *not* appear to affect sexual capacity (potency or libido). Of course, exposure to radiation, even at dose levels well beneath lethal doses, does produce a kind of "sickness" (Section 19.3). This "sickness," whose signs comprise nausea, loss of hair, loss of appetite, malaise, sore throat, petechia, diarrhea, and slight to severe weight loss, is—as is any illness—debilitating. There can, as there can be during any illness, loss of sexual desire and responsiveness, but when the illness has past (its acute phase is over) full restoration of potency and libido occurs.

Animal studies show, however, that while potency and libido are unaffected, *fertility* may be, at least temporarily, impaired. *Permanent* sterility can be produced if sufficiently high doses of radiation are given the gonads (permanent sterility would not be *likely* to result after a *total-body* exposure, because the doses required to produce this result are so high as to bring about one of the radiation syndromes in the irradiated individual and cause death).

After a dose of radiation to the gonads (either as total body exposure or as radiation of the gonads alone), there is a period of continued fertility, followed by a period in which fertility is impaired. Dependent on dose, fertility may be impaired enough to have been lost altogether (*sterility*). This "sterile" period or period of impaired fertility is temporary; in time (the amount of time required is dose-dependent) fertility is restored. Sterility need not consist of a total loss of sperm; rather, to the contrary, normal, viable sperm may even be present. Sterility may be produced if the *number* of sperm is sufficiently reduced so that the probability of fertilization of an egg is reduced to unlikely levels. Such sterility may be termed *functional sterility*.

While, as stated before, the situation in man is incompletely understood, animal data indicate that within the dose range of 400 to 1000 R (the precise dosages are dependent on species) a period of temporary sterility (not simply reduced fertility) is induced in males. At doses *below* 400 R there is no clear-cut period of *complete* sterility. At doses above 1000 R some reduction in fertility is seen even directly after irradiation—in the period where, at lower doses, normal fertility persists. Very high doses are required to induce permanent sterility.

These observed phenomena are usually explained on the basis of differences in radiosensitivity of cells of the germ line. The production of mature sperm begins in the testes with cells which are called *spermatogonia*. These are the undifferentiated cells of the testis in which the first *meiotic* division (Chapter 14) occurs. This division results in two cells called *spermatocytes*. The spermatocytes undergo the *second meiotic* division, yielding four cells called *spermatids*. The spermatids then undergo a complicated cytoplasmic reorganization (the process is known as *spermiogenesis*), to give rise to mature sperm, but no further *divisions* occur. The rearrangement of cytoplasm or spermiogenesis adapts the sperm to the mobile function it must have in order to "seek" and fertilize an ovum.

Of the cells involved in the various stages in spermatogenesis, the spermatogonial cells are the most radiosensitive. Spermatocytes, spermatids, and even the sperm themselves are rather radioresistant. During irradiation, then, with dose-levels to the total body in the non-lethal range (400 R or less) the spermatogonia are affected; some will be killed, and, in others, division will be inhibited. There will be a *reduction* in the number of these cells and, in time and as a consequence of the damage to the precursor spermatogonia, reduction in the number of cells formed during the other stages of spermato-genesis. There will, after a time, inevitably be a reduction in the number of mature sperm, and, if this reduction is severe enough, impairment of fertility or even sterility may occur. Directly after irradiation, then, no change in fertility is expected (none occurs) because the mature sperm are not affected. Similarly, the cells of the intermediate stages (spermatids and spermatocytes) are not unduly damaged and they continue to mature. The supply of mature sperm will only be interrupted when a deficit occurs as a result of the damage done, at irradiation, to the spermatogonia. If the radiation dose is not too high, the dead or damaged spermatogonia will be replaced and the proper number of mature sperm will eventually be restored. Thus, a period of fertility follows irradiation, succeeded by a period of impaired fertility, succeeded in time by a restoration of normal fertility.

It should be stressed that this discussion centers only around *fertility,* i.e., the capacity of a spermatozoon to *fertilize* an ovum (to enter and begin development of an embryo within an ovum). Sper-matozoa are, in respect to fertility, radioresistant. However, genetic mutations may have been produced in the irradiated sperm.

In human beings, as has been stated, little data are available, but the information that does exist indicates that a *single* dose of 400 to 600 R to the testes can or is likely to produce complete sterility. Temporary sterility follows lower doses; a *single* dose of about 250 R brings about sterility for about one year. Very much lower doses (as low as 30 R), however, can reduce the sperm count and impair fertility.

Even the complete loss of fertility is without effect on libido, hormone balance, or on somatic cells of the testes. No impairment of the sex drive or of sexual capacity has been noted.

In *females,* in terms of the results of exposure to the ovaries, the situation is very similar to that in males. The permanently sterilizing dose varies with age; older females require smaller doses to produce sterility than do younger ones. In mice, a 150 R dose of x ray is permanently sterilizing. There is, as with males, a fertile period following irradiation; sterility sets in at a later time. Again, as with males, mature germ cells (in this case, ova) are capable of fertilization or union with the male gamete so that sterility would not be expected to come into existence until the mature form and its radioresistant precursors become depleted and no new eggs mature.

The dose (total-body dose) required to produce sterility in human females is rarely received; it will be high enough (300 or more roentgens) to initiate a radiation syndrome. Radiation given directly to the ovaries (either as therapy to the ovaries themselves or when the ovaries are included in the field of radiation) can, of course, produce sterility. In this case, unlike that of males, radiation sterilization does have important effects on sexual capacity. This is true because ovarian production of hormones is closely related to the development, maturation, and discharge of ova. If these processes are halted (either by radiation or by any other mechanism), an "induced menopause" is the result, with the expected concomitants of natural menopause: diminished libido, "hot flashes," and in some individuals depression, and loss or absence of menstruation.

**23.4  Shortening of Life Span.**  As has been mentioned earlier (Chapter 19), exposure to radiation over the total body shortens the life span. This is true whether the exposures to radiation are given over short or long periods of time (within limits, the effect seems independent of dose-rate). As will be seen in the following section, radiation is a carcinogen (a cancer-inducing agent) and it is to be anticipated that irradiated animals will more often develop cancers than will non-irradiated ones. This is the case, and in consequence, the life of irradiated animals will be expected (on the whole) to be shortened since the exposure induces a fatal disease. But, even if all deaths due to malignant disease are excluded, the life of irradiated animals is shorter by statistically significant amounts than that of unirradiated ones.

In rodents, there are some studies in which results conflicting with the above statements have been reported. Animals exposed to small doses, accumulated over periods of time, outlive non-irradiated controls. Not all data tending to demonstrate this *life-lengthening* effect of radiation are closed to criticism, but the frequency of the appearance of this kind of report lends support to the existence of such a phenomenon. Whatever this effect is, it is at this writing very poorly understood.

The amount of shortening of life of small animals after total-body irradiation appears to be dose-dependent. Smaller amounts of radiation shorten life to a lesser degree than do large amounts. Over a range of doses the response appears to be linear. But it is not known whether any dose of radiation, however small, will shorten life. Some argue and have argued that a "threshold" dose of radiation which is necessary to initiate the life-shortening effect may exist. While no such threshold has been demonstrated, neither has it been shown conclusively that extremely small doses result in the shortening of life. It is an exceedingly difficult point to test effectively, for very small doses will be expected (if the relationship is indeed linear *through-out*) to shorten life very little. Irradiated *populations* must be compared to non-irradiated populations to determine whether, on the average, the non-irradiated ones have a longer life span than do those who were irradiated. When only a small amount of time is involved, *very* large populations (under rather carefully controlled environments) must be used. Thus, any radiation-induced *disease* state (like cancer) which would shorten life must be excluded so that, in both groups, only animals dying from "old age" are compared. Experiments such as these are very difficult to set up and run; their results are often even more difficult to evaluate.

Life-shortening as a radiation lesion is subject to modifying influences; it is more marked if young animals are irradiated than if old ones are thus treated; the presence of oxygen at irradiation enhances the effect; chemical protectors present during irradiation protect against the effect.

Life-shortening is not restricted to the aftermath of *total-body* radiation; if only parts of the body are exposed, this effect can be elicited as well. The length of shortening, however, is less than that which follows total-body irradiation. While that is true, if the length of shortening is viewed as a function of the fraction of the body irradiated, irradiation of parts of the body produces a *relatively* greater effect than does total-body radiation.

**23.5   The Effect of Dose-Rate.**   The life-shortening effect is dependent on *dose-rate* as well as total dose. If a given dose is prolonged over a long period, its life-shortening effect will be much less than that of the same dose given in a short burst. If the dose is given in fractions, i.e., at interrupted intervals, the life-shortening effect of that dose will be greatly reduced compared to the same dose given at one time.

**23.6   Human Experience.**   The bulk of the data on life-shortening in human beings is derived from studies made on the life spans of American radiologists. The life of American radiologists has, at least in the past, been shown to be shorter than that of other physicians. The observed shortening is believed related to day-by-day radiation exposure obtained in the course of the radiologists' work. At first, the suggestion that radiologists might have a shortened life was greeted with criticism and the data upon which the conclusion was based were said by some to have too many shortcomings to demonstrate that point conclusively. However, at the same time, and over the years, American radiologists have become more and more careful to expose themselves to progressively smaller and smaller amounts of radiation. For example, in 1934, a dose of 1 R per week was considered permissible (that is, it was believed to produce no detectable effects *within the lifetime* of an irradiated individual). By 1936 this dose had been lowered to 0.1 R per day. In 1946 a still further reduction to 0.3 R per week was made. The present level is 0.1 R per week, but most radiologists are now quite careful to expose themselves to far less than that. The data relating life-span and radiation exposure of United States radiologists have been substantiated. There has been demonstrable life-shortening among radiologists in the past. But, with each decrease in radiation exposure received, the degree of shortening has been less. At present, and since 1960, no demonstrable life-shortening can be detected.

Similar studies of British radiologists did not give a similar picture. However, this apparent discrepancy between radiologists of the United States and those of Great Britain may be due to earlier adoption in Great Britain of safer radiation procedures.

**23.7 Cancer.** Ionizing radiations (as well as radiations of lesser energies) are carcinogens (cancer-formers); exposure to ionizing radiation carries the risk of cancer induction in the irradiated organism. Ionizing radiation is a *general* carcinogen, that is, it induces or brings about cancers of any tissue in nearly any animal tested, irrespective of species.

Radiation is not the only carcinogen. There are, in fact, a multitude of them. Generally, carcinogens may be classified as: radiations (both ionizing and non-ionizing), chemicals (polycyclic hydrocarbons, azo dyes, to name two classes of compounds), physical chronic irritants (abrasives, cellophane implanted in an organ), and living agents (viruses). Among these, however, only radiation is at present known to be so general a carcinogen. Chemicals may induce a tumor in one tissue but not in another; they may be carcinogenic in one species but not in another. Viruses can be carcinogenic for certain species or strains or in certain tissues.

**23.8 Latent Period.** Following the use of radiation as a carcinogen there is (as there is with chemical carcinogens) *a latent period.* It is a period in which the tissue that has received the carcinogenic stimulus does not appear abnormal. But, in the case, at least, of radiation, the carcinogenic transformations must have been accomplished in the moment of irradiation. They are not apparent and cannot be detected then—indeed, often not until a long time later; but they must essentially have occurred immediately when the tissue was irradiated. What is going on during the latent period cannot now be described, for nothing can be detected. It is possible that, during the latent period, changes in irradiated cells are so subtle as to be beyond the present ability to detect them. On the other hand, it is also possible that nothing happens then, for it is equally possible that the induction of cancer is a two-step process. The first of these might be the *initiation* of a cancer, the *transformation* of normal cells to cells having the capacity to become cancerous. But, a *second* stimulus might be necessary to actually start the *growth* of the cancer. The latent period might be a period of quiescence, the period between the two phases, *initiation* and *promotion* of growth.

Whatever the case, there is usually a long latent period (long relative to the length of life of the irradiated animal) between irradiation and the appearance of a tumor. In human beings the period can be ten, twenty, or even thirty years. In addition to a long latent period, not *every* irradiated individual, even heavily irradiated individuals, will get a cancer.

Repeated doses of radiation will have the effect of shortening the latent period. In spite of the fact that there is such a long latent period, a cause-and-effect relationship between exposure to ionizing radiation and later cancer formation can be established. The major link in establishing this relationship is that the tumor almost invariably appears at the irradiated site (when local irradiation of a part of the body has been done) or in the site of localization of a radionuclide.

**23.9 Leukemia.** Only certain types of leukemias (acute leukemias and chronic myeloid leukemias) are *known* to be induced by ionizing radiation in man. It seems likely that *acute* lymphatic leukemias can also be induced (in particular, in children), but the risk seems much less than that of the *chronic* lymphatic leukemias. Leukemia is observed after short-term, high-level exposure over the total body or nearly all the body (many investigators are convinced that there was an increase in the frequency of leukemia among the Japanese populations of Hiroshima and Nagasaki; yet others remain in doubt concerning this). It is also observed after external radiation in large amounts given at rather low dose-rates over the total body or to large parts of the bone marrow, and after an administration of radioiodine ($^{131}$I) in doses *greater* than *one curie* for therapy for carcinoma of the thyroid gland.

Leukemia is *suspected* (but not solidly established) to occur after deposition in the body of radionuclides such as radium, thorium, or strontium 90; in children exposed to diagnostic pelvic x-radiation *in utero;* after short-term exposures to doses of less than 100 rads; and in children receiving irradiation to the thymus gland early in their lives.

**23.10 Relationship of Leukemia to Dose.** The relationship of induced leukemia to dose appeared to be *linear* among the survivors of Nagasaki and Hiroshima. The precise estimation of dose *received*, and whether it was composed chiefly of neutron or gamma radiation, by the survivors of the atomic attacks upon these cities is very difficult to determine. But, if it were assumed that neutrons and gamma radiation gave about the same result, a linear relationship leads to the conclusion that 1 rad over the total body produced one to two cases of leukemia per million population per year, averaged over the thirteen years following exposure.

In men whose spines were irradiated for the bone disorder, ankylosing spondylitis, similar results were obtained. These studies were also beset with difficulties, although not of the same nature as those encountered at Hiroshima and Nagasaki. The dose in the spine irradiations is known quite accurately, but doses to the same individual were given at different times so that the total had to be obtained by addition. This is a serious shortcoming because the bone marrow is not likely to have been equally susceptible at all times. However, if this difficulty is ignored, a *linear* relationship leads to an expectation that 1 rad of whole body radiation would produce between one and two cases of leukemia per million persons irradiated—averaged over seven years.

In both therapeutic irradiation and irradiation as a result of the atomic explosions, the risk of leukemia as a function of time after irradiation diminishes (the longer time that passes after irradiation the smaller is the probability that any given irradiated individual will contract *radiation-induced* leukemia), but the rate remains higher than is encountered in similar non-irradiated environments for long periods of time.

It must be remembered that these values are *extrapolated* values; they are based on a *presumed* linear relationship through all doses. As yet, this has not been proved to be the case and no *proof* exists that these low doses *do* induce leukemia in adults.

In the fetus there is evidence that doses in the range of 1 to 5 rads induce leukemia, but, in this respect, the fetus is believed very much more sensitive than is the postnatal individual.

A progressive rise in leukemia mortality rates over approximately the last forty years has been described in the United States, England, and elsewhere. It has been suggested that increasing exposure to medical x rays is among the reasons for such an increase. In 1956, reports on the biologic effects of ionizing radiation were widely publicized. A recent report[1] describes the first observed decline in leukemia mortality rates; it may be related to awareness of the potential hazards of medical radiation.

**23.11  Leukemia in U.S. Radiologists.**  Radiation-induced leukemia has been, as has been life-shortening, an occupational hazard for the radiologists of the United States. For these individuals, as with life-shortening, the risk of leukemia has been decreasing (in the decade 1949-1958 the rate was half that of the years before 1949), but it is still above that of the remainder of the population. Some authors feel that the increased incidence now remaining in the radiologist population is due to overexposure in the past. They believe that present good safety practices have eliminated the health hazard for the profession.

**23.12  Mechanism of Action in Radiation-Induced Cancer.**  The etiologic basis of radiation-induced cancer (the mode of action that brings it about) is unknown. As with chemicals, other physical agents, and viruses, the fact that radiation induces cancer is beyond dispute; the dose required and the mode of action are not clear yet. Deductions based on knowledge of cancers themselves and of normal tissues from which they are derived can be made concerning these points. There is much evidence to indicate that cancers arise as a result of a *genetic mutation*. The indications are that (1) cancers seem to arise from normal tissue. Unless cancer cells which begin to grow only upon a stimulus are always present in normal tissues—and this is possible—normal tissue must be transformed to cancer tissue. (2) Cancers "breed true"; cancer cells give rise to other cancer cells, like themselves. (3) When transplanted from one part of the body to another (this process is called metastasis) or from one organism to another, cancer cells continue to breed true. (4) Cancer cells *retain* some characteristics of their tissue of origin.

It may be, then, that radiation produces a mutation in cells, one which frees the cells from growth control by the body in which the radiation occurs. This process would be the *initiation*, the transformation to a cancer cell. Then, if the transformed cell receives a stimulus to grow and divide (freedom from the control of growth need not mean that growth itself *inevitably* follows), it will do so without restraint.

Not all workers accept the mutation hypothesis for the induction of cancer, and, in fact, this hypothesis has not been proved. Yet, the carcinogens as a whole (there are exceptions) *are* mutagens so that this process is, at least, quite possible.

**23.13  Cataracts.**  Cataracts form as a result of an exposure to ionizing radiation in which the eye is involved. They are relatively uncommon late effects of total body radiation, for a rather large dose is required to induce their formation. The cataracts are not the same as those which occur as a result of senility; in appearance and development they are distinct. Neutrons, however, do produce them in good quantity after rather low doses.

# SUMMARY

1. The "late effects" following total-body exposure in low-dose ranges are *impaired* fertility, shortening of life span, cancer induction, and the induction of cataracts.
2. Impairment of fertility occurs because of radiosensitivity of precursor cells to the gametes.
3. Shortening of life span is a true radiation effect, but its genesis is not known.
4. Exposure to radiation increases the frequency of all kinds of cancer.
5. Cataracts occur after irradiation of the eyes, in particular with neutrons. It is not a common consequence of total-body radiation.

## Text Reference

1. Fraumeni, J. F., Jr., and Miller, R. W.: Leukemia mortality: downturn rates in the United States, Science *155*, 1126-1127 (1967).

## General References

1. Hollaender, Alexander, (ed): *Radiation Biology,* Vol. I, Part 2, Chapter 12. *Genetic Effects of Radiation in Mammals,* by W. L. Russell. McGraw-Hill Book Company, Inc., New York, 1954.
2. Bacq, Z. M., and Alexander, Peter: *Fundamentals of Radiobiology,* 2nd Ed., Chapter 17. *Delayed Effects.* Pergamon Press, New York, 1961.
3. Report of the United Nations Scientific Committee: *The Effects of Atomic Radiation.* The United Nations, New York, 1962.
4. Warren, Shields: The basis for the limits on whole-body exposure — experience of radiologists, Health Physics *12*, 737-741, (1966).
5. International Commission on Radiological Protection: Committee I. The evaluation of risks from radiation, Health Physics *12*, 239-302 (1966).
6. Stewart, A., and Hewitt, D.: Leukaemia incidence in children in relation to radiation expoxure in early life. In *Current Topics in Radiation Research,* Vol. I, Part VI, edited by M. Ebert and A. Howard. North-Holland Publishing Company, Amsterdam, 1965.

# 24

# Effects on Developing Embryos

**24.1 Introduction.** The embryo probably represent the most radio-sensitive stage in the life of any organism. This is true for several reasons. Among them are: (1) Many of the cells in an embryo are differentiating, and, as has been implied in the law of Bergonié and Tribondeau, differentiating cells are quite radiosensitive. (2) There is, in the embryo, a high rate of mitotic activity; the system is *proliferative*, and, as has already been shown, mitosis is a sensitive time in a cell's life cycle. (3) An embryo is composed of "few" cells; many of its cells are ancestral to vast numbers of cells in the adult, so that damage done to one of them will be distributed over considerable numbers of descendent cells and over large areas of the post-embryonic body. (4) If an embryonic cell is killed—at any time in the development of certain embryos and after certain stages of development of nearly all embryos—the cells for which it would have been an ancestor will not be formed (sometimes, however, another cell will or can take over its function). These factors, then, make the embryonic period an extraordinarily sensitive time of life with respect to radiation.

Within the embryo itself, as is the case in adult organisms, not every organ or system will be equally radiosensitive. Unlike adults, however, in whom the same relative radiosensitivities always seem to exist (bone marrow, for example, is always about as radiosensitive as lymph nodes but more radiosensitive than the gastrointestinal system), there will be shifting radiosensitivities from one organ or system to another. A broad generalization can be made—the organ system *differentiating* will acquire great radiosensitivity and be profoundly affected by irradiation.

**24.2 Regeneration and Repair.** An embryo possesses, usually in much higher degrees than does an adult, the ability to regenerate lost parts. From the embryo's early stages, phagocytes are present which can resorb dead cells—those damaged and killed by irradiation. At early stages, with the dead cells gone the remaining undifferentiated cells (undamaged ones) will begin to assume the role of the missing ones so that the *function* of the dead cells is not lost to the embryo. As a consequence, however, irradiated embryos are usually *smaller*

than normal ones; the progeny of the deleted cells are never entirely replaced. The irradiated embryos *appear* grossly normal, but
cytologic and histologic analyses show damage to their cells, their
life-span is reduced, and their *behavior* performance may not be equal
to that of their unirradiated kin.

**24.3   Stage of Development.**   Ionizing radiation is not the only agent
that produces embryonic deformities or upsets in development. Nor
are the upsets it produces characteristic of its own actions. Many
agents (chemicals, viruses, other physical agents) produce abnormal
embryonic development and the abnormalities they produce are
identical with those caused by an exposure to ionizing radiation. The
abnormality produced, in fact, is more characteristic of and dependent
upon   the   system   developing   at   the   *time*   at   which   the
embryo-deforming agent is used rather than upon the agent itself.
Differentiating or developing systems will be sensitive to or easily
damaged by any number of agents. The reaction of the system
(damage to the cells in it) will always be expressed in the same
way — incomplete or abnormal development *of that system.* Radiation
interactions are, of course, random and indiscriminate. If an entire
embryo is irradiated, a differential reaction of its organ systems will be
observed, based on which of these is in differentiation at the time. The
*stage of development* of the embryo, then, will determine which organ
system of the totally irradiated embryo will be most seriously
damaged and, consequently, the kind of abnormality that will subsequently be observed. Chemical agents and even viruses *may*
(although not necessarily) be more selective in the system that they
will affect. If this is the case, the defect will probably be a reflection of
non-random distribution in the tissues of the embryo rather than a
specific mode of damaging action of the agent used.

**24.4   The Developmental Abnormalities.**   In mammals, irradiation
of the developing embryo before it becomes implanted into the uterus
usually results in death rather than the production of abnormalities.
The survivors ordinarily appear normal. Fertilization of the mammalian ovum most often occurs in the tubes leading from the ovary to
the uterus. It takes place, then, in the oviducts and the very earliest
embryonic development goes on in these tubes. Even after the
cleaving and developing zygotes arrive *in* the uterus, they need not
implant themselves in its wall immediately. In species (rats and mice)
where implantation times have been determined, the zygotes may
float around in the uterine lumen from several hours to days before
implantion occurs. During this time the ovum continues to develop.
In its preimplantation stages it is evidently very susceptible to the
*lethal* action of radiation. It has been shown that, even with doses as

low as 200 R, up to 80 per cent of early preimplantation embryos of mice are killed. In later preimplantation stages the embryos are less sensitive (for example, 40 per cent are killed if irradiated on the fifth day).[1] Such results are reasonable, for the embryo in these early stages consists of very few cells and these will be in the process of differentiation. The cells will be sensitive to radiation, and a loss of a few of them will not be a trivial matter from the point of view of the entire embryo.

Irradiation of the embryo itself during organogenesis leads to malformations and to *neonatal* death (rather than, as when it is in the irradiated preimplantation state, *prenatal* death). In the mouse this period is from seven to twelve days after fertilization, a period equivalent in human beings to the *second* through the *sixth* week of pregnancy. Within this period the defect produced depends on the system developing when irradiation occurs, but, in the mice, *microphthalmia* (tiny eyes) typically results after irradiation at day 7 to 8. *Colosteoma* (a fissure of the eye), *spina bifida occulta* (a defect in the closure of the spinal canal), *hernia*, and *urogenital anomalies* are seen after irradiation at days 9 and 10.

In rats, other workers have demonstrated *anencephaly* (the absence of cerebrum and cerebellum as well as the flat bones of the skull), *anophthalmia* (missing eye or eyes), and *hydrocephalus* (fluid in and around the brain) as well as other brain deformities after irradiation on the ninth, tenth, eleventh, and twelfth days, respectively. *Microcephaly* (pin-head) is seen after irradiation from the twelfth day (corresponding, in man, to the fourth week) to birth.

Low doses (25 R acute x-ray exposure) in the seven and one-half day mouse greatly increase the incidence of skeletal anomalies, and, in an inbred strain, doses of 18 R given on the eighth day result in malformations in 25 per cent of those irradiated.[2,3]

The greatest abundance of malformations occurs after irradiation *early* in development. During the first third of pregnancy the embryo is the most vulnerable, in the second third it is less so, and in the final third it is quite resistant. Male germ cells, however, become very sensitive during the latter period. In mice, acute x-ray exposure of 150 R at the nineteenth day in gestation (it is a late fetus) results in sterilization. Female germ cells have a similar vulnerability, but one that occurs earlier—at about the fifteenth day. Their sensitivity then declines until birth.

**24.5 Human Experience.** Evidence for the production of anomalies in human embryos by radiation is too scanty to give an accurate picture of the situation. Different abnormalities have been attributed to irradiation of the embryo; of these *microcephaly* and associated conditions with microcephaly are the best documented. Frequently, abnormalities of the central nervous system, the eye, and the skeleton are ascribed to irradiation, but the data are such that reliable prediction of dose related to effect and expected incidence is not possible. It can be said, however, that every anomaly of the human fetus has been produced in either mouse or rat by using x ray at comparable stages of development of the animal embryo. While this does not justify extrapolation or prediction of results in human beings, it does make *reasonable* the assumption that similar results might be expected in irradiated human embryos at comparable stages of development (this does, however, remain an assumption).

Many children exposed *in utero* at Hiroshima and Nagasaki were found to be mentally retarded and to have head circumferences less than those expected or well below the mean for their age (all were seven to fifteen weeks in gestation – a radiosensitive period, but not the most radiosensitive one if predictions made from mice are valid). All the children who were seven to fifteen weeks in gestation and whose mothers were less than 1200 meters from the point of detonation of the bombs (the highest dose of radiation is expected in this area) were affected in this way. Those in the same period of gestation but whose mothers were at a greater distance from the point of detonation were less affected. Of the 22 in this gestation period whose mothers were at 1201 to 1500 meters from point of detonation, only 18 per cent were affected. These abnormalites were not noted in children exposed *in utero* whose mothers were farther than 1500 meters from the detonation point. Lesser abnormalities were also encountered in association with severe microcephaly; among them were strabismus (an abnormality of the eyes in which the visual axes do not meet at the desired objective point; it is a consequence of incoordinate action of extrinsic ocular muscles), congenital dislocation of the hips, and mental retardation. An increased incidence of congenital heart disease and hydrocele (an accumulation of fluid in the sac of the tunica vaginalis of the testes) was observed. Fetal death was greatly increased as compared with that in the unirradiated population; at Nagasaki, the rate of fetal deaths was 23.4 per cent and that of neonatal or infant deaths was 26 per cent in those under 2000 meters from the point of detonation. Among the infants who survived, 25 per cent were mentally retarded. Overall, the morbidity and mortality in this group was 60 per cent; in a similar group from the unirradiated Japanese population it was 6 per cent.

Whether or not abnormalities are produced in embryos during radiodiagnosis is yet uncertain. Some instances of increased frequency of malformations of the eye have been reported, but they are not beyond dispute.

**24.6  Clinical Implications.**  While it is still uncertain whether exposures of ionizing radiation in the clinical dose range are embryo-deforming in human beings, they may well have seriously deleterious effects. In experimental animals, embryos in the preimplantation stages are very sensitive to the killing action of radiation, and this situation *may* be similar in human beings. Findings in mice have shown that 100 per cent of the embryos are malformed (many having multiple abnormalities) after a dose of 200 R acute irradiation.[4] This has led to the recommendation that pelvic irradiation of women of child-bearing age should be restricted, as far as is possible, to the ten days following the onset of menstruation. This is a good recommendation, for not enough work has been done to allow good estimates of the effects of low doses given during early pregnancy. Such doses could lead to death of the embryo (which can go unnoticed) or to a mutation involving very large numbers of cells. Later in pregnancy, irradiation carries a risk of somatic mutation; the most serious risk appears to be the induction of cancer (leukemia is induced).

Pelvic irradiation of women in whom there is a probability of pregnancy, particularly early pregnancy, should be avoided, except in serious emergency. Although isolated and too scanty to draw definitive conclusions, reports of malformations following clinical diagnostic exposure of the embryo to x rays have appeared. In mice, the administration of [131]I to pregnant females produces hypothyroidism in both the mother and her offspring. Tumors of the pituitary (adenomas) of the offspring may occur later. Isolated cases of similar destruction of human embryonic thyroid have been reported following administration of [131]I to the mother, but pituitary tumors have not as yet been known to ensue.

## SUMMARY

1.  Embryos are exceedingly radiosensitive. The sensitivity changes with age; generally, older embryos are less sensitive than young ones.
2.  Critical times for producing radiation damage to various organ systems exist; these times probably coincide with the time the affected system is differentiating.
3.  Human embryos are vulnerable to damage from radiation.
4.  Irradiation of pregnant women should be restricted to necessary exposures; exposures of the pelvis should be limited, under all possible circumstances, to emergency procedures.

## Text References

1. Russell, L. B., and Russell, W. L.: Cold Spring Harbor Symposia on Quantitative Biology, 19, 50-59 (1954).
2. Russell, L. B., and Russell, W. L.: Radiation hazards to the embryo and fetus, Radiology 58, 369-377 (1952).
3. Russell, L. B.: Effects of low doses of x-rays on embryonic development in the mouse, Proceeding of the Society for Experimental Biology and Medicine 95, 174-178 (1957).
4. Miller, R. W.: Delayed effects occurring within the first decade after exposure of young individuals to the Hiroshima atomic bomb, Paediatrics 18, 1 (1956).
5. International Commission of Radiological Protection: Committee I: The evaluation of risks from radiation, Health Physics 12, 253 (1966).

## General References

1. Russell, Liane B.: In *Radiation Biology*, Vol. I., Part 2, Chapter 13, pp. 861-918. Alexander Hollaender (ed). McGraw-Hill, New York, 1954.
2. Ruge, Roberts: In *Mechanisms in Radiobiology*, Vol. II, Chapter 1. Maurice Errera and Arne Forssberg (eds.) Academic Press, New York, 1960.
3. International Commission on Radiological Protection: Committee I. The evaluation of risks from radiation, Health Physics 12, 238-302 (1966).

# 25

# Factors Influencing the Effects of Irradiation

**25.1 Introduction.** As has already been pointed out in several specific instances and implied in others, the biologic effects of radiation are not rigid, precise responses on the part of living things. There are variations in the degree of response, even among populations of individuals which otherwise appear quite identical to each other. Some of the factors influencing the responses to radiation are known; others, of course, are not. The former are the subject matter of this chapter; the latter, of future research.

**25.2 The Quality and Quantity of the Radiation.** The *kind* of biologic response to nearly all types, or at least widely differing types, of ionizing radiation does not differ very much. Most organisms respond to most radiations in about the same manner. The *degree* to which they respond, or the magnitude of the response elicited, depends on the *quantity* of radiation given (the dose) and the quality of the radiation administered. Quantity or dose-dependence has already been discussed in detail; nearly all responses to radiation are dose-dependent. (Survival time as a result of doses in the range producing the gastrointestinal syndrome would appear as an exception to this statement. However, the exception is apparent. Certain dose-levels of radiation block the cell renewal system of the intestinal epithelium to the degree that failure of the gut and death associated with it occur in a given period. Dose-levels higher than that destroy more cells in the gut, but death, within a certain time, has been foreordained at a lower dose—when the stem cell population reached a critical low level. *Survival time* is *not* dose-dependent. Even so, other tissues of the irradiated organism will continue to display dose-response dependency; they will be more grievously affected; as dose is increased more of their cells will be injured or killed.)

The *quality* or energy of the ionizing radiation used will determine the degree of the radiobiologic response. The quantity of radiation needed to elicit a particular response will, in many cases, be dependent on the energy of that radiation. The *biologic effectiveness*, the efficiency of a radiation for producing a given effect, will vary.

Measures or estimates of this variation are called RBE (*relative biologic effectiveness*) values. The variation is due to the fact that the effects of ionizing radiation will depend not only on the total amount of energy absorbed over a given time period, but also on the *distribution* of that energy through the material irradiated. The *ionization density* or the distribution of energy along individual tracks will determine the effectiveness of a radiation for producing a given result. For *most* radiation effects the efficiency of a radiation for producing them *increases* as the ion density along the tracks increases. Densely ionizing radiation (or radiations of high LET) will be more efficient for producing most biologic effects than will the same dose of sparsely ionizing radiations.

The degree of difference can be considerable. When comparing the efficiency of gamma rays to x rays for a number of biologic effects, x rays, the *less* energetic radiation, those that produce less energetic high-speed electrons with higher LET's, are between 1 and 2 times as effective as gamma rays. For example, it has been shown that 200 Kev x rays are about 1.3 times as effective as 20 Mev x rays for killing mice. Approximately 1.3 times the dose of the very energetic x rays is needed to elicit the same effect as that of the 200 Kev radiation.

In human skin the *threshold* dose for producing erythema (reddening of the skin), under controlled conditions of dose-rate and area irradiated, has been given as 1000 R for gamma rays (from radium) and 1000 Kev x rays but only 700 R for 200 Kev radiation (a ratio of effectiveness or RBE value of 1.4); and 500 R for 100 Kev radiation (a ratio of 2).

The increase in biologic effectiveness with diminishing energy holds for most biologic effects save for those where one hit is all that is required for inactivation or change. In the latter, one ionization or a single cluster of ionizations is all that is necessary to produce the effect; any additional ionization will be wasted.

For irradiation of tumors, then, the most heavily ionizing radiation possible would seem to be the radiation of choice since killing of the tumor is the desired result. However, the choice of radiation may not be as simple as that; a number of other factors (to be described below) will enter into the effectiveness of any radiation for producing a biologic result.

**25.3 Intensity-Duration Factor.** For most biologic effects, in particular those observed in animals, the effectiveness of a given dose will be related to the rate at which the dose is delivered. Generally speaking, the effectiveness of a given dose for producing a given effect is *lessened* as the time to deliver that dose is increased. There are apparent exceptions; genetic mutations have been supposed to be dose-rate independent; any dose, given at any rate has been supposed to produce the same total number of these mutations. This is so because the mutation is believed to involve an irreversible change in the molecules of DNA, requiring only a single chemical change to bring them into existence.

Not only is the effectiveness of any given radiation less when given at slow dose-rates than at rapid ones, but also there will be an alteration in the magnitude of the effect if the same dose of the same radiation is given at interrupted intervals, *in fractions*, with some time between each fraction.

The differences in the magnitude of effects observed as a function of dose-rate or of fractioning the dose are usually explained by the supposition that *recovery* can occur following biologic damage and that the damage itself can be repaired. This is true because any dose of ionizing radiation can be expected to produce the same number of ionizations in like material or a fixed number of free radicals irrespective of either the rate or the continuity of irradiation. If the accumulated effect of a fractioned dose of radiation is less than that of the same dose given at once, it is reasonable to expect that some of the damage has, between the fractions, been repaired. Similarly, if a dose given at a low dose-rate produces less damage than the same dose given quickly, repair or recovery is a reasonable assumption. When radiation is given rapidly, all the energy will be transmitted in a very short interval. Enough molecules of living matter may be changed in that interval to cause serious derangement of metabolism, even death. At slower dose-rates, on the other hand, while the *same* total amount of energy is transmitted and the *same* total number of *changes* produced, some molecules that have been changed may have an opportunity to either repair themselves or to be repaired. The total damage sustained at the *end* of the irradiation is less than that experienced in the short exposure, because some of the damage will have been repaired. The total number of changes, of course, is the same in both instances.

This is not to say that *all* damage from irradiation is or can be repaired. Rather, it is believed that some damaged molecules are not repaired following any radiation exposure. Repeated exposures to even small doses of ionizing radiation or exposure to radiation given at very slow dose-rates produces damage that can be expected to accumulate.

There will also be a difference in the magnitude of the biologic response or the biologic effectiveness, dependent upon the size and spacing between fractions when the dose is interrupted. If the fractions are given very close together so that little time separates them, the relative effectiveness will be greater than that of the same amounts of radiation separated by longer intervals. Presumably, in the longer interval, more time is available for recovery from each fraction, and, in that time, more molecules recover. On the other hand, if the fractions are separated by the same time interval but the amount of radiation given at each exposure differs, the relative effectiveness will also differ. A greater biologic effect may be expected from the total dose if the fractions are of unequal size than if they are the same.

More damage will occur if the first fraction is larger than the second. This is true because the number of molecules that must recover *before* the second fraction is given is large. The cell in which they are found will be more profoundly damaged and its over-all capacity for recovery more affected. The second fraction is likely to add insult to a still badly damaged system. If the first fraction is small, more recovery and a more intact entity will exist when the second fraction (the larger) is given. Less *total* damage will result.

**25.4 The Recovery Mechanisms.** Several recent investigations into recovery of irradiated populations of cells have indicated a mechanism of recovery which may explain the variable biologic effects of different dose-rates. In a case where *two* or more events (either ionizations or interactions with free radicals) are necessary to produce *irreversible* cell damage or death, a *single* event will be a *latent* injury (that is to say, no injury is expressed unless the second event follows). If the second event does not follow within a given or *definable* time period, the first or latent injury can heal or be repaired. In such a case, irreversible damage or death will depend on both events occurring within a short time interval, a time interval short enough for the second event to take place before the first has had time to heal. Injuries of this kind will be dose-rate *and* ion-density dependent.

DNA presents a good example of such injuries. If the main chain of a DNA molecule is broken by an interaction with radiation or by one of radiation's by-products, it can, in a relatively short time, restitute itself by rejoining the broken ends. If it is broken in two or more places at the same time or at *nearly* the same time, restitution of the macromolecule — intact — becomes less probable.

Further, it is *believed,* though not yet absolutely proved, that broken or injured DNA can be repaired — in particular after a break in only *one* of the chains of the macromolecules. This kind of repair is less probable after two breaks and would be less probable yet after more than two breaks.

If one of the chains in the double-stranded molecule is broken, an enzyme can remove or digest the broken piece — from the point of breakage to its end. Then, the complementary strand, or chain, synthesizes or directs the synthesis of the digested piece. The orginal molecule is restored intact. When two breaks occur, one in *each* of the

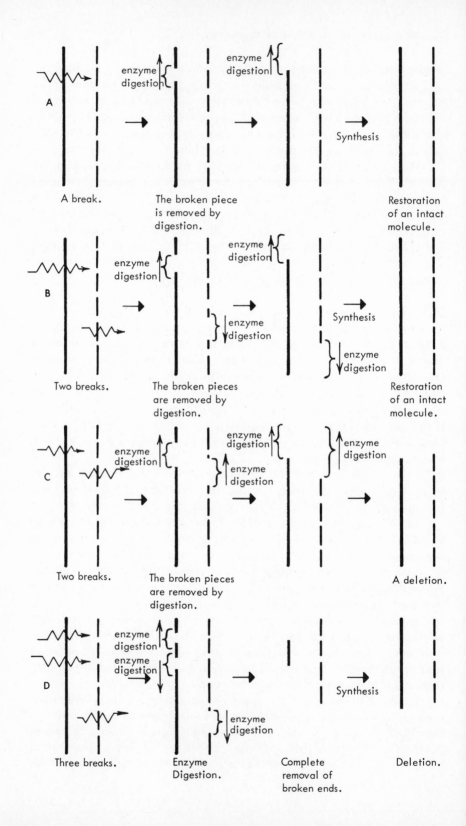

A. A break. — The broken piece is removed by digestion. — Synthesis — Restoration of an intact molecule.

B. Two breaks. — The broken pieces are removed by digestion. — Synthesis — Restoration of an intact molecule.

C. Two breaks. — The broken pieces are removed by digestion. — A deletion.

D. Three breaks. — Enzyme Digestion. — Complete removal of broken ends. — Synthesis — Deletion.

strands, the same process can occur, but, depending on *where* the breaks have occurred, an intact molecule may or may not be restored (Figure 25.1).

Restoration of an intact molecule after this kind of damage (scission of the main DNA chain) will be dependent upon both LET *and* dose-rate. With high LET, more than one ionization or damaging event within the confines of even a DNA molecule would be expected. This is not so likely with sparsely ionizing, low LET radiation. The probability of more than one break occurring will increase as a function of ion density. The dose-rate will also be a determinant in the repair process. If the process is slow enough so that all or most of the chain breakages that occur can be repaired *before* a second occurs, each new breakage (even if it is the end of a long series of breakages) will act as if it were the first one (or as in case a, Figure 25.1) and an intact molecule would be expected to be restored each time. The net effect, of course, would be no damage. As the dose-rate is increased, the likelihood of producing two simultaneous breaks increases, and the probability of repair decreases (cases c and d, Figure 25.1). Some permanent damage will result. In this way, the *dose-rate* will have determined the degree of permanent damage done.

It should be emphasized that, at present, the existence of this repair mechanism cannot be proved beyond all doubt. However, there is much evidence pointing to this concept. DNA synthesis, after irradiation, appears to go on—even outside the S phase (the normal DNA synthesis interval). This is interpreted as the synthesis of the enzyme-digested fragments. In addition, the amount of radiation-damaged DNA in cells where this process is believed to occur is altered with time. Directly after irradiation, if DNA is extracted from these cells, many small fragments can be detected. These are believed to be the broken "ends" of the molecules. But extraction of the DNA from irradiated cells at time intervals after radiation shows ever decreasing numbers of these fragments.

The observations are taken to mean that some of the small fragments present right after irradiation have been digested and replaced by intact molecules.

Some of the workers investigating these phenomena have noted that "innate radiosensitivity" may be linked to the ability to repair damaged DNA. The ability to do so seems limited in radiosensitive strains when compared to radioresistant strains of the same organism.

---

**Figure 25.1.** A possible mechanism of repair of DNA injured from an interaction either with ionizing radiation or one of radiation's secondary products. Where only one event is sustained (A) the molecule can be restored. But, in the case of two or more "hits" (B,C,D), a deletion of part of the molecule *may* result and permanent damage to the cell will follow.

The second recovery mechanism concerns itself with the effect of dose-fractionation. It supposes that inactivation (or death, as the case may be) will be the result of a multi-hit phenomenon (Chapter 10). It will be recalled that, where a number of agents (targets, sensitive sites) are responsible for or direct the vital functions of a living thing, all of these must be inactivated before vital function will cease (or, in a less drastic case, permanent damage will be apparent). The survival of organisms having multiple targets when plotted against *dose* of radiation is sigmoid (Chapter 10): there are doses of radiation that are so low that *essentially* none of the organisms is killed (Figures 10.3 and 10.4).

It can be seen that no organisms are killed at very low doses (the curve does not intersect the origin in Figure 10.3; it is at zero for an appreciable dose-range). Sensitive sites or molecules *are* being inactivated, but at certain dose levels (which will increase as the number of such molecules increases) the probability of all having been inactivated is very high and a sharp increase in the number of cells or organisms that die is then observed. When radiation is given in *fractions*, the shoulder in the log plot (Figure 10.4) tends to *reappear* after each fraction so that the dose required to get on the linear portion (a steep rise in killing) of the curve increases. The time required for the reappearance of the shoulder (repair of damage done) probably will be characteristic of the cells under consideration. Small doses, appropriately fractioned, would be expected to yield a smaller radiation response than the same dose continuously given. Also, many small doses would be expected to be less damaging than a few large ones.

Recovery by this mechanism would be expected to be more dependent upon the *number* of fractions, rather than upon the time between fractions.

While not strictly a modifier of the RBE, changing the time intervals *between* fractions can be expected to permit still a third mechanism of recovery (and thus be a determinant of radiation efficiency). The longer an interval between exposures to radiation, the better the unaffected cells (or those which have recovered, by one of the mechanisms above) will be able to divide, replace the killed cells, and repopulate the tissue. *Tissue repair*, then, is a time-dependent phenomenon. The longer the time after an exposure to radiation, the more nearly normal a tissue will become.

## 25.5  The Pressure of Oxygen.

The tension of oxygen in cells at the time of irradiation is an important determinant of the degree of severity of radiation damage (Chapter 11). Oxygen always *enhances* radiation action.

**25.6 Completeness of Irradiation.** The effectiveness of any given dosage of radiation will depend upon the "completeness" of the irradiation, that is, whether the *entire* cell or organism is irradiated or only a part of it. For a given cell, the nucleus will be more sensitive to radiation than its cytoplasm. Within total organisms, certain systems are more sensitive than others. Generally speaking, irradiation of the total organism is more damaging than the irradiation of any component part.

**25.7 Proliferative vs. Non-proliferative Tissues.** Tissues or groups of cells that are rapidly proliferating or which have a large number of their members in mitosis will be more sensitive to radiation than will more mitotically *static* tissues or groups of cells. The mitotic process is a relatively radiosensitive phase in a cell's life, and, within the process itself, differences in radiosensitivity have been observed. These differences depend on the endpoint observed; for lethality, late $G_1$ and S appear to be the most sensitive period, but the $G_2$ period is the one in which the greatest variety of chromosome breaks will ccur.

**25.8 Age.** There is a general relationship of radiation sensitivity and age of the irradiated organism. Generally speaking, radiosensitivity *decreases* as age increases; older organisms are more resistant than young ones. But, the relationship is a general one. Very old organisms become relatively more radiosensitive than younger ones. This, however, may be a reflection of the loss of resistance to any form of insult (not merely radiation) on the part of the very old. Throughout adult life, with the exception of the period of old age, radiosensitivity changes little. During the period of rapid growth to maturity, most organisms will be more radiosensitive than those having adult status. Puberty is an especially sensitive period.

**25.9 Sex.** In some species and in some strains within species a sex difference in response to total-body radiation has been noted. In mammals, females appear *generally* to be somewhat more resistant to radiation than males, but the differences are not great.

**25.10 Body Weight.** While the precise role is unclear, it appears that *heavier* organisms are more resistant to radiation than are lighter ones of the same kind.

**25.11 Temperature and Metabolic Rate.** The *development* of radiation injury is dependent on metabolic rate. Because this is so, varying the metabolic rate will bring about variations in the *rate* of development of radiation injury. If metabolism is speeded up or caused to race (this can be done by subjecting animals to exhaustive exercise, or placing non-acclimatized animals in cold environments), the lethal effects of irradiation are enhanced, while retarding the metabolic rate (this can be done by lowering body temperature — inducing hypothermia) protracts the period over which radiation damage occurs. The administration of thyroid-stimulating substances or the removal of the thyroid gland, procedures which will change the basal metabolic rate (although in opposite directions), does not, surprisingly, have much effect on radiosensitivity.

**25.12  Species Variation.**  This point has already been sufficiently stressed; there are variations in response to radiation based on species. The origins of such variations are as yet unclear, but their existence is beyond dispute.

**25.13  Diurnal Variation.**  The sensitivity of some organisms to radiation varies according to the time at which they are irradiated. The effect, described so far only for total-body radiation in rats and mice, is similar to many responses of organisms to the effects of a large number of stimuli; they occur with a daily rhythm. Maximum sensitivity occurs duing the active period (the "subjective day").

**25.14  Stress.**  Radiation is more effective (or more damaging) to animals experiencing some kind of stress. For example, small non-lethal doses of radiation may cause death in animals suffering a *non-lethal* thermal burn. Radiation appears to be a stress itself and, combined with other stresses, attains greater magnitude of effect.

**25.15  Medical Implications.**  All of the above-discussed modifying factors will have some bearing on the medical use of ionizing radiation. All should be considered in deciding the dose to be given or the probable response to given doses of radiation. Among them, however, the time-intensity factor, oxygen effect, tissue sensitivity, and effect of age are the most important — at least so far as our present state of knowledge permits the judgment to be made. In both diagnostic and therapeutic work, age of the patient as it bears on his sensitivity to radiation, as well as the probable length of life remaining to the patient in which the late effects may be expressed, must be evaluated whenever radiation is to be used. The tissue to be irradiated is an important factor in making a decision in regard to both the total dose (is it mitotically active?; static?) and the time between fractions. The time-intensity factor will determine the efficiency of irradiation for producing damage; recovery of both normal and abnormal irradiated tissues must be a factor in choosing the type as well as the dose-rate of the radiation to be used.

## SUMMARY

1. The biological effects of radiation are dependent *both* on the kind as well as the quantity of radiation used.
2. Relative biologic effectiveness (RBE) depends on LET, but also upon the dose-rate and upon whether the dose is given all at once or in fractions.
3. Recovery from radiation can occur; restoration of normal conditions depends on dose-rate as well as ion density.
4. The physiologic status of the irradiated organism, as well as its age, sex, and weight, will determine its response to irradiation.

## General References

1. Patt, H. M., and Brues, A. M.: *The Pathological Physiology of Radiation Injury in the Mammal. I. Physical and Biological Factors in Radiation Action in Radiation Biology*, Vol. I, part 2. A. Hollaender (ed). McGraw-Hill, New York, 1954.
2. Fowler, J. F.: *The Effect of Age on Radiosensitivity* in *Radiation Effects in Physics, Chemistry and Biology*. M. Ebert and A. Howard (eds). Year Book Medical Publishers, Inc., Chicago, 1963.
3. Cohen, L.: *Radiation Response and Recovery*, in *The Biological Basis of Radiation Therapy*. F. E. Schwartz (ed). Lippincott, Philadelphia, 1966.
4. Nelson, R. F.: Variation in radiosensitivity of mice with time of day, Acta Radiologic 4, 91-96 (1966).

# 26

# Radiation Effects on Immunity

**26.1 Introduction.** The process of *immunity* is itself very complex; the normal mechanisms are not yet entirely clear. Yet, exposure to radiation does alter the capacity of organisms to respond to the introduction of foreign entities into their systems, and often the changes in this *defense capacity* are closely correlated (although not yet proved to be *causally* related) to certain pathophysiologic changes brought about by the exposure. This chapter will deal in a general way with these changes.

**26.2 Immunity.** In a very broad sense, *immune* responses are reactions of a body in (1) *recognizing* foreign material with which it has come into contact *as* foreign to itself or different from itself, and (2) "removing" it from the body (either by reacting with the foreign material and "neutralizing" or "detoxifying" it, by encapsulating it in a thick membrane and isolating it, or by *digesting* it, causing it to disappear). The foreign substance may be one of a large range of materials; general categories include large parasites (the various worms), viruses, bacteria, tissues or groups of tissues (such as in a skin or tissue graft), and non-living chemicals often elaborated by plant or animal cells (commonly by bacteria) called "toxins."

The mechanisms by which organisms respond (make themselves immune) to the various foreign substances may be of two types, inborn or innate and acquired. The inborn mechanisms are genetically determined and are characteristic of the individual or species. They are usually non-specific; that is to say, the organism or species will be generally quite resistant to infection rather than to infection by a specific organism.

*Acquired immunity,* on the other hand, describes an immunity or resistance to infection, usually by a specific foreign substance or material, which has been gained as a result of prior contact with the same or similar foreign substance or material. This immunity is acquired usually against foreign proteins (the source may vary, but often or commonly the foreign proteins will be elaborated by bacteria). One exposure to these proteins will cause the body to produce substances that detoxify them (these are the *antibodies*). A high level of antibodies will be produced which subsequently falls off. When a second exposure to the same protein occurs (even long periods after the first has been experienced), the process of antibody formation occurs very rapidly with the production of much larger quantities of antibody than were produced the first time. It is a *specific* response (as opposed to innate mechanisms); the body seems to "recall" its first experience with a given protein and can bring forth very quickly the series of events (elaboration of antibody) needed to deal with this protein.

The defense against implantation of foreign tissues is mediated through cells called *lymphocytes.* If foreign tissue is implanted in an animal the animal will recognize it as foreign, and lymphocytes, most often from nearby lymph nodes, will invade the tissue and *digest* the tissue. This response is the reason for the failure of tissue or organ implants (for example, skin or kidney transplants) to persist successfully in an animal host; the host lymphocytes attack, kill, and digest the offending material. This reaction, too, is, like that of an acquired immunity, specific. A second transplant of tissue from the *same* host will also be rejected. The second rejection response will, however, be much accelerated compared to the first. But, implantation of tissue from *another,* even a closely related, donor will be rejected at a rate characteristic of a *first* rejection response. Within limits it is correct to say each challenge by a *new* donor (or, more precisely, a genetically *different* donor) will be a new experience for the host.

**26.3 Tissue Rejection.** Lymphoid tissue and the lymphocytes themselves are markedly radiosensitive. Small doses of radiation (in mammals, a total-body dose above 300 R of x rays) are sufficient to kill most mature lymphocytes and to inhibit the production of new ones in the lymph nodes. The nodes themselves are badly damaged by low radiation doses, sometimes so much so that the architecture of the nodes is completely disrupted (the nodes do regenerate, however, in time, although long periods of time may be required for the restoration of normal architecture).

Therefore, irradiation of an organism will be expected to and, in fact, does prolong the life of tissue implants or grafts in that organism. That is to say, the tissue-rejection response of an irradiated host takes a much longer time than that of a non-irradiated host. The delay itself is evidently due to destruction of lymphoid tissue, and the length of the delay will depend on how much is destroyed—itself a reflection of dose.

If massive doses of total-body radiation are given, complete or near complete destruction of the immune response can be brought about. (The dose levels needed would cause death unless something is done to prevent that outcome. The way this is done is the subject of the next chapter.) Tissues transplanted to such a host "take" and are not rejected. Organisms bearing such grafts produce two genetically *different* kinds of cells: their own genotype and that of the *donor* cells. Such organisms are called "chimeras."

The existence of radiation-produced chimeras is the rationale behind the use of total-body radiation in preparation for organ transplants in human beings. In the case of some kidney diseases, both kidneys may become non-functional. An approach for saving the life of an individual thus afflicted involves the transplantation of a kidney from another individual. Except when an identical twin is available as a donor, a kidney from any donor will, in the usual course of events, be recognized by the host as foreign tissue and will be rejected. Total-body radiation, in the proper dosages, *prior* to implatation of the donor organ, increases the length of time that the donor organ will remain viable. The production of large numbers of chimeras, however, has not been realized; the kidney grafts are, in time, rejected. While this approach appears a good one to use in organ transplantation, and, after more time and experimentation, might be fruitful, at present it does not give good results.

**26.4 Increase in Susceptibility to Infection: Innate Immunity.**
Acute irradiation impairs the *barrier function* of certain tissues against penetration through them of infective agents. Of these, skin, lungs, and the intestinal mucosa are affected. As has already been described in the sections on total-body radiation, intestinal flora, normally kept in the lumen by the barrier presented by the mucosa, may invade or infect the bloodstream of irradiated animals. The destruction of the continuity of the mucosa by exposure to radiation results in the loss of the natural barrier to infection of this kind and so reduces natural or innate immunity. Skin and lungs, two other natural defense barriers against penetration by infective agents, are similarly affected.

The *barrier* function of tissues is but one of the ways in which the tissues help in preventing infection. There are, as well, *cellular defense mechanisms.* Certain cells (those in the appendix of the rabbit, for example) can block and destroy many cells that might penetrate a barrier tissue, even in its intact state. These cells are affected by irradiation and some, if not all, of their function is lost. Phagocytes may engulf but not digest bacteria. The enclosed bacteria may again be set free. The engulfing property may itself be affected.

The clearance of bacteria from the body may be incomplete after irradiation. Animals, recovering from an infection, have *usually* cleared the infective agent and are not themselves disease carriers. After irradiation, there will be an increased susceptibility to the same diseases and the recovered animals may "carry" the infection for rather long periods.

**26.5 Acquired Immunity.** An organism exposed to foreign material can, as mentioned in the beginning of this chapter, synthesize substances (antibodies) to counteract or destroy the foreign material. The reaction is specific; that is, antibodies are elaborated against a particular foreign matter (antigen). Some of the classes of antigens include proteins and polysaccharides, but foreign cells such as bacteria may also elicit the response. The antibodies may agglutinate bacteria (causing them to clump) or dissolve them (lysis). Exposure to radiation will *alter* the ability of an organism to synthesize antibodies and, as a consequence, the speed with which antigens (whether purely chemical or total cells) are removed from the infected animal.

**26.6 Time of Irradiation.** The time radiation is given will influence the degree to which the ability to elaborate antibodies is affected by the radiation exposure. If antigen is administered *before* irradiation, the antibody producing response is *less* affected than when antigen is administered to an irradiated organism. It appears that maximum damage to the process of antibody formation is caused when irradiation is carried out twelve to twenty-four hours before administration of the antigen. This is evaluated by comparing the maximum amount of antibody formed (titer), the length of time required for antibody to be formed (the induction period), and the relative rate at which antibody is formed (once its formation has started) in unirradiated animals and in animals irradiated at various time intervals before and after antigen administration. If antigen is administered just *after* irradiation, the process of antibody formation or production will not itself be impaired (exposure will have occurred before this process is elicited), and nearly normal amounts of antibody will eventually be formed. However, the production will take longer and the relative rate of production of antibody will be slower than in non-irradiated subjects. If antigen is administered four days *before* irradiation, normal amounts of antibody are produced, but the rate of production is slower than normal. The four-day period is *longer* than the normal *induction period*, and antibody production is not affected by irradiation. But, if antigen is administered just *before* irradiation, antibody levels are near normal, but the production is *higher* than normal.

**26.7 Phases of Antibody Production.** These responses of the process of antibody formation have led to the following hypothesis on the mechanics of the process itself. There are said to be three phases involved. The first of these, the *preinduction phase* or period, is thought to be very brief (probably lasting—for certain antigens, at least—one to four hours) and is believed essential for *initiating* development of the *antibody-synthesizing* mechanism. This phase is quite radiosensitive and, for certain antigens, appears to require certain clearly defined threshold doses of radiation.

Following this period will be an *induction* period; irradiation to rather high dose-levels during this period does not affect the total *quantity* of antibodies produced, but the *time* required for them to appear is very long. The quantity produced can actually exceed normal expectation (see Section 26.8). Irradiation during this period may affect antibody formation by slowing down or inhibiting the development of the *apparatus* that synthesizes antibodies.

Finally the *production period* will occur. In this time, antibodies will actually be produced—a process which is relatively radioresistant. There are species differences in resistance, but the process is generally thought of as resistant. Irradiation in this period has little effect on antibody production.

**26.8  Secondary Reactions.**   The influence on *secondary reactions* or responses of irradiation is less clearly defined. The effect seems to depend, at least in part, upon the antigen used: the secondary responses of some appear radiosensitive while others are resistant.

## SUMMARY

1.  Immunity appears to be of two types: *natural* or innate (this is non-specific) and *acquired*, specific immunity.
2.  The immune response consists in *recognizing* foreign material as foreign and *removing* it from the body.
3.  Foreign material falls into three categories: viruses and cells, groups of cells (tissues or organs), non-living chemicals (toxins).
4.  Radiation, in particular total-body radiation, *inhibits* the immune responses, but cases are known in which an enhancement of response has been described.

### General References

1.  Hasek, M., and Lengerova, A.: *Immunology,* in *Mechanisms* in *Radiobiology,* Vol. II, M. Errera and A. Forssbergs (eds.), Academic Press, New York, 1960.
2.  Taliaferro, W. H., Taliaferro, L. G., and Jaroslow, B. N.: *Radiation and Immune Mechanisms,* Academic Press, New York, 1964.

# 27

# Treatment of Irradiated Organisms

**27.1 Introduction.** The *syndromes* leading to death in lethally irradiated organisms and even the "sickness" following irradiation at non-lethal, total-body dose levels have been ascribed to radiation damage to cells of *all* the tissues of the body. But death, after exposure to a wide range of dose-levels, has been presumed to result *primarily* from radiation damage to and failure of the cell renewal systems of two major organ systems, the bone marrow and the gastrointestinal system. Accordingly, if this presumption is correct, a therapy or course of treatment for irradiated organisms could be devised which might make it possible to mitigate the symptoms of the syndromes and to measurably extend the life of irradiated organisms, hypothetically, for periods of many years.

**27.2 Rationale.** The treatments developed have been based upon examination of the primary and secondary consequences of total body radiation. Lost or vanishing functions or cells, those that are destroyed by total-body exposure, are carefully *replaced* until such time as the irradiated organism can begin to regenerate its missing cells or functions.

This can be done; the principle is well established. *Successful,* long-term treatment, however, depends to a great extent on the total dose received. After exposure to very high dose-levels, the damage done to the central nervous system and the consequences that flow from it (Chapter 22) are, at present, beyond treatment. But, that category aside, even at lower doses the actual dose received will still determine the ultimate success of treatment. This is true, because dose is the determining factor in how long natural regenerative processes are delayed following radiation exposure. Replacement therapy, the replacement of cells or functions, cannot, at present, go on for protracted periods of time; successful treatment presupposes that the irradiated organism can soon again become self-sufficient.

**27.3  Secondary Manifestations.**  The secondary manifestations following total-body radiation exposure that *must* be treated if even short-term survival is to be possible are granulocytopenia (the absence or scarcity of granulocytes — mature polymorphonucleocytes — from the circulating blood), thrombocytopenia (the absence or scarcity of thrombocytes — platelets, red blood cells — from the circulating blood), and, in species where this occurs, anemia. At higher doses, the watery, often bloody diarrhea, which causes fluid loss and electrolyte imbalance, must also be controlled.

**27.4  Susceptibility to Infection.**  Resistance to infections by nearly any kind of bacteria is markedly reduced following total body radiation. While it is true that this increased susceptibility may be due *in part* to a breakdown of the *barrier function* of various tissues (in particular that of gut after relatively high doses of radiation), a correlation can also be made between the time of onset of infection and depression of *granulocyte* count following radiation. Such a correlation suggests that these cells are an important part of the defense against infection by and rapid growth of bacteria in the body after irradiation.

Further, after total body radiation, when granulocytopenia becomes detectable, replacement of granulocytes (by transfusion) clears up or mitigates the bacterial infections that follow lethal exposures.

Replacement therapy with granulocytes establishes a very important point even if its practical application gives, as yet, disappointingly poor results. *Replacement* does modify the progress and outcome of the syndrome. The poor results are due primarily to the rather short life expectancy of transfused granulocytes. The half life in man has been estimated at between six and eight hours.[1,2] Such a brief survival time means that, for replacement therapy, a very large supply of fresh granulocytes will have to be available. Repeated transfusions will have to be made during the period of granulocytic insufficiency (a period that will vary in length with dose). This in itself is a difficulty, for large supplies of these cells are not freely available. In addition, repeated transfusions of granulocytes lead to a shortening of their already short life span after transfusing. Nevertheless, none of these shortcomings of the treatment obscures the importance of the principle it establishes; replacement of granulocytes can modify the extent of infection and the course of the syndrome following lethal irradiation exposure.

**27.5  Treatment of Infection with Drugs.**  Since the multiplication and proliferation of bacteria in the blood and the products that these bacteria produce are believed to be of major importance in radiation-produced lethality, it is reasonable to expect that antibiotics could substitute for the presence of granulocytes, prevent or mitigate infection, and extend life after lethal irradiation. This is the case; in the period of severe granulocyte depression, antibiotics do provide protection against radiation and forestall death. After exposure to radiation in low dose-ranges, antibiotics and platelets have been used in dogs and have prevented death. Antibiotic therapy is begun when signs indicate that infection is present, when the temperature becomes elevated. Unfortunately the infecting microorganisms in time become resistant to the antibiotic being used; the temperature again becomes elevated. But, if a different antibiotic is then given, the organisms can be controlled, and fever will again drop.

Equally successful therapy has not been reported for every study using antibiotics. In some irradiated species, better results appear attainable than in others: certain strains of bacteria appear more susceptible than others. Nevertheless, the principle seems established; granulocytopenia can be treated either by transfusion of fresh granulocytes or antibiotic therapy. Either alternative modifies the consequences of total body radiation and can extend life beyond that expected after lethal doses of radiation.

**27.6  Control of Hemorrhage.**  Even if granulocyte replacement therapy is successful and infection is avoided, the hazard of hemorrhage due to loss of thrombocytes remains. In the untreated or unmodified acute radiation syndrome, infection and bleeding occur so closely together that it is not possible to separate their individual roles in bringing about death. But, in granulocyte-treated irradiated organisms, those in which infection is controlled, the role of bleeding and the extent to which it may be responsible for radiation death can be evaluated. Acutely irradiated, infection-free organisms die as a result of their exposure to radiation. Moreover, in such animals, death coincides with the time at which thrombocytes become markedly depleted. When platelet levels drop very low, irradiated animals will die unless they are treated.[3] If *fresh* platelets *are* transfused, however, bleeding dramatically stops, and death is averted. While an absolute causal relationship is not yet established, the strong inference implicit in such findings is that death would have been caused by *thrombocytopenia.*

The effect of *fresh* platelet transfusion is evidently linked to the fact that such transfusions increase the level of circulating platelets. No significant prevention of bleeding has been noted with the use of platelets treated in various ways: frozen, disrupted, or lyophilized. Platelets in any of these forms do not increase the levels of circulating platelets[3] nor do they prevent bleeding. The storage and preservation of platelets are, in fact, important factors in limiting the usefulness of this technique for treatment of radiation exposure. *In vivo* survival time of transfused platelets is relatively long compared to that of granulocytes (five days, but there are significant species variations), long enough, in fact, so that a method of storing platelets would have considerable clinical significance. These cells, under normal storage conditions, quickly lose the qualities that are needed in the treatment of radiation exposure.

When repeated platelet transfusion is necessary, the efficiency of this therapy for stopping bleeding gradually decreases and the life of the transfused cells grows shorter with each succeeding transfusion. This appears to be due to the development of an immunologic response on the part of the host against the foreign cells. Antibodies are formed (although rather more slowly in totally irradiated hosts than in unirradiated hosts) which agglutinate and destroy the transfused cells.

**27.7  Treatment of Dehydration.**  When, after relatively high doses of total body radiation, the gut is denuded, severe fluid loss with subsequent electrolyte imbalance occurs. This dehydration and electrolyte imbalance are believed to be the responsible entity in bringing about death within a short time after irradiation. If time enough is to be given for the mucosa to regenerate and reline the gut, the water loss and electrolyte imbalance must be treated so that early death does not occur. Fluid and electrolyte replacement combined with antibiotic therapy is useful; in dogs it is effective in the early acute phases. Later, when infection is likely to be present, it is less useful.

**27.8  Bone-Marrow Replacement.**  The transfusion of bone-marrow cells to lethally irradiated individuals would be expected to confer significant beneficial therapeutic results. This supposition is based on the observation that, in animals irradiated to high dose-levels but in which the spleens were shielded, significant protection against the radiation was obtained. Hemopoietic cells appeared to be able to repopulate the bone-marrow spaces, thereby averting bone-marrow depletion. This could be taken as presumptive evidence that if bone marrow were transplanted to lethally irradiated organisms, the transplanted marrow would multiply to fill the depleted marrow spaces, and, in time, begin to supply mature circulating cells for the irradiated organism.

The hypothesis has been tested in many places and at many times, bone-marrow transfusions do indeed increase the probability of survival of lethally irradiated organisms. The degree of increase is dependent upon the amount of bone marrow transplanted. The more that is transplanted, the better the chance for survival. The transfused bone marrow begins to multiply and replaces the irradiated organism's lost marrow. The more marrow transfused, the more rapid and the earlier is this replacement and the shorter the period in which the irradiated organism will have a shortage of mature circulating cells.

However, the probable success of bone-marrow transplants will vary in relation to the genetic relationship between the donor of the bone marrow and the irradiated host. Any tissue transplant will be more "successful" (persist longer in the host) the more closely the donor and the host are related. This is true, of course, for bone marrow. If, in the case of an irradiated host, the host's *own* bone marrow is used as the donor (this is called an autotransplant; it can be made only if bone marrow is removed before irradiation and then injected after irradiation), a permanent "take" can reasonably be expected; no complications are likely to result. If an exchange is made between *identical* twins (biologically, since such twins result from the separation of the cells of a zygote in very early development, both individuals have the same genes and can be regarded as one individual), permanent transplants can also be expected. But, the more genetically separated donor and host become, the less successful are the transplants. If *homologous* bone marrow is used as a donor (the donor and host are of the same species but are not identical twins), much larger amounts of bone marrow must be transplanted to confer "protection" against the bone marrow phase of the syndrome than when *autologous* bone marrow can be used. In addition, when homologous and *heterologous* transplants are compared (in heterologous transplants, the donor and host are *not* of the same species), more heterologous than homologous tissue is required to obtain the same result. Beyond that, the *length* of the extension of life (protection against the *immediately* lethal effects of irradiation) is also dependent upon the genetic relationship of donor and host. The more closely related donor and host, the longer the survival (or, stated another way, the better the protection). If homologous marrow is used, it does protect against the immediately lethal effects; treated animals survive longer than untreated irradiated animals. Later, these same animals begin to die; the numbers that die greatly increase with time after irradiation. Death, however, during this period seems unconnected with the radiation exposure itself. Rather, it appears to be the result of an *immunologic* reaction—a tissue response—of the donor cells *against* the host (of the graft against the host). The response, called "secondary" or "runt" disease, is characterized by a wasting of the treated organism. The intensity and time of onset of this "runt" disease will be determined by the genetic relationship of donor and host. The more closely the two are related, the longer it will be before the secondary sickness starts and the slower this sickness will progress.

**27.9  Human Experience.**  The principles described in this chapter may be expected to apply to the therapy of overexposed human beings as well as to the laboratory animals in which they have been discovered and demonstrated. Not all, however, have been of value in actual practice, and some cannot, at present, be expected to be useful. The most useful is the treatment of symptoms: the administration of antibiotics, fluid, and electrolytes, and the transfusion of platelets. Bone marrow transfusions are at the present time impractical. Except in the rare case in which an identical twin will be available as a donor, any donor will be homologous to the irradiated person; runt disease or secondary disease can be expected as a result of homologous transfusions.

In occupations in which there is a significant danger or hazard of high accidental exposure to radiation, the possibility of *removing* bone marrow from the workers and storing it for reinjection as a precaution against the day when that danger might be realized is being and should be explored.

## SUMMARY

1. Substitution or replacement of lost cells or functions can protect against the damaging effects of irradiation.
2. Susceptibility to infection and bleeding can be prevented by granulocyte transfusion, by antibiotic therapy, and by fresh platelet transfusion. Control of fluid loss and electrolyte imbalance can be corrected by salt and fluid therapy.
3. Bone-marrow transfusions will repopulate depleted marrow and protect against death. But runt disease is a lethal, complicating factor.

## Text References

1. Mauer, A. M., Athens, J. W., Ashenbrucker, H., Cartwright, G. E., and Wintrobe, M. M.: Leukokinetic studies II. A method for labeling granulocytes *in vitro* with radioactive diisopropylfluorophosphate(DFP[32]), Journal of Clinical Investigation 39, 1481-1486 (1960).
2. Athens, J. W., Raab, S. O., Haab, O. P., Mauer, A. M., Ashenbrucker, H., Cartwright, G. F., and Wintrobe, M. M.: Leukokinetic studies III. The distribution of granulocytes in the blood of normal subjects, Journal of Clinical Investigation 40, 159-164 (1961).
3. Fliedner, T. M., Sorensen, D. K., Bond, V. P., Cronkite, E. P., Jackson, D. P., and Adanik, E.: Comparative effectiveness of fresh and lyophilized platelets in controlling irradiation hemorrhage in the rat, Proceedings of the Society for Experimental Biology and Medicine 99: 731 (1958).

## General References

1. Bond, V. P., Fliedner, T. M., and Archambeau, J. O.: *Mammalian Radiation Lethality,* Academic Press, New York, 1965.
2. van Bekkum, D. W.: In *Mechanisms in Radiobiology,* Vol. II, M. Errera and A. Forssberg (eds.). Chapter 5, pp. 297-360. Academic Press, New York, 1960.

# Index